YOU CAN BEAT THE ENERGY CRISIS!

YES, THERE REALLY IS AN ENERGY CRISIS!

We live in an increasingly industrialized world. A world that—quite foolishly—relies far too heavily on two non-renewable fossil fuels (natural gas and petroleum). We've already burned up the most easily tapped reserves of these power sources . . . and it will be both more difficult and more costly to supply ourselves with gas and petroleum in the future. Many experts even predict that we'll completely exhaust the remaining stocks of these fuels within 30 years.

AND IT'S GOING TO AFFECT THE WAY YOU LIVE!

The days of cheap and virtually unlimited energy are over. If you continue using our society's "traditional" forms of power, you're going to pay more for the privilege of consuming less. Your house will be cooler in winter and warmer during the summer. You'll spend your vacations closer to home. Breathe more pollution as you burn "dirtier" grades of petroleum. And always suffer from the nagging thought that "they" might shut off your source of fuel at any time.

BUT THERE ARE WAYS TO BEAT THE PROBLEM!

Surprisingly enough, you don't have to put up with the hard times that are ahead. And you don't have to put up with them now! You can heat or cool your home, run a shop or factory, operate your car, cook your food—in short, supply all your energy requirements—with largely non-polluting, completely renewable sources of power that you control. TODAY! The necessary hardware, in most cases, is already available and this book tells you where to find it. Or you can build your own and this book tells you how.

COOK AND HEAT WITH THE SUN! USE THE WIND TO MAKE ELECTRICITY! POWER YOUR SHOP WITH A WATER WHEEL! RUN NATURAL GAS APPLIANCES OR A CAR ON "FREE" METHANE

IN THIS EYE-OPENING
ENERGY SOURCES TH

D1108743

CREDITS

Research for this book was done by John Boll, Kenny Hodges, Kay Holmes, Linda Holt, Carolyn Kimsey, Jim Morgans, Julie Needham, Dianne Reed, Priscilla Rhodes, Jane Shuttleworth, John Shuttleworth, Craig Sponseller and the authors whose names appear on some of the articles contained herein.

Copy written and proofread by John Boll, Kenny Hodges, Carolyn Kimsey, Jim Morgans, Julie Needham, Jane Shuttleworth and various named authors under the direction of John Shuttleworth.

Typesetting by Fred Mahaffey, Mary Redmon, Dianne Reed and Lucy Wilmoth under the direction of Linda Holt.

Layout by Kay Holmes, Priscilla Rhodes and Craig Sponseller under the direction of Jane Shuttleworth.

Bibliography by John Boll, Kenny Hodges and Mary Redmon.

Index by Jim Morgans.

Superior artwork by Craig Sponseller.

SPECIAL ACKNOWLEDGMENTS

Some of the material in this book originally appeared in different form in the magazine, THE MOTHER EARTH NEWS ®, published by THE MOTHER EARTH NEWS, Inc., P.O. Box 70, Hendersonville, North Carolina 28739, and/or was used on the syndicated radio program, NEWS FROM THE MOTHER EARTH NEWS, distributed by THE MOTHER EARTH NEWS, Inc., and/or appeared in the syndicated newspaper feature, THE MOTHER EARTH NEWS, distributed by The Register and Tribune Syndicate, 715 Locust Street, Des Moines, Iowa 50304, and/or appeared in LIFESTYLE! magazine, published by THE MOTHER EARTH NEWS, Inc.

Special thanks to *Popular Science Monthly*, Popular Science Publishing Company, Inc., 380 Madison Avenue, New York, New York 10017, for permission to reprint the used-oil burner article on pages 56—61 and permission to reprint the five-part water power article on pages 68—109 of this book. Special thanks, also, to D.S. Halacy, Jr., for permission to reprint the three solar energy projects on pages 252—277 of this book. Special thanks once more to Ram Bux Singh for permission to reprint the methane gas information on pages 280—289 of this book. Special thanks yet again to Henry Clews for permission to reprint the electrical energy consumption chart on page 128 of this book. And a Super Special Acknowledgment to Winnie Red Rocker for writing and *Alternative Sources of Energy* for making freely available the windplant article on pages 198—203 of this book.

THE MOTHER EARTH NEWS®
HANDBOOK OF
HOMEMADE
POWER

BY THE STAFF OF
THE MOTHER EARTH NEWS®

BANTAM BOOKS
TORONTO · NEW YORK · LONDON

THE MOTHER EARTH NEWS®
HANDBOOK OF HOMEMADE POWER

A Bantam Book | published May 1974

2nd printing .... November 1974	7th printing .... June 1976
3rd printing ..... February 1975	8th printing ..... February 1977
4th printing .... July 1975	9th printing ...... August 1978
5th printing ...... February 1976	10th printing .... April 1979
6th printing .... May 1976	11th printing .... June 1980

ISBN 0-553-14310-7

Published simultaneously in the United States and Canada

---

*Bantam Books are published by Bantam Books, Inc. Its trade-
mark, consisting of the words "Bantam Books" and the por-
trayal of a bantam, is Registered in U.S. Patent and Trademark
Office and in other countries. Marca Registrada. Bantam
Books, Inc., 666 Fifth Avenue, New York, New York 10019.*

PRINTED IN THE UNITED STATES OF AMERICA

20 19 18 17 16 15 14 13 12 11

This Book

is dedicated to

THE ENDURANCE OF THE PLANET,

A GENTLER TECHNOLOGY

and

THE SURVIVALISTS

that Patrick Rivers writes about.

TABLE OF CONTENTS

INTRODUCTION

Unlike most of the books, articles and TV reports on the developing energy shortage, this manual will *not* bore you with endless projections of gasoline consumption or the use of electricity in the year 2000. Nor will it rehash the virtues of geothermal power versus nuclear fission versus the so-called "hydrogen economy" versus other pie-in-the-sky "solutions" to our society's increasingly unsatisfied appetite for energy.

Instead, this handbook is designed to help *you* sidestep the energy problem once and for all—on a very personal basis—right here and right now.

In the pages of this guide, you'll learn how to heat and cook with that most traditional of all renewable fuels, wood. You'll find working plans for the construction of two kinds of water wheels and the dams and other hardware that go with them. You'll discover how to find and rebuild an old wind-driven electrical generator, build your own from scratch or—if you aren't that handy—buy a brand-new unit and have it installed.

This manual shows you how to construct a solar stove, oven and water heater. It explains—in simple, uncomplicated language—just how Steve and Holly Baer heat their New Mexico home with ninety 55-gallon drums and the sun. It takes you step by step through the production of a usable fuel—methane—from waste . . . in both test quantities and batches large enough to heat your house and power your automobile.

The following pages, in other words, are packed with information about "alternative" energy systems that really work and that you can put to work right now . . . today! Yes, there *are* answers to the developing energy crisis . . . and you hold a rich collection of those answers in your hand at this very moment. ◗

WOOD
A RENEWABLE RESOURCE

If there's any one section of this book that can be criticized, this is it . . . on the grounds that burning wood does put some pollution in the air. On the other hand, hickory smoke can do delicious things to a curing ham and, like it or not, wood *is* one of our renewable resources. When all the oil and natural gas have been pumped out of the ground, we'll still be planting, growing, cutting and burning timber.

If we haven't forgotten how, that is. A very large proportion of our current population, you know, wouldn't recognize a crosscut saw—let alone be able to figure out how to use it—if they saw one. And more's the pity. There's something almost sinfully satisfying about cooking food and heating your house all winter with cords of fuel that you've felled, buzzed up and split out yourself.

If you've never known that feeling, the following section will help you learn how to identify the best-burning woods, handle an axe, ready your home for this most natural of all heat, cook on a cast-iron kitchen range, get every bit of warmth from the wood you use and cut twice as much of the fuel with half the effort.

As an extra bonus (just in case you don't have a ready supply of timber at hand), this part of our manual also tells you how to make newspaper "logs" and recycle used motor oil into a fuel good enough to heat a shop or barn at virtually no cost.

One way or another, then, the following 64 pages should help you "keep the home fires burning" long enough for you to read the rest of this book. And *then* you'll be ready to set up a water wheel, windplant, solar collector and/or methane digester that will supply you with all the "alternative" energy you'll need from now on! We hope. We hope. ●

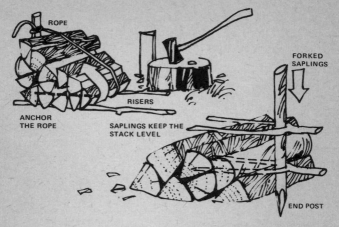

ROPE

FORKED SAPLINGS

RISERS

ANCHOR THE ROPE

SAPLINGS KEEP THE STACK LEVEL

END POST

The following article originally appeared as THE MOTHER EARTH NEWS *syndicated newspaper feature for December 16, 1973.*

As recently as last summer most of us considered fireplaces and wood-burning furnaces to be little more than quaint reminders of the past. This winter, however—as the continent's stock of fuel oil and natural gas shrinks to a crisis level—such "old time" heating equipment will once again mean comfort (even survival!) to hundreds of thousands of U.S. and Canadian families.

Perhaps your household will be one of the many that gets converted wholly or in part to wood heat during the coming weeks. If so, you're almost sure to appreciate a quick brushup on the nearly forgotten art of living with a "hand fed" blaze.

First off, of course, you must consider just where and in what you intend to build your fire or fires. Lucky indeed is the family residing in a home already well-equipped with wood-burning cookstove, fireplaces or furnace. New stoves are now back-ordered an average of ten months and used, wood-fired space heaters are scarce as hens' teeth in most sections of North America.

To be sure, if your situation is truly desperate, you can always have a local welding shop convert a 55-gallon drum into a "barrel stove" for you. It won't look too pretty sitting in your living room, but it most certainly will keep you warm until you can replace it with something more picturesque.

COLD? YOU CAN ALWAYS HEAT WITH WOOD!

New, used or converted from a drum, make sure your wood-burner is located well away from all walls and high enough so that its heat will not set your room's linoleum or floorboards on fire. Just to be extra safe, set the heater on an asbestos pad and place a fireproof shield between the stove and any nearby flammable curtains, panels, furniture, etc.

Correct placement, construction and operation of stove-pipes, chimneys and flues—although actually quite simple—can often completely baffle a fresh convert to wood heat and I'd be foolish to try to explain a "typical" vent system here. Consult with the folks at your local hardware store if you buy and install stovepipe . . . or pay a reputable sheet metal shop to do the job for you. Just make darn sure that whoever does the task adequately insulates any ceilings or sections of roof through which the flue is run.

If you don't feel qualified to saw out your own firewood, the chances are good that you'll pay someone to cut and deliver the fuel to you. And, more than likely, that someone will quote you a price "by the cord".

Now a cord of firewood is supposed to be a fixed measure (a stack 8' long by 4' wide by 4' high) of 128 cubic feet. Depending on how that stack is put together, however, you can get somewhat more or a good deal less fuel than you think when you buy one.

Due to the open spaces between a few, large logs—for instance—the buyer of a cord of firewood made up of such timbers will receive somewhat less for his money than the purchaser of a cord composed of carefully selected and closely stacked random-sized logs. It stands to reason, then, that you'll get more for your money if you specify that some small kindling sticks be mixed with the large-diameter timbers in any cord of wood you buy.

You should also bear in mind that a cord of softwood usually weighs out to slightly more than a ton while the same measure of hardwood tips the scales in the neighborhood of 1-3/4 tons. Hardwood, obviously, is the better bargain.

There's yet another consideration to take into account when you plunk down money for firewood: every tree is slightly different and each variety has a heating value all its own.

Shellbark hickory is just about the best natural fuel you're likely to be offered on today's firewood market. If you assign it a heating value of 100, you'll find that pignut hickory rates about 95, white oak comes in at 84, white ash stands at 77 and dogwood ranks 75.

Apple (at 70), red oak (69), white beech (65) and black walnut (65) are next in line . . . followed by black birch (62), yellow oak (60), white elm (58) and hard maple and red cedar (both rate 76). Wild cherry at 55, yellow pine's 54, yellow poplar with 51, butternut's 43, white birch at 43 and white pine with a rating of 30 bring up the rear.

To keep the insects that sometimes hide under a log's bark out of your house, store all firewood outside and at least 20 feet from your home. Bring it in only as needed.

Any edition of the *Boy Scout's Handbook* will show you how to "lay" a fire that will start (and continue) burning on the first match. After that it's merely a matter of experimenting with your particular heater for a few days until you learn to regulate the blaze with draft (down on the stove) and damper (up on the flue). You'll figure out soon enough that a big steady bed of hot coals is better than a series of roaring flames punctuated by cooling-off periods. A couple of big chunks that burn slowly, in other words, will maintain a comfortable temperature far better than any combination of kindling, branches or shavings. ●

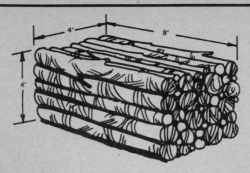

A CORD IS A CORD IS A...

Although a cord of wood is supposed to be a fixed measure of 128 cubic feet (a stack 8' long by 4' wide by 4' high), this "precise" specification leaves much to be desired. Due to the open spaces between a few, large round logs—for instance—the buyer of a cord of wood made up of such timbers will receive somewhat less for his money than the purchaser of a cord composed of carefully selected and closely stacked random-sized logs. It stands to reason, then, that you'll get more for your money if you always specify that some small kindling sticks be mixed with the larger-diameter timbers in any cord of wood you buy. You should also keep in mind the fact that a cord of softwood usually weighs out to slightly more than a ton while the same measure of hardwood tips the scales in the neighborhood of 1-3/4 tons. Hardwood, obviously, is the better bargain.

Reprinted from The Mother Earth News Almanac
(Bantam Books, $1.95) ©*1973. Reprinted by permission.*

ROHN ENGH:
HERE'S HOW WE HEAT WITH WOOD

Six years ago, when we bought our farm in northwestern Wisconsin, we found the toolshed filled with quaint memorabilia: a two-man saw, six-pound maul with rough-hewn handle, a rusted Swede saw, several wedges and a sizable double-bladed axe. We hung the items up on the toolshed wall as museum pieces, and proceeded to "civilize" the farmstead by installing an oil furnace and hot air heat in the house.

For the next five years we sat there, thinking we were satisfied with our oil burner . . . and paying the price which it annually extorted from us. Up here in northern Wisconsin, where stretches of 20°-below weather—with wind—are not uncommon, it's easy for a family to spend upwards of $400 a year on fuel (especially if they live in an old, not-so-airtight farmhouse).

Then, last winter—just as snow flurries began blowing in from Canada—we got to know and love wood heat. As an efficient and economical source of warmth for our entire house—with an intimate, personal quality all its own—this "primitive" method is (perhaps surprisingly!) *it*.

I'll admit that we didn't discover this all at once or completely on our own. In fact, we initially made the change from oil to wood because we were forced to do so (after giving up our preliminary visions of camping for the winter in the backyard of some friends who live on the Gulf of Mexico). A

doctor had traced the severe allergy of our youngest son to the hydrocarbons in petroleum products, and advised us to switch to some fuel other than oil or gas. Electric heaters were, however, totally impractical for our elderly farmhouse. Wood alone was left.

This prospect was sprung on us in October, which meant a lot of scramblin' before the cold Wisconsin winter set in. At that point, I'd never felled a tree in my life . . . but the "quaint memorabilia" in the shed had just become vitally important to us.

We started by stoking up our old country home's fireplace and a small "showcase" wood-burning stove in the kitchen. (There were enough deadfalls out in the pasture to feed these two without my facing the task of cutting down a tree.) But the stove would burn out in the middle of the night, and the fireplace, with its serious heat loss, was no match for the winter wind. We nearly froze during our first two weeks.

Then we cried "help" in our local *Tri-County Advertiser* and located a big, secondhand, wood-burning heater for $50.00. With it—plus the aid of a neighboring old-timer and a little ingenuity—we not only survived but enjoyed our initial winter of wood (the first of many, since our change of fuel has indeed helped to relieve our son's allergy problem).

The heart of our system, an Ashley heater, is located in the center of the kitchen where it provides the family with atmosphere, a handy "meetin' spot" and—of course—warmth. It's a great help if you want to take some of the stiffness out of your hands and feet after a frigid taste of the outdoors (or you just need to stop your whole self from shaking on a chilly morning). Our boys use the stove to dry their mittens, and my wife Jeri finds it ideal for keeping food and cocoa—a winter staple at our house—warm.

The crackling of the fire in the stove is in itself a basic earth-sound attraction. The steady subtle murmur of burning logs casts a comfortable feel around the kitchen, and encourages long, lazy daydreams when you tilt back in—yes!—the old rocker with your stockinged feet stretched out toward the solid warmth. Such closeness to one's needs is a rare pleasure these days and a welcome contrast to the increasingly indirect lighting, heating and communication patterns "enjoyed" in our society at large.

On a cold morning 11-year-old Danny absorbs as much heat as he can, then takes off for the barn to milk his goat before the school bus arrives. And I, after storing up some of the stove's radiation myself, pull away from the warmth and activity in the kitchen to go outside to the woodpile. There I start the day with fifteen minutes of axe work . . . which keeps me in better shape than the jogging I used to do every morning.

With the wind whistling at my back, I then carry an armful of good chunks in to the woodbox and toss some of the fuel into the stove. The special warmth of wood heat permeates the house, and gives me a sense of full accomplishment . . . because I've personally completed the cycle of finding, cutting and splitting my own energy source and transforming it into warmth for both family and home.

Our big Ashley will take a log two feet long and eight inches thick. It has an airtight firebox and ash door (a very good feature) and a special draft system that prevents the waste of a lot of heat which would otherwise be lost up the chimney.

Air for combustion of the wood enters the heater's firebox at the top, is warmed by the blaze as it passes through a downdraft stack and is then distributed evenly along the length of the burning logs by an intake manifold. An automatic thermostat, with which you dial the degree of heat you want, opens and closes the damper at the top of the downdraft

stack to admit just enough air to maintain the desired temperature.

We've found the Ashley to be highly effective . . . even on the few days last winter when temperatures dropped to 30° below zero and the wind came up to give us a chill factor equivalent to −60°. We conserved fuel by putting blankets over the kitchen doorways, brought out the Monopoly set and kept more comfortable than our nearby friends . . . who had their oil burners' thermostats set on high and still couldn't get really warm unless they stood in front of their kitchen ovens. That's the real advantage of a wood-fired stove over "modern" heat: You can get close to the source and toast comfortably, yet still have warmth evenly radiated to the rest of the house.

Another good thing about an Ashley is that it doesn't require a huge supply of wood which has been dried and seasoned for a year. The unit is perfectly content when fed with logs freshly cut no more than an hour before. This is possible because the design of the heater (and certain others on the market) causes the contents of the firebox to burn from the bottom up, not from the top down. Thus the upper wood— even if it's green—dries out as it gradually falls, and is consumed so completely that carbon and creosote deposits in the chimney—caused by unburned wood gases—are kept at a minimum. As one neighboring old-timer commented, a stove like ours "even burns up the ashes".

If your wood burner isn't that good—or even if it is—you should definitely be aware of the inflammable wastes that may well build up in your home's chimney. A large roaring flame,

like that which leaps up when you throw a wastebasket of paper into the stove, could ignite the soot and resins in the flue and possibly trigger a serious house fire.

Although the chance of such a flare-up is remote, it's wise to be conscious of the hazard. Some old-timers prefer to let any chimney blaze burn itself out (as long as the fire doesn't spread), while others keep a large bag of salt handy to dump down the flue as an extinguisher.

One useful item I found up in our homestead's barn was a ladder with hooks on its top end. It was the same length as the pitched portion of the house roof and had been kept up there in the old days just in case a chimney fire did get started. We put the "antique" back in its rightful place atop the house and left it there all winter. Though we've never had to use the ladder, we'd rather be safe than sorry.

The best answer to the problem of chimney fires, of course, lies in preventing the buildup of inflammable residue in the first place. Every now and then, some people give their stoves' fireboxes a sprinkling of salt . . . which seems to help keep the chimneys soot-free. I do the same thing with a commercially available (from M.E.E. Company, 1137 S.W. Hanford, Seattle, Washington 98134) product called Red Devil.

Or—if you forget occasional applications of the cleaners mentioned above—just look down your flue now and then and knock off the soot with a long pole or a chain swung in the shaft (be careful not to dislodge any mortar).

By the way: If this all sounds terribly complicated or dangerous, it's not. Any kind of equipment should be kept clean

and in good operating condition. Do the same for your chimney and the chances of its catching fire are less than those of a backup or other malfunction in an oil or gas furnace.

A close look at your home's water pipes is also in order if the house has wood heat. Any line that runs along an outside wall, as some of ours do, can be wrapped with insulation to protect it from freezing. And, if you leave the house for any length of time, it's most important to have a dependable friend pop in and reload your heater for you. The better models hold 100 pounds of wood at one filling and will burn up to 18 hours unattended. If you plan to be gone several days or more, of course, it's best to drain the water pipes. Anyhow, the pleasures of wood heat make it more fun to stay put and keep the home fires burnin'.

During our first season of heating with wood we were too caught up in the initiation throes of chain saw maintenance, log-splitting techniques and tree-felling traumas to keep a considered record of how much fuel we used. This year we intend to be a little more scientific, especially since our research indicates that an Ashley will heat a six-room house all winter on *only two to three cords of wood* . . . depending on home layout, insulation and the severity of the weather. (Our house has nine rooms. We closed off two, and the other seven stayed totally comfortable.) Heaters differ in performance, of course, and one farmer told us that our model uses only a third as much wood as he'd needed with another brand.

Last winter gave me my education in fuel gathering. Before I'd "graduated", I mangled three axes, one chain saw bar and one six-pound maul. My mistakes were my teachers . . . and when the temperature plummets to the below-zero mark and stays there, a student learns fast. Perhaps my experience might be helpful to others who are interested in burning wood.

Spring and fall are the best times to cut fuel (no bugs, no weeds, no burrs, no prickly heat). If you're using a good automatic heater, the wood can be burned immediately. Otherwise, if possible, it should be left out to dry for a season.

Which timber makes the best fuel? The hardwoods burn slower—and usually hotter—and oak, ash, birch and maple are generally the favorites. Elm is good, too, but tough to split. A first-rate heater will burn even poplar (low fuel on the totem pole), however, and keep your house warm while doing it. Fireplaces and less efficient stoves won't.

It's handy to have your own source of fuel supply, but it's not a necessity. A little scouting around can turn up many possibilities: neighbors who want a tree taken down, telephone and electric company prunings, outlying farmers or country dump locations with groves to be cleared, new construction sites where you might be *paid* to haul away timber.

In our case, we're lucky enough to have a built-in supply of oak (a great fuel!) in the woods on our south 40. Our house and barn were built back before the turn of the century with timber from this same stand, and I feel an intangible "rightness" to the whole process when I go out there and haul in each load for the stove.

To handle the wood, my old-timer neighbor told me, "First thing you need is a chain saw. And don't buy a used one. Get it new, so there won't be any mysteries about how it's been treated." Chain saws, he explained, have to be coddled. They dislike sand and dirt and need regular cleaning and maintenance checks.

Of several good brands of chain saws, the McCulloch was highly recommended to us and we invested in a Mac 10 model. We made that choice partly because there's a McCulloch service center in town . . . a factor that becomes not just handy but *critical* if you need repairs in midwinter.

When you begin to use your new tool, remember that its power-packed cutting action is equal to the strength of several workhorses and deserves a lot of respect. Work slowly, and follow the good and sensible precautions listed in any chain saw handbook. Many old-timers say that two woodsmen should always work together, with one clearing twigs and branches from the ground to give the other open space to do his sawing.

My own biggest challenge was learning to cut a tree down singlehanded, and I'd like to pass on some important do's and don'ts.

First, make sure your chain saw is properly oiled and well filled with gas. Then give an eye to which way the tree leans

and gauge your cuts to let it fall in that direction. Or, if your prospect is good and straight, check which side holds the most and/or heaviest branches.

Unlike the tall pines of Walt Disney movies, thick oaks with hundred-pound boughs won't give you much cooperation. Whenever possible, let the branch weight of a tree be your guide to where it's going to fall. Once last winter, when I tried to fell an oak against its natural direction in order to miss a nearby fence, the weight of the tree shifted halfway through my cutting, pinched the saw, broke its chain and bent its bar. Then, as I tried to retrieve my tool with wedges, the big oak decided to fall anyway . . . right through the fence.

When you can, begin felling a tree by first removing some of its branches. Do this with a first-cut into the limb from the bottom with your chain saw. Then sever it from the top.

Your initial cut into the trunk itself should be horizontal, about one-third of the way through the diameter (see Fig. 1), and into the side toward which you want the tree to fall. Next saw diagonally downward to the deepest point of the first saw mark.

Always start with the cut which is parallel to the ground for at least three reasons: [1] It's probably the most tiring of all, and is best done when you're still fresh and energetic. [2] The weight of the tree is less likely to pinch the saw if you make

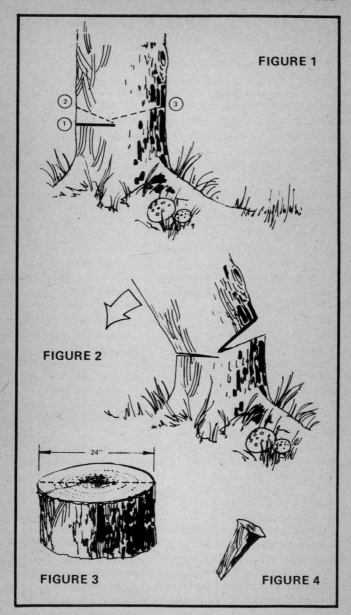

FIGURE 1

FIGURE 2

FIGURE 3

FIGURE 4

the diagonal cut second. [3] If you were to reverse the order of these operations, you'd find it more difficult to make the two incisions meet.

When you make your third and final cut (from the opposite side) don't saw all the way through the trunk. Leave enough wood to serve as a hinge, which you can sever after the tree falls (see Fig. 2). Otherwise, when the great mass crashes to the ground, the branches will act as springs and cause the trunk to kick back. Many a folk song has been inspired by the death of a logger who misjudged this recoil.

Begin trimming out your fallen tree by cutting away the small crinkly branches (loggers call these "hair"). Throw them into piles and, when you have enough, burn them where they lie. Cut the bigger boughs and the trunk into convenient lengths for your stove or heater . . . but don't attempt to use the section of the tree where a main branch has grown out of the trunk. These pieces are impossible to split and are usually too large for the door of a stove. Leave them on the ground to be burned with the smaller branches.

Among still more "memorabilia" up in our barn I found two handmade wooden sleds with metal runners that were used for transporting wood from the forest in the old days. These served us well for the hauling of fuel until the snow got too deep. Then I switched to a flat, plastic sled that glided along the tops of the banks.

I pile all our cut logs by the back door . . . and whenever I feel the urge, I step outside and do some wood splitting. The colder the weather, the easier the job: When the mercury drops, the moisture in the chunks freezes, and the smaller sections will cleave with one blow.

Thick chunks are a little more difficult . . . and here's how I break up hard white oak: First, I examine the face of the wood for any existing cracks (which serve as my splitting guide). Then, with a six-pound maul, I start swinging away at the center of the drum (see Fig. 3). Sometimes the piece splits open quickly. Other times, not. It's satisfying but tiring work.

Wedges (Fig. 4) are excellent tools for a woodsman. If a log refuses to be split with an axe or maul, place a wedge along the grain and drive it in with your maul's flat end. You may have to use two or even three wedges on a stubborn chunk.

What about kindling? Automatic heaters—which burn all night—don't need it. In fact, one fire built at the beginning of the season can be kept alive all winter. If you're using a fire-place or smaller wood stove, gather your small fuel early and keep it from getting damp. The drier the sticks are, of course, the easier it is to get your fire going on a chilly morning.

Dry twigs make good kindling, but for a real tried and true fire starter, split some of your logs two or three times, let the pieces dry well and split them again into thin strips. Another first-class kindling source is the log trimmings from a local lumber mill. Some operations give these away, while others charge a dollar for a pickup load.

Does all this sound like a lot of work? It is . . . but it's labor of a very satisfying kind. Axe swinging is a safe, non-toxic tranquilizer (even when you think you don't need one) . . . and I find it a sure-fire way to get lots of fresh Wisconsin air into my lungs in a hurry.

Perhaps it's those moments between axe swings, however, that are the most valuable benefit of all. Many of us have forgotten the delight of examining in close focus the small things around us . . . and the chopping of wood offers its prac-titioner a chance to . . . well, to pause and look.

While I rest between blows I find myself counting the rings in a large oak, watching a squirrel scamper down a branch, comparing the bark of a hickory to that of a birch or examining the way a branch grows from a tree's main trunk . . . all manifestations of a rhythm and beauty of growth and life that somehow refresh the soul.

Smells, too, take on a new importance when you heat with wood. The job makes you get outside in the snow in spite of yourself, and you find that you love it. The great winter outdoors has a fragrance all its own when you're sawing or splitting fuel . . . a fresh, clear sharpness leavened with the pungent scent of inner wood newly opened. Inside the house, the soft odor of burning logs greets you like incense and wraps you with warmth and comfort.

As I fill our heater, I look upon every piece of split fuel as a special event of my own making. Each chunk represents a swing of the axe . . . a movement of my own muscles transferred directly into heat that keeps my family warm. It tells me—with certainty—that I'm directly involved in the trilogy of human needs: food, clothing and shelter. ◓

MARK GREGORY:
BASIC
AXEMANSHIP

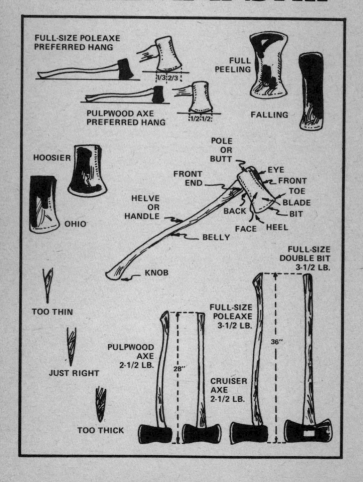

FULL-SIZE POLEAXE
PREFERRED HANG

1/3 2/3

FULL
PEELING

PULPWOOD AXE
PREFERRED HANG

1/2 1/2

FALLING

HOOSIER

OHIO

POLE
OR
BUTT

FRONT
END

HELVE
OR
HANDLE

BACK

BELLY

FACE

EYE
FRONT
TOE
BLADE
BIT
HEEL

KNOB

TOO THIN

JUST RIGHT

TOO THICK

PULPWOOD
AXE
2-1/2 LB.

28"

FULL-SIZE
POLEAXE
3-1/2 LB.

CRUISER
AXE
2-1/2 LB.

FULL-SIZE
DOUBLE BIT
3-1/2 LB.

36"

When it comes right down to basic survival, there is one tool that definitely outclasses all others and that's a good double-bitted axe. In fact, with a sharp axe there's not much you can't do in the way of providing food and shelter . . . even to making a new axe handle if the old one breaks. This tool must be kept sharp, however, and you must know how to use it correctly. Otherwise, an axe can be extremely dangerous, as many would-be woodsmen have learned by badly gashing a leg.

Growing up on a Missouri farm I learned to use an axe at an early age; there was firewood to cut, brush and hedgerows to clean out and fenceposts to cut and split. I learned much from a part-Cherokee uncle who, shunning the rest of the world, made a living doing a little trapping and dog training (hunting dogs) for city folks. To watch him cut and split a pile of logs was sheer joy. The axe was an extension of his arm that did his absolute bidding and never seemed to tire him.

You should know the first rule of good axemanship if you're interested in mastering this tool: Buy a quality axe that is well suited to the jobs you'll put it to.

There are many styles and brands of axes and, sad to say, many are of poor quality. Stay away from surplus stores and bargain military axes. They're made of inferior metal and their edges become round as doughnuts after a few blows. There is absolutely no way you can sharpen such a tool and keep it sharp.

If you want a bargain "cheap" axe, watch the country auctions. An axe may be old and its handle may be cracked or loose . . . but if the head isn't chipped or broken, the axe can be easily repaired and it will probably sell for less than a dollar. *(Such an axe was likely bought new from a small town hardware store so, if you can't find a bargain at an auction, try the local outlet in any farming or mountain town.—MOTHER.)*

As for axe "style" or design, decide what you want the tool to do and then try to find the ideal axe for the job. If you plan mainly to split fireplace logs, for instance, get a single-bit (blade) axe with a fat, wedge-shaped blade. It won't stick in the log ends so easily and the extra weight of the head will help provide splitting force. For tree felling or building a log cabin, get a heavy (3-1/2 pound) double-bit axe with a long handle. This combination will almost swing itself through long hours of work . . . especially if you keep both blades extremely sharp and thin.

I've used many axes and my all-around favorite for anything from cutting a sapling to splitting a few fireplace logs to providing shelter and fire while camping is a small version of the double-bitted Hudson Bay style. I prefer a handle about six inches shorter than standard. For me, this is a beautifully balanced tool but you must realize that an axe is a very personal thing. If you plan to use one much, try several styles and weights to find exactly the one for you.

I hone one blade edge of my favorite axe razor sharp and, with it, I can slice off a two-inch limb with one blow. The opposite edge of the blade is never sharpened quite so drastically and is used for everything from splitting to cutting roots.

Sharpening an axe blade is no mystery but does take a bit of patience and time. Merely file the nicks out of the blade

Always clear full area of swing before you begin any axe work. The debris underfoot in this illustration can cause trouble.

(keeping the existing bevel), then hone with a round axe hone.

And there's the catch: It takes a lot of elbow grease to put a sharp edge on a blade and most beginning axemen just won't take the time. A seasoned woodsman, however, knows that a really sharp edge makes a safer axe: It's the dull blades that glance (rather than bite in) and make the bad gashes on legs and feet.

While you're putting an edge on your axe, check the head and see if it's loose. If it is, drive a wooden or metal wedge into the head end of the handle.

Hang your axe up in the cabin when you're not using it. Never leave it leaning against a wall or sticking in a live tree. An axe can be an extremely dangerous hazard either way and, in the second case, the tree will be permanently scarred and—possibly—killed.

To slash small branches away from the side of a fallen log, stand on one side of the downed timber and reach over for the cut.

An axe left sticking in a block of wood may be picturesque but is also very dangerous. This is hard on the blade, too, as it draws moisture from the green wood and can become rusted and pitted. The best idea (for both the blade and innocent bystanders) is a sheath that is kept on the blade at all times the axe is not in use. Such a sheath should be kept well oiled with a good grade of gun oil.

Although an axe can be used (and is, often, by farmers) to chop holes in ice, the blade should always be warmed first near a fire or by blowing on it. A cold blade is extremely brittle and can break quite easily.

Before you do any work with an axe, make sure the area around you—the ground, overhead, left, right, front and back—is completely clear of brush, branches and debris. The smallest limb can catch the blade and jerk you off balance and

Place small logs in crotch of larger for splitting. An axe can easily glance off a piece of wood lying loose on the ground.

the tiniest twig under your feet may roll and cause you to fall and badly injure yourself.

Plant your feet firmly in a comfortable, wide stance and look directly at the place you plan to hit with the blade. Hunting archers have a trick of concentrating on the smallest spot they can see, rather than the overall target. If you do the same you'll come closer to hitting the mark.

Grasp the axe handle about two inches from the end with both hands close together. Position the blade on the spot in front of you and—with a smooth swing—pull the axe back, letting it swing up and past you on one side. You'll have to *swing* the axe up to keep it going but when it reaches the top of its arc it will start to fall of its own accord. All you have to do then is guide it for an easy, effortless cut.

The way *not* to handle an axe (and often tried by begin-

Good axemen always work from the butt of a tree toward its top when lopping off limbs . . . and they always chop across the main log.

ners) starts with the axeman picking the tool straight up in front with one hand on the end and the other in the middle of the handle. Folks trying this method usually slide the middle hand back to the end of the handle at this point as they lift the axe straight above their heads. With a mighty heave, they then "force" the axe down, nearly always missing the mark and wearing themselves out with the first blow.

Using a natural swing, the axe does most of the work. You provide only a bit of help at the start and, with some practice, even an out-of-shape beginner will be surprised at how long he can "work" at this without getting tired. The trick is to establish a rhythm that suits you and that you can keep going until you finish the job.

One summer I worked as a laborer pouring concrete street

Cut small firewood over a larger log. This technique will prevent the severed pieces from flying up and hitting you in the face.

gutters. This requires miles and miles of forms and thousands of stakes to hold those forms in place. The mallet swing of the stake drivers is exactly like the motion I'm describing here for axe work. With this easy approach, the 68-year-old, 120-plus pound man I worked with could drive stakes all day just as fast as I could position and hold them. He never missed (believe me, I know) and you could count cadence to the blows of his mallet. Although this idea applies most directly to chopping rather than splitting or lopping off limbs, the principle carries through and you'll find yourself using much the same rhythm for these jobs.

When felling trees, first make sure that everyone else is out of the area. Then determine the direction in which the tree leans (and they all lean a little). It will be easiest—but it's not

Medium-sized firewood should be cut over a larger chunk of timber also. It's safer that way and your axe will stay sharper too.

necessary—to fell the tree in the direction in which it leans. Once you've decided the way you want the tree to fall, make a cut on *that* side of the trunk.

Make this cut somewhat more than halfway through the tree. Then start another cut on the *opposite* side of the trunk and a little *above* the first cut. Keep chopping until you hear a crack . . . then lay down your axe and run as fast and as far as possible. That may be a slight overstatement . . . but never, never stand behind a falling tree. The butt can kick back and kill you faster than you can possibly move out of danger.

With the tree down, you can begin trimming off limbs. Start at the base and cut toward the top. On larger trees, always determine beforehand if the tree will roll or fall toward you when a limb starts to break. Many loggers have been killed or maimed this way.

Once the branches are removed, you're ready to cut them

Never, but NEVER, leave an axe sticking in a stump or log. It's hard on the blade and just invites you to trip and fall over it.

and the main trunk into desired lengths. If the tree is extremely large and you've had a bit of axe practice, stand on top of the trunk—with feet spread wide and firmly planted—and chop on the *side* of the log between your feet. For smaller trees use the same principle and, standing on one side of the trunk, reach over to chop into the opposite side.

Cut small pieces of firewood to length over a larger log. Never lay the pieces directly on the ground for this job; the ends can fly up and cause injury. When splitting short chunks, stand each piece on end or lay it in the crotch of another log.

Splitting a log for fenceposts or rough beams requires an altogether different technique. As before, if you use an axe, use one with a fat wedge-shaped blade and—as my uncle always stressed—let the log split itself. Give each stroke a little time before removing the blade for the next. In many cases, if you wait just a bit, you'll hear a faint pop as the fibers

Bend small saplings over with one hand and slice them off as close to the ground as you can. Make the cut as square as you can.

grudgingly release and separate.

You may need to use wedges and a heavy mallet to split some woods such as wild cherry and Osage orange. There are wooden wedges (sometimes called gluts and made on the spot when needed), heavy steel wedges, wooden mallets (mauls) and steel sledges. Although real purists still refuse to drive a steel wedge with a steel sledge, such practice is generally accepted these days. No self-respecting woodsman would ever drive a steel wedge with his axe, however, nor would he ever drive one axe with another axe or a sledge.

An axe is not a wedge, nor a sledge, nor a maul. It is a chopping tool and should be used for that and that alone. Driving steel wedges with an axe and using an axe as a maul or a wedge will sooner or later (and probably

Square-sawn, seasoned firewood splits easily with an axe. Wait a few seconds after each stroke to give the wood a chance to separate.

sooner!) ruin it.

Wedges come in sets since you always require at least two—one to release the other—and, once you start driving them in, you're committed until the log splits. If you find both your wedges frozen in a particularly difficult log, you can split out a few gluts (which *can* be driven with an axe) to relieve them.

There's a rich sense of accomplishment in learning the correct use of an axe and this general introduction should go a long way toward helping any beginner master the tool. Don't be discouraged if your original attempt at axemanship produces little more than kindling, however. You'll probably improve rapidly and—if you get nothing else from your first day—you're sure to sleep well that night! ⬤

Right idea . . . WRONG driving tool! Split stubborn woods with a set of metal wedges . . . but never, NEVER drive those wedges with an axe.

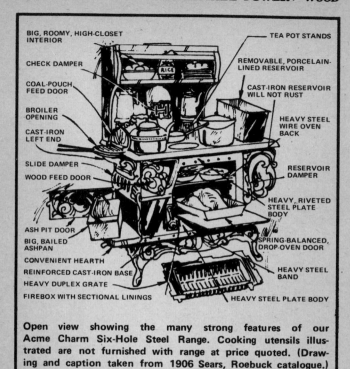

Open view showing the many strong features of our Acme Charm Six-Hole Steel Range. Cooking utensils illustrated are not furnished with range at price quoted. (Drawing and caption taken from 1906 Sears, Roebuck catalogue.)

My husband, Theo—bless his practical heart—looked at me with his mouth wide open, trying for the umpteenth time in our years of marriage to understand the workings of my mind. Finally, he found his voice. "Billie, surely you aren't serious about wanting a wood cookstove. Have you any idea of what using one is like?" He shook his head.

"Yes, I think I do. In fact, I'm sure of it." Boy, that last crack closed off every avenue of escape. If I weren't sure, I'd better get that way.

Theo went on. "Why, you'll probably break your foot the first day kicking the blamed thing when it doesn't do to suit you." He threw back his head and laughed. Theo had grown up with a wood-burning cookstove and claimed to know all their quirks.

His arguments were sound enough but I had a few of my

B. TOUCHSTONE HARDAWAY:
I LIVE WITH A WOOD-BURNING COOKSTOVE AND LOVE IT

own: "I know a wood-burning range would be sheer purgatory for many, but I think it will be therapeutic for my impatient nature. Also, think of the money we'll save on the electric bill and it's a great way to get rid of all that scrub timber growing everywhere . . . and, besides, I WANT IT."

A smile played at the corners of Theo's mouth. How well he knew me. "All right. We'll buy you a wood-burning cookstove but, once it's bought, there'll be no turning back. OK?"

OK! I swallowed hard because I knew I had some research work cut out for myself before the stove arrived.

THE OLD WAYS WERE OFTEN GOOD WAYS

I guess you could say I'm semi-old-fashioned. I like sturdy iron bedsteads, big-legged tables, well-sunned mattresses, skirts to the knees, a fresh-scrubbed look and cakes made from the flour up. I enjoy watching hens scratching in the yard for their biddies and—occasionally—I like to scrub my floors with a bucket of lye water and a worn-out broom.

The latter could be a carryover from childhood, since I always associate lye-scrubbed floors and sunned mattresses with my growing-up period. The finishing touch on spring cleaning days was to place a large, fragrant bouquet of wild sweet williams in the center of an oilcloth-covered table. I can smell them now!

Because I am fond of so many things and traditions of yesterday, the idea of a wood-burning cookstove had sort of eased into my mind over the years even though I knew absolutely nothing about using one . . . and—suddenly—my stove was here!

Theo put the cookstove up with its long, glossy black pipe leading into the new brick chimney. Our little issues ran about gathering kindling and bits of wood for the first blaze in mama's new stove that was just like the one Martha Washington had used to cook meals for George.

Theo built a fire and I transferred supper from the electric range to the wood burner. Then, as the new stove got hot, smoke began seeping out of every nook and cranny and rose in sheets off its top. The thick haze filled the kitchen and quickly forced us—coughing and sputtering—to open every available window and door (in January yet). The condition was temporary, however, and only lasted a few minutes until the "new" wore off. We soon had the house buttoned up again and I eagerly looked forward to fathoming the mysteries of the wood-burning cookstove.

STARTING THE FIRE

Since I grew up without the privilege of brothers and the knowledge bestowed on very young ladies by that fine organization known as the Girl Scouts, I knew absolutely zero about starting a fire. I had halfheartedly watched my husband and sons build a blaze in our fireplace . . . but never with the interest needed to really learn how, and the first time I faced the ordeal of firing up my new stove unassisted, I nearly panicked.

On that wretched day I burned three Sunday editions of the paper and a whole log of rich pine and—an hour later—all I had to show was a lot of filmy ashes floating about, a streak of soot across my face and a stove that was still as cold as a wedge (in this case, a wedge of ice).

It was thus that Theo found me when he came home weary from the field for his supper. In my romantic imagination, I had planned to quote from Oliver Goldsmith's *The Traveller*, this beautiful little verse:

> *At night returning, every labour sped*
> *He sits him down the monarch of a shed*
> *Smiles by his cheerful fire, and round surveys*
> *His children's looks, that brighten at the blaze;*
> *While his lov'd partner, boastful of her hoard,*
> *Displays her cleanly platter on the board.*

Well, the only part that now applied was the cleanly platter. It was clean indeed and there was *no* fire, cheerful or otherwise. I suppose the one thing which saved his lov'd partner from rebuke was the wretched look on her soot-streaked face. Theo's only comment, in a very sober voice, was, "Is there any kindling left?"

With those not-kind-but-not-scolding words, I fled to the

woodshed and scraped up a few chips. In no time at all, Theo had a cheerful fire spittin' and poppin'. It just made me sick.

After what seemed an eternity, I finally got the hang of it. Now, I only need a tiny bit of kindling or dry blocks and a sheet of newspaper to start a roaring blaze. Here's how I do it:

It's all-important that you don't let your stove's ash container get too full. This is because the ash box is usually so close to the firebox that, full, it can cut off the oxygen needed to make a fire "draw". I empty the ashes from my stove about twice a week. Since hot ashes always contain sparks that can ignite in the slightest wind, this job should be done in the morning, before a fire is built.

Next, I open the damper all the way so the air will draw and I lay my fire by taking one single sheet of newspaper (dry leaves, pine needles or tar paper will do if no newspaper is available), wadding it loosely and placing the wad in the front of the firebox. On top of this I crisscross some splinters. Then, on top of it all, I place a few sticks of dry wood and "light 'er up". In no time at all she's ready for the coffeepot and kettle.

The damper, by the way, regulates the blaze (and, therefore, the heat) by controlling the flow of air (oxygen) through the firebox. You want the damper wide open when starting a fire. Once it's burning nicely, close the damper a bit to hold the heat in the stove or to slow down the blaze.

One afternoon I was busy and called to my teenage daughter, Bonnie, to turn the chicken for me. She yelled, "How do you turn this darn thing off?" We had a good laugh (one of many) before I introduced her to the indispensable damper. I explained there was no ON or OFF *per se*, only an UP and DOWN, which is controlled with the damper. When you need OFF, you simply remove the pot; when you want to hold the heat DOWN, you turn the damper or push the pot to the side of the stove away from the heat. Simple! Bonnie grinned and shook her pretty head.

I never use kerosene or gasoline as a quick starter. They are highly dangerous and they really don't help. If the wood is dry enough to burn at all, it will start with a little encouragement from newspaper, pine needles or dry leaves. If it's not dry enough, kerosene or gas won't help. Once the fluid burns itself out you're right back where you started. I do keep a little hatchet handy, though, to tailor-make splinters when they're brought in too big.

FUELS AND FUELING

To each his own about the kind of wood to burn in a cookstove. You'll probably want to experiment until you find your favorite. In my opinion, ash makes the hottest fire and hickory is best for steady heat. Now that we live most of the year where cedar is plentiful, I cook quite a lot with it and enjoy the added benefit of a nice aroma.

If you live where you can't afford to be choosy, don't fret: Any wood will give a good, substantial fire once you get it going. And, if you have no wood at all, most of the old-time cookstoves will cheerfully accept hard coal, soft coal, coke or even corncobs.

While we're on the subject of wood, I should mention—for those who don't know (and I was among them until two years ago)—the difference between *green* and *dry* wood. Well do I remember the first time I sent our youngest daughter out to bring me a turn of green wood. She came back empty-handed and said sadly, "There is no green wood . . . only brown and sort of blackish."

Green wood is wood that hasn't been cut too long. It's full of moisture and quite heavy. *Dry* wood has been cut long enough to dry out. It's quite light and burns rapidly.

A good formula to follow is: For quick heat, use *tinder dry*; for standard baking, use *year-old wood* (dry); and for a slow, steady, long-holding fire, use *nearly green* wood.

Green wood is usually added after the fire is really going good. You'll soon learn to mix green and dry wood too. This gives a "just right" fire for most any kind of cooking except deep-fat frying which takes a blaze "hot as hell". For this, you need all dry wood and the damper tightly closed.

One of the most difficult things I had to learn—or rather, not forget—was to keep the firebox full of wood while cooking a meal. I would be cooking away and—suddenly—my french fries were just "sitting there" before I realized that I hadn't fed the fire recently. This, of course, is a must so you have to make like a railroad man and keep "firing that ole boiler".

I get up in the mornings an hour before I am ready to cook. This gives the fire a chance to "do its thing" and gives me some quiet time before our little ones are up and about. When the fire is ready, I have everything prepared to cook.

WOOD SUPPLY

If one lives on a tiny place or has no scrub timber to use for firewood, there are solutions. Almost any farmer or landowner will allow you to cut scrub timber from his place, clearing the way for more pasture and tillable land. The only requisite is that you pile the brush neatly or take it with you. This, too,

can be used for firewood if broken or chopped and piled.

If you live in the vicinity of a sawmill or lumberyard of some sort, there are always discarded strips and shavings that will burn. In Louisiana, when we don't want to go "pine knot huntin' " we visit a nearby box factory where scrap lumber has been piled many feet high. This scrap burns great.

As I walk in the woods of Louisiana and the Ozarks I see what amounts to literally truckloads of rotten, dry limbs and felled trees. In Europe, this would be a gold mine since many a serious livelihood is earned by gathering such wood and peddling it to townspeople for fuel.

There's no need to invest in a noisy chain saw for your wood-hunting expeditions. If you want something more traditional, less expensive and quieter, try a crosscut. You know . . . the long, two-man saw that you pull back and forth until the tree is felled. I've been on one end of such a saw and it's a splendid body conditioner. If you can't afford a saw you might do as Thoreau did: Borrow one. Just be sure you return it sharper than you found it . . . again, as Thoreau did.

CLEANING THE STOVE

The cleaning of a wood-burning stove involves very little effort. If you spill grease or food on it, the spill *burns* right off. I keep a bundle of newspapers handy and, after each meal, I wipe my cookstove vigorously with a wadded sheet. Then, once every two weeks or so, I "black" the stove.

Blacking consists of dipping a limber paintbrush (39¢) into the stove polish or blacking (49¢ a bottle and enough for three applications) and painting it on. The process gives a newness to the stove and makes it look pretty . . . also keeps it from rusting, I understand.

I then wipe the white part of the cookstove until it's shiny clean with my dish towel. Now and then I also wipe out the oven with a damp towel and scrape away any spills.

Once or twice a year I take all the burners off the top and clean out the soot and ashes that have blown between the oven and the burners. This collection doesn't interfere with the stove's performance, but cleaning it out makes me feel as good as when I move the refrigerator to sweep and mop away a year's collection of dust.

I am no slave to housework, so I really enjoy the easy care of my wood-burning range.

SECOND THOUGHTS

One of my glutton-for-gloom friends said I'd change my mind about the cookstove after one good, hot summer. I gave this a lot of thought before we bought the range and frequently considered how our grandmothers—attired in their several long skirts, with cheeks a-blazin' and hearts a-singin'—worked diligently in all kinds of weather and prepared menus fit for any old king on an iron stove. I couldn't believe summer cooking would be such an ordeal.

And it isn't. At this writing I've just finished the second hot summer with my wood stove and I wouldn't go "back" to the modern method under any circumstances.

Although the question of summer cooking hadn't bothered me, I did have one concern about the stove: I didn't want it to be a traumatic experience for Bonnie since—even before the cookstove arrived—it had seemed to highly embarrass her. She had, in fact, detested even the thought of the range and hoped to the last minute I'd "come to my senses" and not bring that monstrosity into our pretty, sunny kitchen.

I think somewhere in her young, sensitive mind, she associated the wood-burning stove with deprivation . . . or maybe she didn't know how she would explain my actions to her peers.

Then, as if by a miracle, the boy she was dating came early one evening and watched as I fried chicken (we eat a lot of chicken). We chatted while he waited for Bonnie and—although he said not a word about the stove—he sure eyeballed it.

Later, Bonnie told me the boy had asked her if that was a wood cookstove her mother was using and when she sadly confessed that it was, he beamed. "Really? Gee, I hope you'll ask me to eat sometimes. The food's great cooked on one. My granny had a wood stove until last year."

Bonnie said the young fellow even mentioned that he thought her mother was "cool". I *like* that boy.

A BIGGER STOVE . . . AND A BETTER LIFE

Henry Thoreau, God rest his soul, knew his stuff when he said, "Simplify, simplify". This—for at least nine months of each year—we have literally done. We now have two homes: One in the midst of the "rat race" in Louisiana where everyone's in a mad dash, racial tension is thick and trust for each other is a thing long gone. The other, a little four-room "unmodern" house we rent for twenty bucks a month, is in the heart of the beautiful Ozark Mountains.

Here, in our second domicile, I wash our clothes on a rub board outside next to nature; I carry our wood and water inside; we have no telephone, television nor neighbors for a mile in any direction. Daily, we walk a mile up the mountain and a mile back for our mail. The local people are slow to anger, slow to criticize and quick to help. The school at the foot of the mountains is unsophisticated and undemanding in every way.

We live in our retreat house nine months of the year. Then we're forced back to that "other way" to earn enough to live our simple and quiet life here in the hills.

We have only the barest furniture necessities and every item in our mountain house is "useful". To quote Thoreau again, "Most of the luxuries, and many of the so-called comforts of life are . . . positive hindrances." Amen!

We considered ourselves lucky as all get out when we found a beautifully cared for Home Comfort wood-burning cookstove for our retreat. It is truly an antique, but sturdy as the mountains surrounding our house. The white on the stove still gleams except where pots have been scraped back and forth over the years.

I wouldn't take ten times the price we paid for the range nor 50 times that much for the friendship we made with its sellers, two lovely little ladies in their seventies who care tenderly for each other. They used the stove for 50 years before selling it.

This range is much bigger than the one I have in Louisiana and I could cook for a battalion of men on it. The food warmers on top are large enough to hold a full meal with the doors closed. The giant oven will cook six loaves of bread at once and the copper-lined water reservoir heats 15 gallons so hot I have to cool it to do dishes.

Each time I stand cooking at this stove I think of all the fine old women who must have stood just as I, meditating as they stirred a bubbly pot. The date of manufacture is 1864, so probably a hoop skirt has been worn here too.

During the course of a meal's preparation, I bend and stoop and squat many times to fill the firebox or punch around to liven the coals. Needless to say, this is good for my matronly waistline.

Then, of course, there is that special treat of going to the woodshed, or *woodpile* here in the Ozarks. It gives me a chance to listen to the songs of a variety of birds and enjoy nature a bit while I load my arms with the aromatic cedar wood. It seems only natural for me at this time to thank my Creator for allowing me to be cast in the lot that I am.

Ah, the wood chopping . . . the inevitable wood chopping. When my strong-armed husband cuts the wood, he hauls it to the house in blocks to be split later. He and the boys do this chore for the most part but, sometimes, I enjoy taking a whack with the axe.

Most of the time I miss the block completely and stab the ground. When I am able to hit the block, the axe mostly bounces off the silly thing (and my sons double over with laughter). Once in a while I am able to strike a cruel blow and split a block. Then, of course, I am filled with incentive and wear myself down trying for a repeat performance. By the time I have a pitiful little pile of wood, I am hot as a pistol. One ole-timer put it well, "My wood warms me while I'm cuttin' it and again when I burn it."

Though my accomplishments are not great on my wood choppin' days, I can eat like a horse and not worry about calories. In fact, I haven't thought much on dieting since being here in the mountains. There's no need. We work hard, we eat wholesome foods, we sleep nearly ten hours a night and the calories take care of themselves.

We are in bed before nine each evening unless we feel reck-
less, and then we stay up another thirty minutes to read a few
more chapters. Six o'clock in the morning finds me searching
for the light string in my little kitchen and preparing to lay my
fire.

THE STOVEPIPE OVEN

While looking for a wood range to buy, my husband and I
were browsing in a local hardware store here in the Ozarks and
found a quaint little *stovepipe oven*. The first I had ever seen,
but the salesman said they'd been around for as long as he
could remember. He said they fit between the first and second
joint of the stovepipe on a heater or range and the heat scurry-
ing up the pipe gets the little oven hot enough to bake anything you like. It's plenty big for a loaf of bread, cakes or a
hen, yet. Just perfect for the small family.

If a family didn't want to invest in a wood-burning range
but found it necessary to buy a wood-burning heater for
warmth, they could purchase one of these ducky little ovens
and insert it in the stovepipe of their heater. They'd then be all
set for cooking, heating and baking. The little ovens cost in the
neighborhood of nine dollars. They are substantially built and,
in my opinion, are well worth the price.

I wouldn't mind at all cooking on such an ensemble and I
plan to buy one of these ovens and mount it on our heater's
pipe. Then—if I should take the notion to bake a cake and the
range isn't fired up—I can still bake. Sort of like killing two
birds with one stove!

IN CONCLUSION

I can now look back two years and laugh at my anxieties about starting a fire in my wood-burning range. In fact, I find that—as I put more years behind me—I am able to laugh at most things I once thought were major catastrophies. And I did have my problems with that stove.

The first time I baked biscuits I burned them to ebony. Also the second and third times. But on the fourth try they came out golden brown. And I burned my hands and wrists every day until I finally got it through my blockhead that EVERYTHING on or near that stove was HOT! But surely—if somewhat slowly—I mastered the wood range.

There's one thing about my cookstoves—no, there are many things about them, but this one in particular—they simply won't be hurried. They take their own sweet time. No begging, wringing the hands or kicking their backsides will get them hot any faster. They force me to slow my quick-moving self to a snail's pace, which is good for me.

I am compelled to wait for the fire to get hot enough before I put the bacon in the skillet, or else it will just boil gently *(gag)*. Then I'm compelled to wait for the fire to cool down enough to pop the biscuits into the rosy-red oven or I have burned-on-the-outside-and-gooey-on-the-inside *(shudder)* biscuits. I like to think of these "waits" as character building.

I should explain here that, for me, there's a vast difference in doing a thing that can be aggravating at times "by choice" rather than "by necessity". When I feel forced to accept a situation that irritates me, I can moan and complain louder than any soul for miles around. But when the thing or situation is my own choice, I feel pretty silly griping about it . . . in fact, I'd better not, if I know what's good for me.

To be even more honest, there are times when cooking on a wood-burning range can be pure hair shirt, UNLESS I channel my attitude into the right groove. Honestly though, these times are rare.

Once I learned to operate my wood stove I began to really enjoy its coziness. While I'm writing I can see to dinner and mind the firebox. It gives me a warm, everything's-fine-with-the-world feeling to fill the firebox with "just right" green wood for gently boiling a big pot of vegetable soup or turnip greens and a good ham bone.

Yes, I enjoy my wood-burning stove, but a word of caution to the would-be owners of one: If you're geared to live in a mad dash, stewing in your own juice AND you don't wish to change . . . you'd better not tinker around with a wood-burning cookstove. Chances are you'll flip your lid as well as the stove's.

But if you're able to slow your pace, you don't mind some of your friends clucking their tongues or lifting their eyebrows at your action, if you like a taste of yesterday, the wonderful smell of wood smoke, apples in your cheeks AND you have a jim-dandy supply of wood and fat pine kindlin' . . . you just might get the same pleasure from your wood stove that I have from mine. I hope so. ◓

Some wood-burning cookstove suppliers are listed in this book's bibliography (see Wood, Hardware*). A word of warning, however: Most are months behind on their orders at this time (early 1974).*

It can be a ticklish thing, this baking bread on a wood-burning range the first time. I have had many a failure and many successes. We eat the failures as well as the successes.

This is a basic whole-wheat recipe I'd like to share with you:

> 2-1/2 cups milk, scalded
> 1/4 cup honey
> 1 Tbs. salt
> 1/2 cup nutritional yeast
> One pkg. active dried yeast softened in
> 1/2 cup lukewarm water
> 3 Tbs. cooking oil
> 6 to 8 cups whole-wheat flour

Blend milk, honey, salt and nutritional yeast. When this cools to lukewarm, add softened yeast, oil and three cups of the flour. Beat until bubbles rise to the surface. Add enough of the remaining flour to make a soft dough that comes away clean from the sides of bowl. Turn dough onto floured surface and let rest ten minutes. Then knead until smooth and elastic. Place in oiled bowl, turning dough over several times to coat with oil. Cover. Let rise again. Divide dough into 3 equal portions. Shape into balls and let stand for five minutes, then mold into loaves. Place in oiled bread pans. Let rise until nearly doubled in bulk, about an hour. Bake about an hour in moderately hot oven.

B. TOUCHSTONE HARDAWAY:
COOKSTOVE BAKING

I always start my fire when I place loaves in bread pans for last rising, which takes about 30 or 40 minutes. This gives the fire time to get "moderately" hot.

My oven has a temperature gauge which says simply SLOW—MODERATE—HOT. No numbers for degrees, just those three words. When that needle registers HOT, let me tell you, it is exactly that. I would judge it to be about a thousand degrees in the oven.

So you'll want to "baby" your fire on bread-baking day. Sometimes in spite of all I can do, the fire will nearly reach the HOT mark before I can slow 'er down. Then I call upon that modern invention, aluminum foil, and make a nice little cap over all three loaves. After that, the old fire can get as hot as it likes while the bread cooks to perfection inside. If I am out of foil, I put a large tray or several lids on top of the loaves after they have crusted over. This is not too desirable, but will do in a tight. Even then, sometimes, I have to leave the oven door ajar.

This problem of too much heat too fast doesn't happen too often, but it does happen occasionally. (I like to think of these times as some more of that character-building stuff I mentioned.)

If you place a pan of water on the floor of the oven under the loaves, it seems to give them volume and keeps the temperature easier to control. The bread is delicious and well worth the effort. ◗

AN INDIANA FARMWIFE, ESTHER SHUTTLEWORTH, TELLS ABOUT...

"COOKSTOVES I HAVE KNOWN"

During the depression I cooked and canned on a "stove" made of bricks stacked five high with a piece of tin or metal laid across the top for a grill. I kept the fire going underneath with twigs, any bits of lumber I could find, corncobs and wood split from trees we cut with a crosscut saw.

Our first iron cookstove, believe it or not, had a door on both the front and back of the oven ... and a tiny little hole under the grates from which we had to dip the ashes with a large spoon. It was strictly a wood-burning range ... but you will never taste ambrosia until you have eaten potatoes panfried in an iron skillet on an old cookstove *(especially if those potatoes are waiting for you after you've been cleaning the barn, cutting wood or hunting cottontails all day in below-freezing weather—MOTHER)*.

The second cookstove we owned was more modern. It had four lids (burners to the present generation), an oblong cooking space, big oven and a reservoir which—kept filled—always yielded scalding hot water for many and various uses. Above all, it had an ashpan with which you could clean the firebox with a minimum of mess and effort. The warming oven at the top was another extremely handy feature and, to make the range perfect, it would also burn coal and hold a fire overnight.

The stove required no thermostat for either its top or oven. You simply moved your pans from the reservoir toward the front of the range to get any desired heat and you soon learned to judge baking temperatures by touching a wet finger to the oven door.

Our next cookstove was a wondrous enameled job with a water coil in the firebox. We connected this through a wall into a tank in the bathroom and the stove then supplied us with cooking and baking facilities, heat and hot water for bathing! Alas, we moved during WW II and had to leave our treasure in the old house. Through some government agency we got a paper that allowed us to buy another cookstove, but this one was not exactly new and a little enamel was missing here and there. It was still a good range to heat and cook by.

Youngsters sometimes ask if a wood-burning stove isn't hot to cook on in the summer. No, not especially. In the summer you use cobs, old shingles, twigs and small splinters of wood to build a quick fire that burns out rapidly. And you do it again for the next meal. Besides, the proper place for a wood-burning range is a big, old farmhouse kitchen that you can open up in the summer.

Whenever I see advertisements for "new" ovens that clean themselves, I have to chuckle. My old cookstoves never had places (not even the ovens) that required scouring like the electric range we have at present. Of course things ran over and burned . . . but soon thereafter you could lift or wipe the ash away and no spot remained at all. Nothing ever seems to happen to the top of a cookstove except that, over the years, it will lose its intense black look. A quick wipe with a greased paper will take care of that.

There's one more point in favor of the old iron stove and that is, yes, food cooked on one really does taste better. I don't actually know why but I suspect that—in the case of baking anyway—the intense, dry heat of a cookstove's oven browns on a crust so fast that almost all the flavor is immediately locked into the pie, loaf of bread, roast or whatever. It's a simple matter then to slide the dish or pan forward to "just the right spot" nearer the oven door so that the goodies within can bake at their own deliberate pace. There *is* a difference! ●

A. MICHAEL WASSIL:
STOVEPIPE POWER

With all the discussion that's going on about natural power for home use, no one yet seems to have expounded at length on one source of energy that's readily available to homesteaders: namely, the heat that goes up the old stovepipe. Seems a shame to let those calories get away . . . especially when you think of them in terms of firewood and all the energy you've expended cutting it.

Although I've never actually measured the Btu's roaring out the top end of a stovepipe, I *have* toasted bread (in about one second) and boiled pots of water in the hot blast from a small stove. Perhaps some thermal buff out there in MOTHER-land would like to do the measurements on the quantity of heat that escapes up the flue . . . given various-sized stoves, different lengths and diameters of stovepipe and varying intensities of flame in the firebox. At any rate, while the rest of us are waiting for such a report, here are a few suggestions for utilizing some of that energy.

[1] Use the stovepipe itself as a radiant heater, the way many pioneer builders did in New England, here in Ontario and elsewhere. In a single-storied structure, put the stove at one end of the building and carry the pipe horizontally to the other end and then out as shown in Fig. 1.

When there's more than one story, just run the vent straight up through the rooms above (see Fig. 2). Whatever you do, though, don't put your stovepipe up in the manner depicted on the cover of MOTHER NO. 18!

FIGURE 1

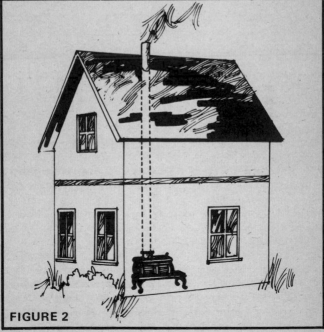

FIGURE 2

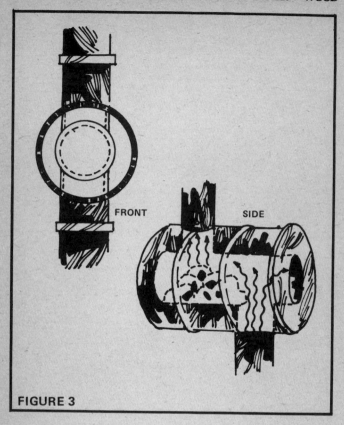

FRONT   SIDE

FIGURE 3

[2] The Palace Grand in Dawson City, Yukon Territory has a unique (the owners claim) variation on Suggestion Number 1. This device—which they call a double stove—is simply a large hot air chamber partway up the stovepipe that traps some of the escaping heat and radiates it into the room.

The model in Dawson is a bit complicated, and consists of a modified 45-gallon steel drum (see Fig. 3). I imagine that an unmodified steel drum (Fig. 4) would also work. Either version would be more efficient filled with pebbles or stones, which would absorb heat—sauna-style—and radiate it back even after the stove itself had burned low. Don't pack in the rocks very snugly, though, or you'll kill the draft.

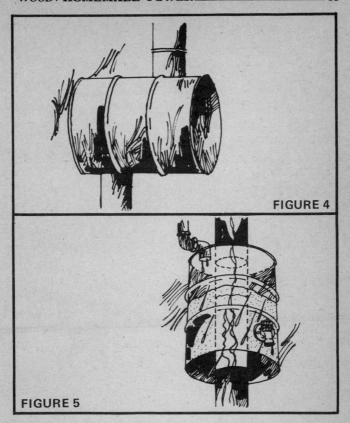

FIGURE 4

FIGURE 5

[3] Instead of an air chamber, put a water tank (Fig. 5) on the stovepipe. This involves a little plumbing since you have to run the pipe through the middle of the water container. You'll need a tap at the bottom of the tank and some sort of inlet at the top (this could be as elaborate as a float valve hooked up to your main water source to keep the reservoir full automatically, or as simple as a movable lid that allows you to dump in replacement water by hand). There you are . . . a convenient hot water supply.

Although insulation will keep the water in the tank hot longer, I'd advise against it. In the winter, when the stove is going all the time, the water will never get cool anyhow . . .

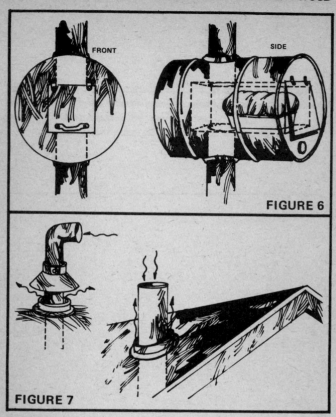

FRONT　　SIDE

FIGURE 6

FIGURE 7

and the bare metal of the reservoir will act as a radiator.

[4] Put an oven (Fig. 6) in the stovepipe. Units that fit into a standard smoke vent used to be available commercially *(and as far as I know they still are . . . from the Louisville Tin and Stove Company, 737 South 13th Street, Louisville, Kentucky 40210.—MOTHER).* Or you can make your own.

[5] In MOTHER NO. 18 (pg. 112), Bill Lange suggested a concentric double stovepipe in which one of the conduits draws outside air into the heater and warms it in the process.

I suggest using the center pipe as the intake and extending it a couple of feet higher at the upper end than the surrounding output duct (see Fig. 7). At the lower—or stove—end, the

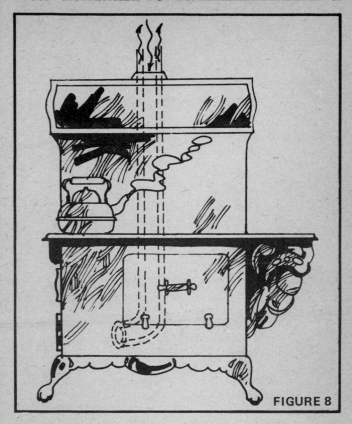

FIGURE 8

intake pipe should be taken right through the bottom of the firebox into the ash box chamber (Fig. 8).

This arrangement, of course, would necessitate some modi-fication of the damper so, instead, you could run the intake pipe around the damper . . . or eliminate the damper itself and regulate the firebox by a smaller valve in the intake pipe only.

[6] Finally, and most elaborately of all, you could use that stovepipe heat to boil water to run a small steam engine, either a conventional piston type or a more efficient turbine. The steam engine in turn could power a small generator to supply a modest amount of electricity . . . sufficient, maybe, to operate a few light bulbs. ●

So you got the dome up this summer and it shot your entire budget. You've already moved in, but winter's comin' on and you have no idea how you're gonna keep warm. Wouldn't it be nice if you could find some way to heat the thing free . . . and wouldn't it be even nicer to get paid for keeping warm?

Yes, indeed. And you can do it too. Bill Cheney does. Although Bill heats a shop and not a home with the rig described in this article, there's no reason why it can't see you through that first homesteading winter . . . or more.

Naturally, MOTHER advises that you follow construction drawings exactly and observe proper precautions when using your heater.

The burner and blower assembly on Bill Cheney's heater is bracketed to a conventional bottled-gas cylinder, ready to be connected to a fuel line. Rheostat (below bracket) regulates blower motor.

BILL CHENEY:
CHEAP HEAT

Reprinted courtesy of Popular Science
Monthly. ©1961 *by Popular Science Publishing Co., Inc.*

The fuel I burn to heat my shop doesn't cost me a penny. In fact, I'm *paid* a buck for every 100 gallons I haul away. It's old crankcase oil, and gas stations are happy to have me pump it out of their waste tanks.

I built my own stove from a condemned bottled-gas cylin-

Rear of stove needs damper if gas is burned instead of oil. Disk is 1/8" steel plate. 1" smaller in diameter than exhaust pipe; shaft is 1/2" steel rod. Platform welded on top of stove is optional.

der. You can pick one up for peanuts because legally they can't be used again, and it's too costly to cut them up for scrap. If you can't get one, a 30-, 50- or 100-gallon steel drum can be substituted. My stove cylinder is 14" by 40", but these dimensions aren't critical. The ones for the throat and firing

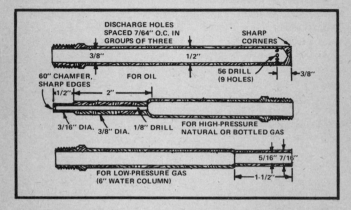

All jets machined from 6" lengths of 5/8" brass rod, with standard 1/4" pipe threads on one end for screwing on fuel-regulating valve. The main shank of each has a 1/2" outside and a 3/8" inside diameter.

Three interchangeable jets (for different fuels) can be used on heater. They're slipped through bored plug and deflector made from bushing, as shown in insert. Braze blade at 15-degree angle from axis.

port *are*, since they guarantee the hot throat that's required to burn any fuel. I circulate the heat with a small electric fan, and there's plenty to spread around: With clean oil, the heater can produce up to 500,000 Btu's per hour.

It's clean heat, too, although some smoke is generated when the burner is first started. To carry this (and all carbon monoxide fumes) outside, a stack is required. Where erecting one is impractical, you can burn natural or bottled gas, instead. You just insert a different jet nozzle. When burning gas fuels, I exhaust right into the shop . . . there's some water vapor, but not enough to cause troublesome condensation. Better check local regulations, though. If they specify a stack for gas, too, you might as well enjoy the economy of crankcase oil.

Start with the stove. If you've been able to pick up an old bottled-gas cylinder, you must prepare it in a special way. Set the tank upright on its base and fill it with water (to prevent any possibility of igniting and exploding gases that might be inside). Lay out an 8" circle at the crown of the domed top. Using a cutting torch, pierce the tank with a short arc cut out on this circle. (As the cut will be below water line, water will flow out until level with it.) Complete the circle and drain the tank.

With the tank upended, cut a 6" diameter hole in the center of the base for the exhaust. It's in the center so heated air will

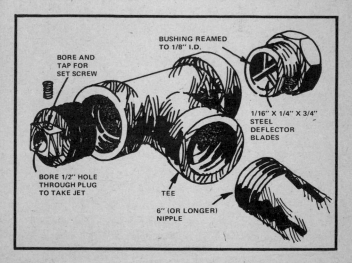

BORE AND TAP FOR SET SCREW

BUSHING REAMED TO 1/8" I.D.

1/16" X 1/4" X 3/4" STEEL DEFLECTOR BLADES

BORE 1/2" HOLE THROUGH PLUG TO TAKE JET

TEE

6" (OR LONGER) NIPPLE

build up in the top of the stove, improving combustion as well as retaining heat. I formed my exhaust pipe by bending a sheet of 1/8" steel plate, but lighter material can be used.

Weld the throat at the other end, and complete the stove by placing it on its side in a sturdy stand. Mine is a pipe frame welded to the cylinder and equipped with casters so the stove can be rolled around the shop or used outside.

You need lots of air to burn the fuel properly. I bought a used vacuum cleaner blower and brazed a 1" pipe coupling into its outlet for attaching the burner pipe. Since throttling the air output causes the blower to speed up, an airflow valve could damage the motor. Instead, I installed a rheostat, salvaged from a sewing machine, to regulate the motor speed.

Drilling the discharge holes in the closed end of the oil jet is a critical operation. Sharp edges are essential for clean burning. Be sure drill runs true at high speed and don't hold jet in fingers.

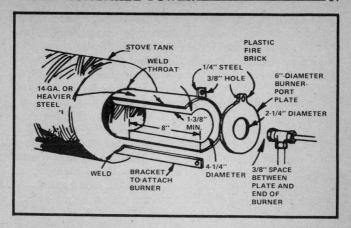

The heart of the heater is the burner itself. It's made of four black-iron 1" pipe fittings. The deflector imparts a swirling motion to the blower air that helps mix it with the fuel from the jet. The jet is secured with a setscrew so it can be adjusted . . . or replaced with another type if the fuel is changed. The position of the jet, in or out, depends on the choice of fuel, and—if it is gas—the fuel pressure. When oil is used, the bottom of the supply tank should be about a foot above the burner.

To start the burner, if oil is the fuel, open the port plate and thrust a crumpled newspaper or oil-soaked rag well into the throat. Light this, close the port, turn on a little air and slowly open the fuel valve until oil ignites in the throat. Gradually increase the air supply, then give more oil. Once the throat becomes hot, increase the flow of both air and oil, experimenting for the best mixture and proper jet position. When properly set, there should be no smoke or soot. To shut the stove off turn off the oil first, letting the blower run until the fire is completely out. If this isn't done, oil may drip onto the hot throat and flame will puff out of the burner port.

When firing with gas, start the blower at low speed and hold a piece of burning paper just below the closed port while slowly turning on the gas.

Whatever your fuel, never look directly into the port . . . always inspect it at an angle or use a small mirror. While the fuel can't explode, the great heat might singe your whiskers. ●

A number of companies now market machines designed to help you roll your family's old newspapers into "logs" that can be burned in a fireplace or stove. After testing a couple of these devices, I think the idea is a good one for two reasons: [1] it puts recycling on a real grassroots basis by allowing you to directly convert part of your waste into something useful and [2] it gives you a small, partial answer to today's fuel shortage.

There's no need to shell out good dollars for a "log rolling" machine to realize these benefits, however. Just get yourself a length of old broomstick and start tightly rolling one section or sheet of newspaper after another around it as shown in Fig. 1. When the "log" is about two inches thick, slip the broomstick out, tie the bundle with light wire and soak the paper in one pint of charcoal lighter or kerosene (*never* gasoline). If you have no other soaking tray, you can make one that will last for years from a sheet of heavy-duty aluminum foil (Fig. 2).

Once the rolled paper has soaked up the fluid, wrap more waste newsprint around the saturated core . . . enough to make a log about four to five inches thick. Tie the bundle with light wire and set it aside. Three of these logs will burn all evening in a fireplace. ◓

NEWSPAPER LOGS

FIGURE 1

FIGURE 2

FIGURE 3

TOM MURRAY:
TWICE THE WOOD IN HALF THE TIME

Here's a way to cut firewood that not only increases productivity on a cords-per-day basis, but makes the job easier too. This secret allows you to saw a number of logs, slabs or whatever at once . . . so you won't have to reposition yourself and your tools every time you cut a piece to proper firebox length.

To use the method, you need to own or have access to the following: a maul or sledgehammer, a steel bar about five feet in length (for starting postholes), eight or ten fenceposts five to seven feet long and a chain saw.

OK. Choose a spot for the cutting operation. Since you're going to the trouble of driving eight or more posts, the location should be at least somewhat permanent. Pick a site that's handy for the unloading of your truck or other wood-hauling vehicle, and close to the shed where the cut fuel will be stored.

Now drive the posts. To do so with a sledge or maul, you need "starter" holes . . . and that's where the steel bar comes in. Take a firm grip on the rod, ram it down into the spot where your first upright is to go and move it back and forth sideways to widen the opening. Continue this operation until the hole is around eighteen inches deep (width is relatively unimportant). Next, start three more holes in a straight line

You'll find it much easier to make a "starter" hole for each post and then drive the upright in with a maul . . . rather than dig a hole to fit.

with the first. If your logs are long, you may want to set five or even six posts in each row. The distance between excavations should be the same as the desired length of firewood . . . in my case, eighteen inches.

Go ahead and drive the four to six posts with your maul, just far enough into the ground to anchor them securely. Then make an imaginary mark parallel to the row and about twelve inches away (farther if your logs are fat), and hammer in a second line of stakes, each one directly opposite its counterpart in the first line of uprights.

That's it! Your woodsman's aid is ready to use. Take your logs or slabs and lay them lengthwise between the two lines of posts (stacking the firewood to just below the top of the hold-

Once your crude "jig" is finished, you can cut a week's supply of wood in minutes with a chain saw and just a little muscle work.

ers). Then start the chain saw and—after centering your cut in the middle of the gap between two sets of stakes—slice right down through the whole pile. Repeat this action in the next bay, the one after that, etc.

As you near the bottom of each cut, take care not to run your saw through the undermost log and damage its chain on the dirt and stones beneath. In fact, it's a good idea to leave a large uncut timber or railroad tie on the ground between the lines of posts as insurance.

You'll be amazed how much this simple trick shortens the time and work of preparing firewood. In fact, when you use my system, it'll take you longer to stack your wood in the shed than it'll take you to cut it! ◓

WATER
MAKE IT WORK FOR YOU

It seems almost certain that man's use of the water wheel dates back at least 100 years before the birth of Christ. Today —in the form of the turbines at the heart of our monstrous hydroelectric systems—it goes on stronger than ever.

Perhaps too strong. For somehow, during the past 50 years or so, we seem to have convinced ourselves that only the giant water power installations are "worth fooling with" in this modern age. Whereas every little village and hamlet on the North American Continent boasted a water-driven mill in 1900, the few that now remain in working order are scarce as hen's teeth and, generally, are operated only seasonally for the tourist trade.

Once again, however, the pendulum is starting to swing in the other direction. As today's "back to the land" movement continues to gain strength, more and more "new pioneers" find themselves sitting on a little patch of land beside a stream . . . but with either a definite distaste for the local electrical utility or no local utility to feel distaste for. Naturally enough, a growing number of such individuals sooner or later begin to think about harnessing that stream with "a little water wheel of our own".

Well, as this section shows, it can be done. Overshot wheel, Pelton turbine or hydraulic ram . . . whichever way you want to go, you'll find the plans here. And, if you need reassurance that a homemade hydropower system will really work, you're sure to find Thomas Oates' story (he's been operating such a system in the mountains of North Carolina for 40 years) of particular interest. Or, if the seeming complexity of things like hydraulic rams and Pelton turbines tend to scare you away from a personal water power system before you begin, take a quick look at the simple rock tumbler which closes out this part of the book. See! Getting useful work done by a flowing stream doesn't have to be complicated at all! ◉

Back in 1947, Popular Science *printed a five-part article that very concisely sketched out every step necessary for establishing a small water-power plant on a farm or homestead. That information is just as valuable today for many of MOTHER's readers as it was 25 years ago and* Popular Science *has kindly given us reprint rights to the whole package.*

C. D. BASSET:
BUILD YOUR OWN
WATER
POWER
PLANT

Reprinted courtesy of Popular Science *Monthly.* © *1947 Popular Science Pub. Co., Inc.*

PART ONE:
THERE'S ENERGY
IN THAT STREAM!

Many farms, ranches and other fair-sized tracts of land embrace at least one brook within their limits. In most cases, the idea that a small stream can provide a useful source of power has never occurred to the property owner or—if it did—has been rejected as silly. The fact remains, nevertheless, that impressive advantages can spring from small water power installations.

Electricity can be generated for general use, for pumping water and for standby or emergency purposes; and the pond that is usually created can serve additionally as a means for watering livestock in dry times, for fire fighting, as a swimming pool, as a place to raise fish for sport or as a "crop" . . . and for landscaping or scenic purposes.

Power can be obtained from any flowing stream, no matter how small. Whether it's desirable to harness this power depends on two factors. First, does water flow all the year round, even in the late summer months? Second, does enough water flow to make the harnessing of it economically sound? The first factor is, of course, known to the property owner by observation; the second may be determined by simple measurements.

What's the least amount of power that is worth developing? There is in this country at least one water wheel manufacturer who makes a line of small-capacity units, and this company's smallest hydroelectric unit develops 1/2 kilowatt. From this it can be inferred that, in this company's experience, it is not economically wise to harness a stream that will not develop at least 500 watts dependably at the switchboard. Half a kilowatt will light 10 fair-sized lamps or supply 2/3 hp to operate, say, a deep-well pump. With this figure in mind as a criterion, the reader can make a preliminary reconnaissance of the water power available on his property. The chances are he will be surprised; even a seemingly insignificant stream can deliver many times this minimum.

The power available at the site of a water wheel (that is,

before deductions for inefficiencies in the wheel and generator) is expressed in this formula:

$$Hp = \frac{62.4 \times Q \times H}{33,000}$$

Here Q is the cubic feet of water passing through the wheel in one minute, H is the "head" or vertical distance in feet through which the water falls, 62.4 is the weight in pounds of 1 cu. ft. of water and 33,000 the number of foot-pounds per

This 4" impulse wheel, built for war requirements, was direct-connected to a small generator. It can be run off an ordinary water faucet. Note the removable nozzle and the tiny bucket, lower right.

IF LOCATED AT A WATERFALL, RIGHT, A DAM WILL OFTEN BE SMALL AND INEXPENSIVE AND THE TOTAL HEAD FAIRLY LARGE.

A WIDE VALLEY CALLS FOR A LONG DAM, AS HIGH AS POSSIBLE TO PROVIDE THE MAXIMUM HEAD.

SWAMPY MEADOWLAND INDICATES THE PRESENCE OF A NATURAL RESERVOIR. PLACE THE DAM AT THE NARROWEST POINT WHERE THE BROOK LEAVES.

FIGURE 1

You can cut your water power installation costs noticeably if you locate your dam [1] where the greatest fall can be realized in the shortest distance and [2] at the narrowest part of a stream.

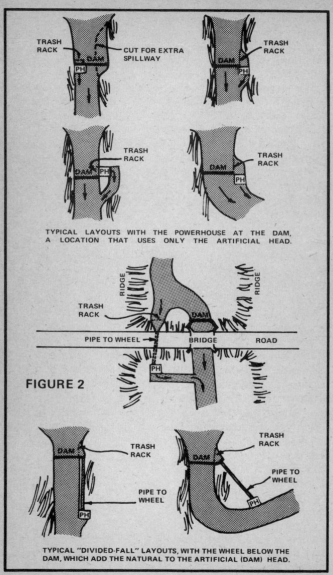

TYPICAL LAYOUTS WITH THE POWERHOUSE AT THE DAM,
A LOCATION THAT USES ONLY THE ARTIFICIAL HEAD.

FIGURE 2

TYPICAL "DIVIDED-FALL" LAYOUTS, WITH THE WHEEL BELOW THE
DAM, WHICH ADD THE NATURAL TO THE ARTIFICIAL (DAM) HEAD.

A water wheel may be situated either right at a dam or some distance below it. Either location has advantages and disadvantages.

minute in 1 hp. A number of methods exist by which the variables Q and H can be determined, but—before considering them—it's well to examine first the possible sites for the dam and wheel, since they will necessarily affect the amount of head secured.

The location of the dam, as suggested in Fig. 1, should be governed by two principles. It should be placed where the greatest useful head is obtainable . . . that is, where the greatest fall occurs in the shortest length of stream. Such a site is often indicated by a natural waterfall, by a conspicuously steep slope or by the swiftness of the current. The second locating principle is a simple matter of cost: a dam should be placed where it can be smallest and still impound the most water. This means, in general, that it should be placed where the stream valley or cut is narrowest.

The site of the water wheel, Fig. 2, may be either at the dam or some distance below it. The former location is the more common, being simpler to build and eliminating the need for a pipe or penstock to deliver water to the wheel. Disadvantages include the fact that the spillway must be of ample capacity to protect the powerhouse in time of high water, and the fact that only the "artificial head"—that created by the dam itself—is available. In cases where the ground falls away abruptly below the dam site, the "divided-flow" layout may be desirable, for it greatly increases the head.

Another preliminary calculation should be made as to the height of the proposed dam. This is restricted, as a rule, only by the height of the valley walls at the site, and by the materials, equipment and money available for building it. The higher it is, the greater the head and the larger the pond that will be created. "Pondage"—water stored for use in times of peak demand—is an important factor in water power calculations. Power is rarely needed 24 hours a day, and construction of a dam of sufficient height to provide water storage will greatly increase the power available at the time of day required.

If, for example, a wheel is to be run for 16 hours a day, and if a dam is built that will impound all water flowing into the pond during the idle eight hours, the power capacity will be increased by 50 percent. Don't neglect to distinguish between "live storage"—the volume of water represented by the difference in height of the spillway flashboards and the wheel

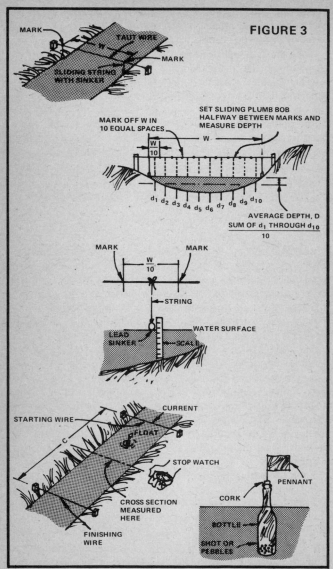

FIGURE 3

MARK

TAUT WIRE

W

MARK

SLIDING STRING WITH SINKER

MARK OFF W IN 10 EQUAL SPACES

SET SLIDING PLUMB BOB HALFWAY BETWEEN MARKS AND MEASURE DEPTH

W

$\frac{W}{10}$

d_1 d_2 d_3 d_4 d_5 d_6 d_7 d_8 d_9 d_{10}

AVERAGE DEPTH, D
$$\frac{\text{SUM OF } d_1 \text{ THROUGH } d_{10}}{10}$$

MARK

MARK

$\frac{W}{10}$

STRING

WATER SURFACE

LEAD SINKER

SCALE

STARTING WIRE

CURRENT

FLOAT

C

STOP WATCH

CROSS SECTION MEASURED HERE

FINISHING WIRE

PENNANT

CORK

BOTTLE

SHOT OR PEBBLES

One of the easiest methods of measuring the flow of a stream is with a float. (See full explanation in the accompanying text.)

intake—and "dead storage": the volume of water below the level of the wheel intake. The former is power-banked against a time of need; the latter is worthless, powerwise.

Once the dam and powerhouse are tentatively sited, and the height of the first is provisionally set, it is time to measure the power available. Assume that all water flowing in the stream can be made to flow through the wheel, which is a fair assumption on small installations. This flow (Q in the power formula) can be determined by the "weir method", which involves constructing a temporary dam of controlled proportions and which will be detailed in a subsequent installment, or by the "float method", which is theoretically a trifle less accurate, though still quite satisfactory.

The float method (Fig. 3) involves the formula:

$$Q = A \times V \times 60$$

in which Q is the volume of water flowing in cubic feet per minute, A is the cross-sectional area of the stream in square feet at the site, and V is the average velocity of the stream at this point, expressed in feet per second.

Select a length of the stream that is fairly straight, with sides approximately parallel, and unobstructed by rocks or shoals for a distance of about 100 feet. Stretch a taut wire squarely across the stream near the middle of this length and measure the width of the stream here in inches. Mark this width off on the wire and divide it into ten equal divisions. From the center point of each division, measure the depth of the water in inches. Then average the depth figure by adding each value and dividing by 10. The cross-sectional area of the stream, A, is now secured by multiplying this average depth by the width, and dividing the result by 144 to obtain the answer in square feet.

Your next step in determining Q is to measure the rate of flow. Using a steel tape, mark off a course along the bank that is 100 feet long; the midpoint of this course should be at the line where the cross section was measured. Stretch wires or rope tautly across the stream at each end of the course, and make a float by filling a bottle so that it rides awash. Provide it with a pennant so that you can follow it easily. Then set the float adrift in the middle of the stream, timing its progress over the course with a stopwatch, beginning just when the pennant passes the first wire and stopping just as it passes the second.

Make a series of runs, averaging the results. The speed of the float in feet per second is then the length of the course divided by the average time. This result is not, however, suitable for immediate use in the flow formula, since not all the water in a stream flows as rapidly as that in the center and near the top. If you multiply the float speed by the coefficient 0.83, the resultant value will serve as V in the flow formula.

Given an estimate of the amount of head to be present at the wheel, you can now make a rough determination of the horsepower your stream can provide. It's worth emphasizing, though, that this figure is necessarily only as accurate as the measurements that produced it, and that the power indicated is that present *at the time of measuring.* A single stream-flow value is not of itself particularly useful unless it is obtained at the time of lowest water, usually in the late summer months. Moreover, even if you have measured the flow at slack-water time, the figures should if possible be supplemented by others secured during maximum springtime flow . . . so that you can calculate the size of spillway needed to prevent damage to your installation in times of high water.

It's a good practice—for backyard engineers as well as for professionals—to refine, cross-check and test your measurements by all means at your disposal. Such checks will not only reduce the chance of disappointment in the final result, but will also permit calculated economics in construction and greater efficiency in operation.

Your estimate of the head present at the wheel, for instance, should be carefully checked, since head is a vital element in the efficiency of any water power project. Several methods for determining the head rather precisely will be given in the next installment, together with the weir method for measuring flow. Subsequent installments will consider types of dams, methods of construction, wheels best suited to small plants and plans for building them.

Before you begin even a preliminary reconnaissance of water power on your property, the writer suggests you secure a loose-leaf notebook to be devoted solely to the project. Develop the habit of neatly entering all data as it is obtained, not forgetting to note dates and stream conditions at the time measurements are made. Such a record is a great help in performing sound calculations and producing excellent results.

PART TWO: PUTTING WATER TO WORK

Inches Depth over Stake, D	1/8 in.	1/4 in.	3/8 in.	1/2 in.	5/8 in.	3/4 in.	7/8 in.
1 inch	.40	.47	.55	.65	.74	.83	.93	1.03
2 "	1.14	1.24	1.36	1.47	1.59	1.71	1.83	1.96
3 "	2.09	2.23	2.36	2.50	2.63	2.78	2.92	3.07
4 "	3.22	3.37	3.52	3.68	3.83	3.99	4.16	4.32
5 "	4.50	4.67	4.84	5.01	5.18	5.36	5.54	5.72
6 "	5.90	6.09	6.28	6.47	6.65	6.85	7.05	7.25
7 "	7.44	7.64	7.84	8.05	8.25	8.45	8.66	8.86
8 "	9.10	9.31	9.52	9.74	9.96	10.18	10.40	10.62
9 "	10.86	11.08	11.31	11.54	11.77	12.00	12.23	12.47
10 "	12.71	12.95	13.19	13.43	13.67	13.93	14.16	14.42
11 "	14.67	14.92	15.18	15.43	15.67	15.96	16.20	16.46
12 "	16.73	16.99	17.26	17.52	17.78	18.05	18.32	18.58
13 "	18.87	19.14	19.42	19.69	19.97	20.24	20.52	20.80
14 "	21.09	21.37	21.65	21.94	22.22	22.51	22.70	23.08
15 "	23.38	23.67	23.97	24.26	24.56	24.86	25.16	25.46
16 "	25.76	26.06	26.36	26.66	26.97	27.27	27.58	27.89
17 "	28.20	28.51	28.82	29.14	29.45	29.76	30.08	30.39
18 "	30.70	31.02	31.34	31.66	31.98	32.31	32.63	32.96
19 "	33.29	33.61	33.94	34.27	34.60	34.94	35.27	35.60
20 "	35.94	36.27	36.60	36.94	37.28	37.62	37.96	38.31
21 "	38.65	39.00	39.34	39.69	40.04	40.39	40.73	41.09
22 "	41.43	41.78	42.13	42.49	42.84	43.20	43.56	43.92
23 "	44.28	44.64	45.00	45.38	45.71	46.08	46.43	46.81
24 "	47.18	47.55	47.91	48.28	48.65	49.02	49.39	49.76

The table above will allow you to very quickly and easily calculate the quantity of water passing over a rectangular weir in cubic feet per minute (cfm) for each inch of notch width. Depth D is read as a combination of the lefthand column and the top row. For example: If the depth over your stake is 5-3/8", follow over the 5 (fifth row) to 3/8" (fourth column), and read the value as 5.01 cfm. That's the volume of flow for each inch of notch width. To find the total flow for your weir, multiply this figure by the notch's width in inches.

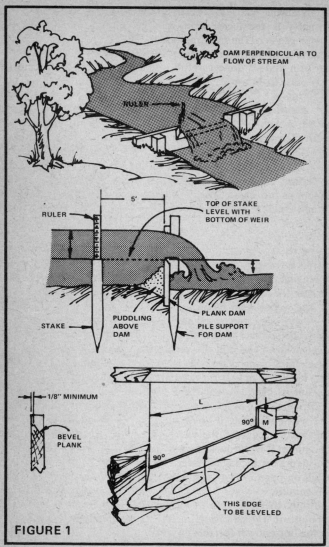

FIGURE 1

It's more trouble to measure the flow of a stream with a weir than with a float . . . but it's also more accurate. The weir method of calculation, it should further be noted, is especially handy for figuring the flow of a stream that is shallow or already has a dam.

Measuring the flow of water in the stream or brook on your property is the logical first step in planning a small water power project. The float method of making this measurement, described in part one of this article, is generally the easiest to perform and—if done carefully—is accurate enough for most purposes. If, however, a stream is so shallow at low-water time as to impede the progress of a weighted float, the weir method of measuring flow has advantages. Essentially a kind of water meter, a weir is a rectangular notch or spillway of carefully controlled proportions located in the center of a small, temporary dam. Two simple measurements permit the volume of flow to be accurately calculated.

Before constructing the dam, measure the depth of the stream at the site . . . the depth of the weir notch, M in Fig. 1, should equal this. Since the dam need not be permanent, simple plank or tongue-and-groove lumber will serve adequately. No water must flow except through the weir, so care should be taken to seal the ends and bottom of the dam by extending planks into the banks and below the bed of the stream. Clay or loam puddling on the upstream side will stop minor seepage. Be sure the dam is perpendicular to the flow of the stream.

The weir should be located in the center of the dam, with its lower edge not less than 1 foot above the surface of the water below the dam. This lower edge should be accurately leveled. Both this and the vertical edges of the weir should be beveled with the sharp edge upstream (a 1/8" flat on the bevel will keep the edge from breaking down). Proportion the weir so that its length L is not less than 3M, and larger if possible.

Drive a stake in the streambed at least 5 feet upstream from the weir, pounding it down until its top is exactly level with the bottom edge of the weir. Allow the stream to reach its maximum flow through the weir and then measure with a ruler the depth in inches of water over the stake. Referring to the table on page 77, you can now read the number of cubic feet per minute of water for each inch of L, the weir width. If you multiply the figure from the table by L, the result is the total amount of water flowing in cubic feet per minute, which is Q in the horsepower formula given last month.

If your stream is already dammed, there is no need to construct another dam just to measure flow. It is quite possible to employ the existing dam, using its spillway as a weir, provided that all water can be made to pass through the spillway. Con-

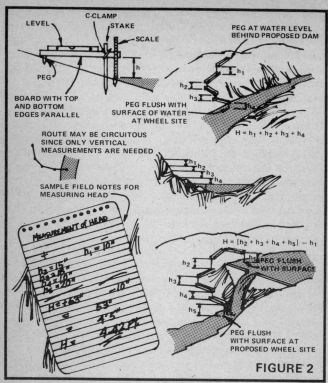

FIGURE 2

The information above illustrates how to measure a stream's head with a carpenter's level, straightedge and pegs. Best of all, the calculations can be made either before or after a dam is built.

struct a wooden or metal frame to fit the spillway and seal it in place snugly. The center of this frame should incorporate a properly proportioned weir notch. As before, M should equal the depth of the water flowing through the spillway before the weir is installed, and L may in most cases be half the width of the spillway.

To get an accurate estimate of available horsepower, you will need a precise figure for H, the head of water that will be present. "Head" may be defined as the vertical distance in feet from the surface of water in the pond behind the dam to the surface of the stream below the dam at the site of the wheel. This figure may be obtained by any of several methods in cases where a dam is already present, and with scarcely greater difficulty at the site of an unbuilt dam.

Measuring a difference in elevation can be quickly and accurately done with an engineer's transit and leveling rod. But—since not everyone has access to these instruments, and since those who do would not need instruction on so simple a job as running a level—we'll pass on to other methods.

Fig. 2 illustrates a very simple way of measuring a vertical distance. The equipment required is a carpenter's level, a folding rule or steel tape, a 1" by 2" by 6' board with two edges planed parallel, two wooden pegs, a stake and a C-clamp. These are items that can be found in almost any home . . . and certainly on any farm. Though the method can be somewhat tedious if the difference in elevation is large, the results will be quite accurate with ordinary care in leveling and measuring. Note in the drawing that in the case of a pre-existent dam, one or more measurements needed to carry around the edge of the dam are subtracted from—rather than added to—the total.

Less practical in most cases, though still of occasional special value, are two other ways to determine head. Elevations can be measured quite readily by the techniques of photographic surveying. For those who are familiar with the procedure, it is a simple matter to take the required pictures in the field and then scale the required elevation at the desk from the developed photographs. Another method involves the use of a barometer, either mercury or aneroid, to indicate differences in height. However, this method is useful only where the head to be measured is considerable, say more than 25 feet, and calls for special techniques to hold the probable error down to acceptable proportions. Except in unusual circumstances, the writer recommends that the method in Fig. 2 be employed, inasmuch as it requires little special equipment and with ordinary care gives good results.

With sound figures for both H and Q, you are now ready to calculate the available horsepower of your installation with the formula given in the first installment. If the power is found to be sufficient to warrant continuing with the project, say 2/3 hp at the least, your next step is to determine the nature of your power requirements. Here individual variations are so many as to make it difficult to outline a specific procedure. It's possible, however, to suggest factors you should consider in planning your power plant.

A simple method of measuring head. With a straightedge held level, the vertical height between a pair of pegs is read off and noted.

Some of the uses to which small-capacity installations are successfully put include directly powering pumps, mills, machine tools or other small-demand machinery and driving a generator to supply electricity for either lighting or power purposes. The latter type of installation is, of course, the more flexible and generally useful. Determine, then, the uses you propose for your water power, and tabulate the horsepower required after each item. In the case of electric motors or appliances rated in amperes or watts, remember that watts are volts times amperes, and that 746 watts are equal to 1 hp.

From this tabulation, the peak load can be determined. This is the sum of the power demands made by different pieces of equipment that may probably be in use at one time. Knowing power and load, you can now determine if the proposed installation will be on a sound basis.

Do not use your available horsepower figure directly, since deductions should first be made for losses in the water wheel . . . and in the generator, if one is to be used. For small installations, assume wheel efficiency to be 75 percent. (Many small wheels will better this, but the assumption will provide leeway for possible optimism in measuring H and Q.) Generator efficiency can be assumed to be 80 percent . . . a figure that will also be bettered in many cases, but is on the safe side. Thus,

Your last measurement, when using this method of calculating head, should be to the surface of the water at the power wheel's site.

switchboard power may be expressed at .75 X .8 X hp, or .6 of the available horsepower.

At this stage of the game, it's well to mull over the possible variations and combinations, rather than to proceed with specific construction plans. Consider for example the decision required if the indicated switchboard power will seemingly handle the peak load ... whether to build a dam just large enough to do this job, or to build one substantially larger to handle possible future increases in power requirements. The former choice will be obviously cheaper at first but may not be so in the long run, since power demands have a way of growing and since it is rarely satisfactory to increase the structure of an existing dam.

If the peak load is apparently too high, various possibilities should be considered. Will "pondage"—water stored behind the dam overnight or in slack periods—help out? Can the use of equipment be dispensed with? Is the project necessarily a year-round enterprise or can the low-power characteristics of the dry season be ignored? A word of caution on these points may not be amiss: it's far better to plan an installation that will provide more power than you need than one which doesn't supply enough.

Whether, in the event that you decide to generate electric-

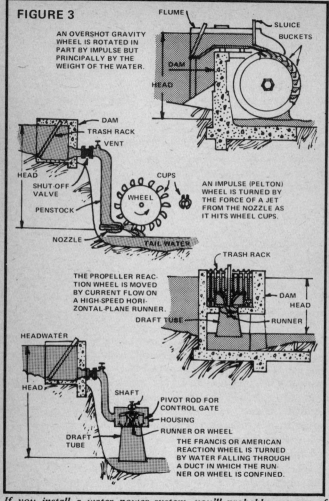

FIGURE 3

AN OVERSHOT GRAVITY WHEEL IS ROTATED IN PART BY IMPULSE BUT PRINCIPALLY BY THE WEIGHT OF THE WATER.

FLUME

SLUICE

BUCKETS

DAM

HEAD

DAM

TRASH RACK

VENT

HEAD

SHUT-OFF VALVE

PENSTOCK

NOZZLE

CUPS

WHEEL

AN IMPULSE (PELTON) WHEEL IS TURNED BY THE FORCE OF A JET FROM THE NOZZLE AS IT HITS WHEEL CUPS.

TAIL WATER

THE PROPELLER REACTION WHEEL IS MOVED BY CURRENT FLOW ON A HIGH-SPEED HORIZONTAL-PLANE RUNNER.

TRASH RACK

DAM

HEAD

DRAFT TUBE

RUNNER

HEADWATER

HEAD

SHAFT

PIVOT ROD FOR CONTROL GATE

HOUSING

RUNNER OR WHEEL

DRAFT TUBE

THE FRANCIS OR AMERICAN REACTION WHEEL IS TURNED BY WATER FALLING THROUGH A DUCT IN WHICH THE RUNNER OR WHEEL IS CONFINED.

If you install a water power system, you'll probably use one of these four wheels to convert the fluid's energy to useable work.

ity, to use AC or DC is another decision to make. In circumstances where the generator must be located some distance from the load, AC is the only choice, for DC transmission losses would be too high (amounting in small installations to a

prohibitive percentage of switchboard power). If your buildings and equipment are already wired to receive one type of
current, it would obviously be sensible to fix on the same type
of power. If, for example, your farm is already wired for a
battery-type lighting system, there would be little reason to
revamp the installation for AC. If on the other hand you are
starting from scratch, the writer recommends the use of DC
wherever possible. An AC generator must be closely regulated
at or slightly above synchronous speed, and close regulation
requires complicated governing equipment that is tricky to
build or expensive to buy. A compound-wound DC generator,
on the other hand, provides inherently close voltage regulation
over a wide speed range . . . and even a shunt-wound DC generator with a direct-acting field-rheostat regulator would be satisfactory.

Selecting the right wheel for your plant is perhaps the final
step in your preliminary planning. There are three general
types of water wheel—impulse, reaction and gravity—and several fairly common varieties of each type. However, for small
plant purposes, it's possible to narrow the number down to
those shown in Fig. 3. Note that two types of reaction wheels
—the Francis and the propeller—are shown, and but one variety of gravity wheel, the overshot one.

The impulse or Pelton wheel, operated exclusively by the
force of the water from the jet, includes among its advantages
very slight leakage and friction losses, good efficiency under
varying flows and a sufficiently high shaft speed to drive a
generator. It is more resistant to pitting by water containing
sand, silt or minerals than the reaction type. Its disadvantages
include the fact that it cannot use all the available head, is
larger than a reaction wheel developing the same power and
will wallow in high tail water. It must be mounted as close to
the tail water as possible.

The reaction wheel, either the Francis or propeller type, is
turned by the fall of water through a duct or pipe in which the
wheel is confined. It is the most compact of all wheels for a
given power, uses all of the available head and operates at a
satisfactory speed for direct coupling to a generator. It is an
efficient wheel over a wide range of conditions, and it can be
mounted at any convenient height above tail water. Disadvantages include rapid corrosion with silted water and relatively
high leakage and friction losses, especially in small units.

Finally, there is the overshot gravity wheel, which is turned largely by the weight of the water and partly by impulse. It has good efficiency under varying flow and is unaffected by sand, silt or minerals in the water. Gravity wheels turn at a low speed, which is undesirable for driving a generator or high-speed machinery, but suitable for some pumping and grinding applications. Such a wheel will wallow in high tail water, is the largest wheel for a given power and will be obstructed by ice in winter unless housed.

PART THREE:
DAMS TURN WATER
INTO KILOWATTS

Concrete, though desirable, isn't necessary for damming a small stream. Beavers have gotten by for years without it. Suitable materials can be found on almost any farm. Logs, rough-hewn timber, rock, masonry, planking, gravel, sand and clay are all useful. Choose the materials most readily available on your property, or the least expensive if you must obtain them elsewhere.

You will have determined, on the basis of the first two installments of this series, the height and width of the dam you will need to convert your stream to power. The summer months provide an ideal time for its construction, for then most brooks are at their lowest level and the water will not impede the progress of work.

Four basic types of small dams are shown in the accompanying drawings. All are adaptable in general to the kind of materials likely to be on hand and also to the head of power desired.

There are two basic principles of design to bear in mind no matter which you build. First, a dam should be sealed both above and below its foundation to prevent the seepage of water through or under it. Seepage through a dam, if permitted, weakens the structure and will eventually break it; that under a dam will undermine its foundation. Then, too, some means must be provided to prevent undermining of the dam

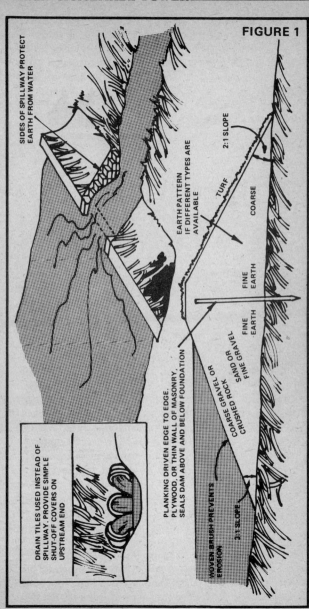

FIGURE 1

SIDES OF SPILLWAY PROTECT EARTH FROM WATER

EARTH PATTERN IF DIFFERENT TYPES ARE AVAILABLE

TURF

2:1 SLOPE

COARSE

FINE EARTH

FINE EARTH

COARSE GRAVEL OR CRUSHED ROCK

SAND OR FINE GRAVEL

PLANKING DRIVEN EDGE TO EDGE, PLYWOOD, OR THIN WALL OF MASONRY, SEALS DAM ABOVE AND BELOW FOUNDATION

2:1 SLOPE

WOVEN BRUSH PREVENTS EROSION

DRAIN TILES USED INSTEAD OF SPILLWAY, PROVIDE SIMPLE SHUT-OFF COVERS ON UPSTREAM END

There's more to the design and fabrication of an earth dam than meets the eye . . . as the above illustration clearly shows.

by the water that flows or spills over it.

In addition, you should check with your local authorities and possibly file plans for your dam with them. States have widely varying regulations, some extremely lenient and some fairly strict. In most, general supervision comes under the state board of health, but a visit to your local county offices will give you correct guidance.

Fig. 1 illustrates the earth dam, which blends well with its surroundings and hence is particularly suited where landscaping or scenic qualities are to be considered. Sealing this type of dam is most important since seepage will literally carry it away if allowed to progress. The seal is put in first and the dam built around it. How far down it should go depends upon the kind of soil. A sand foundation, for instance, requires the seal to extend deeper than clay. If planking is used, it would be well to apply a protective coat such as tar or creosote.

A general pattern for depositing the earth fill is shown in the drawing, but it is not necessary to follow it unless different types of earth are available. Deposit the fill by layers, rolling and tamping each layer well. Then protect the waterside surface from erosion by covering it with a matting woven from brush. Plant turf on the top and downstream side to hold the earth.

Such a dam obviously cannot have water spilling over its crest since this action would wash it away. Two suggestions for handling the excess water are shown. The spillway must be of some material—such as masonry or planking—resistant to the erosion of rushing water, and the sides must protect the open ends of the earth dam from spillage water. An alternative method of handling runoff water is with drain tiles instead of a spillway. Some means must be provided for shutting them off. A simple cover on the upstream end would serve.

Fig. 2 shows the framed dam, which likewise can be easily built, particularly on a farm where lumber in any form from logs to planks is abundantly available. Each frame consists of one joist on which the surface timber is laid and one or more struts. Once the height of the dam is determined, the size of individual frames will vary depending on the contour of the gully (those frames located at the lowest part being the largest). The frames are spaced according to the support the surface timber needs . . . that is, the thinner the surfacing the more supports.

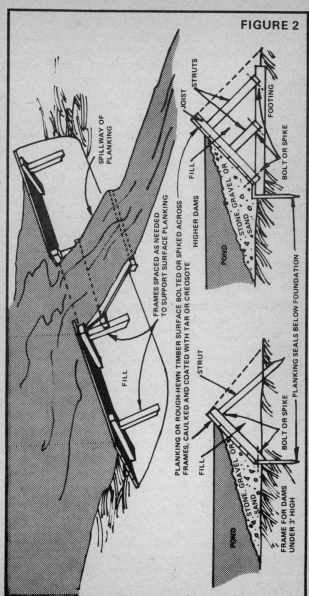

FIGURE 2

SPILLWAY OF PLANKING

FRAMES SPACED AS NEEDED TO SUPPORT SURFACE PLANKING

FILL

HIGHER DAMS

PLANKING OR ROUGH-HEWN TIMBER SURFACE BOLTED OR SPIKED ACROSS FRAMES, CAULKED AND COATED WITH TAR OR CREOSOTE

JOIST

STRUTS

FOOTING

BOLT OR SPIKE

FILL

STONE, GRAVEL OR SAND

POND

STRUT

FILL

STONE, GRAVEL OR SAND

POND

BOLT OR SPIKE

PLANKING SEALS BELOW FOUNDATION

FRAME FOR DAMS UNDER 3' HIGH

Framed dams are fairly easy to construct, but are seldom used . . . quite possibly because their planks can rot away in time.

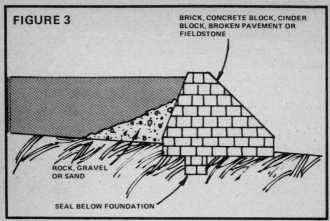

FIGURE 3

BRICK, CONCRETE BLOCK, CINDER BLOCK, BROKEN PAVEMENT OR FIELDSTONE

ROCK, GRAVEL OR SAND

SEAL BELOW FOUNDATION

The gravity dam is relatively complicated to construct. It relies upon brute weight and the binding of its mortar for its stability.

Lay the planking surface or rough-hewn timber horizontally and edge to edge across the frames, and bolt or spike each in place. Caulk the joints and apply a protective coating. Fill is put in behind the downstream side. Build the spillway entirely of planking or similar material.

The gravity dam (shown in Fig. 3) relies upon its weight for its stability. This dam would be most feasible where large rocks or fieldstones abound. Bricks, concrete or cinder blocks —and even chunks of broken concrete pavement—are also excellent materials. The dam is strictly a masonry type, each block being laid with mortar.

Length is not a critical factor for any of these three dams, but it *is* important for the arch dam illustrated in Fig. 4. The placement of such a dam in a gully is limited not only to the point of least width but also to the point where the banks are highest. Otherwise, this dam would impound little water. It would seem unwise to build one to span more than a width of 10 feet. If the heavy timber is used only as a frame on which to spike or bolt a surface of planking, as shown in one of the drawings in Fig. 4, the number of timber arches will depend on the strength of the planking and also on the height of the dam.

Only earth foundations are considered in the drawings, but you may be fortunate enough to have a solid rock foundation on which to build. In that case a seal below the foundation will not be necessary, but some means must be provided to anchor the dam to the rock (such as with anchor bolts in the case of either the framed or gravity dam). Likewise the dam should be sealed at the rock foundation to prevent seepage under it.

In most instances it will be found best to restrict the width of the spillway for excess water to some part of the total length of the dam. This will always be necessary in the case of an earth dam to prevent washing. The spillage water may be allowed to pour over the entire length of framed, gravity and arch dams, however, if the precautions shown in Fig. 5 are taken.

If the downstream side of the dam, or of the spillway, is a curved hard surface of masonry or timber approximating the natural curvature of the water flowing over, it will guide the spillage water so it will be directed downstream without actually falling. Such a curved spillway surface is particularly satisfactory for an earth dam. Large rocks, bricks or other hard objects placed on the downstream side of a spillway not having a curved surface will break the force of the free-falling water and prevent erosion.

The spillway in its simplest form takes the shape of a rectangular depression in the crest of the dam. It should usually be large enough to carry off sufficient excess water so that impounded waters will not top the dam at any season of the year. This, of course, is quite a problem, since accurate determination of spillway capacity requires a knowledge of the total area drained by the creek being dammed plus data on the amount of rainfall at all seasons.

However, most of us will know whether or not the creek we are damming stays within its banks during the year. If it does, then a safe rule to apply would be to make the area of the spillway equal to the cross-section area of the creek at the dam when it is brimful or just ready to flood. The formula is illustrated in Fig. 6.

If the stream does flood, then either construct a dam that in an emergency can allow water to top its full length or build some sort of floodgate into the dam so it can be opened when necessary. One form such a floodgate could take is a group of drain tiles through the dam, as shown in Fig. 1.

The height of the dam you build will be determined by the area of the land to be covered by the impounded water. In

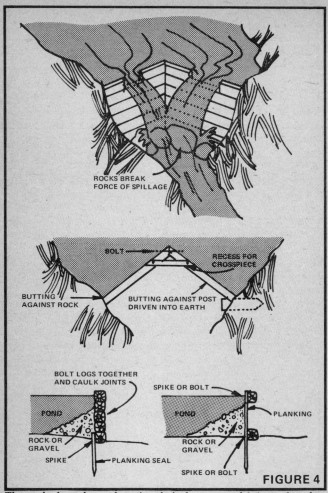

ROCKS BREAK
FORCE OF SPILLAGE

BOLT

RECESS FOR
CROSSPIECE

BUTTING
AGAINST ROCK

BUTTING AGAINST POST
DRIVEN INTO EARTH

BOLT LOGS TOGETHER
AND CAULK JOINTS

SPIKE OR BOLT

POND

PLANKING

ROCK OR
GRAVEL

POND

SPIKE

PLANKING SEAL

ROCK OR
GRAVEL

SPIKE OR BOLT

FIGURE 4

*The arch dam shown here is relatively easy to fabricate, but does
have some severe limitations. It's best kept less than ten feet long.*

general, the higher the dam, the greater the area covered by
water above it.

All vegetation, brush, floatage and the like in the area to be
flooded and for about 15 feet around it should be burned out
or otherwise cleared before the dam is built. This keeps down

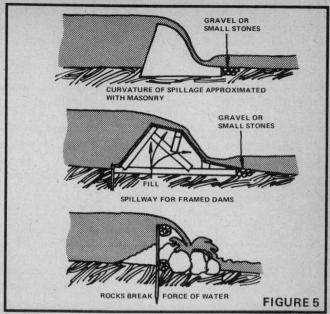

GRAVEL OR
SMALL STONES

CURVATURE OF SPILLAGE APPROXIMATED
WITH MASONRY

GRAVEL OR
SMALL STONES

FILL

SPILLWAY FOR FRAMED DAMS

ROCKS BREAK FORCE OF WATER

FIGURE 5

Improperly handled spillage water can quickly undermine a dam and the methods shown above are a few ways to prevent such a mishap.

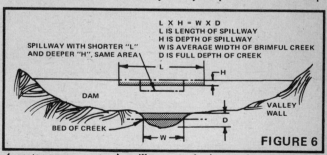

$L \times H = W \times D$
L IS LENGTH OF SPILLWAY
H IS DEPTH OF SPILLWAY
W IS AVERAGE WIDTH OF BRIMFUL CREEK
D IS FULL DEPTH OF CREEK

SPILLWAY WITH SHORTER "L"
AND DEEPER "H", SAME AREA

L

H

DAM

VALLEY
WALL

BED OF CREEK

D

W

FIGURE 6

A water power system's spillway can be just as important as the dam it protects and here's how to determine the spillway's size.

the breeding of mosquitoes and helps retard pollution. It is required in the regulations of some states and is a wise precaution even when not covered by law. In addition, all trees in the area to be flooded should be cut reasonably close to the ground.

PART FOUR:
HOMEMADE WHEEL
DELIVERS OVER 3 HP.

Though one of man's oldest prime movers, a water wheel is still a fascinating piece of machinery. Perhaps this is because it appears comprehensible at a glance (although an efficient wheel is actually a product of subtle and inconspicuous design refinements), and because it seems to be a way of getting power for nothing. The homemade wheel described here was especially designed for this series on harnessing small streams and will reward a careful craftsman by delivering years of constant service. It's particularly suited for an installation having a moderate head (25' to 60') and relatively small flow (.45 to .75 cubic feet per second). Subsequent installments will describe the construction of wheels suited for lesser heads of water and other varied conditions.

As is apparent from the drawings, this is an impulse wheel, driven by the impulses produced as water strikes revolving blades or buckets. In a perfectly designed wheel, the water strikes at high speed, exhausts its energy in driving the wheel to which the bucket is attached and then falls free of the wheel.

Known as a Pelton wheel, this type was developed from the "hurdy-gurdy", a paddle wheel used in California by the forty-niners. The hurdy-gurdy was a wheel that rotated in a vertical plane, had flat vanes fixed around its circumference and was driven by the force of water striking the vanes. It was not an efficient machine, but it was simple to construct. Then an engineer named Lester Pelton substituted a cup-shaped, divided bucket for each of the vanes, and by that step added a high degree of efficiency to the wheel's other virtues.

No single wheel will meet all operating requirements, but some will perform under a reasonably wide range of conditions. The following table indicates the rpm and horsepower output that will be delivered by this wheel under given conditions of head and flow. The latter is measured in cubic feet per second:

HEAD	FLOW	RPM	HP
25'	0.43	350	1.0
30'	0.51	390	1.3
40'	0.59	450	2.0
50'	0.66	500	2.8
60'	0.73	550	3.75

Thus, if a survey of your stream indicates a head and flow close to these values, this Pelton wheel will fit neatly into your plans.

Strictly speaking, a water wheel is an engine powered by water, just as an automobile engine is powered by gasoline. The important power-producing elements of the wheel are the buckets and the nozzle . . . and considerable care should be exercised to see that these parts are made correctly. The nozzle meters the correct amount of water to the wheel, and forms and directs the jet against the buckets. Both the inside diameter and the location of the nozzle with respect to the

While the penstock may be set up to provide either a precipitous or sloping fall, it should be of as large a diameter as possible, have minimum bends and hold down flow friction to the least amount.

wheel are very important, since the jet must impinge upon each bucket at the correct wheel radius or lever arm. It must also be divided equally by the center ridge of each bucket.

The function of the bucket is to convert the energy of the jet—represented by its high speed—into mechanical energy at the wheel shaft. To do this it must slow the water from its high speed in the jet to practically zero speed when it drops into the tail water. Maximum efficiency with this wheel will be obtained if the buckets have the form and size shown in the drawing. This shape acts to slow the jet by turning it smoothly through 180 degrees. The surface of each bucket must be as smooth as possible. A mirror finish is desirable on the inside, and even the back of each bucket should be ground and polished to minimize spray.

Important also is the correct orientation of the bucket to the jet. When the full jet strikes, the bucket should be perpendicular to it. Both the nozzle and the buckets will wear under the action of the high-speed water—at a rate determined by the silt content—and should therefore be made easily removable for replacement.

Above all, buckets must be uniform. If you can get access to a metal-cutting band saw, cut the blanks according to a single pattern. This pattern can be shaped so as to form the end bevels automatically when the blanks are bent, and the bending itself can be done in a jig or hammering form. This jig may be made of a piece of pipe of about 2 inches outside diameter mounted in hardwood end plates. Also provide a holding fixture that will slide in the table groove of the band saw to assure that the slots for the end lugs are cut and spaced uniformly. A holding jig should also be made to line up the lugs and buckets for welding. On completion, balance the wheel by laying weld beads along the backs of any light buckets. Beads should be laid carefully and ground smooth.

Ball bearings may be employed, but are not necessary since the wheel turns at comparatively low speeds. If the builder prefers to use plain bearings, it will simplify machining the shaft, which should present a shoulder to the inside of the bearing so that the wheel may be positioned. If plain bearings are employed, babbitted linings are satisfactory, provided provision is made for proper lubrication.

One vital job that the foundation must do is hold the wheel and the nozzle in correct relative positions. It should be placed on firm ground or piling so that it will not settle unevenly, and must, of course, take advantage of all the head possible. The penstock from the dam should have easy access to the nozzle, and the tail water easy escape to the stream. If possible use 4-inch or larger pipe for the penstock and lay it out to hold frictional losses to a minimum. The width of the foundation is such as to allow the water to fly clear of the buckets. The removable cover over the upper half of the wheel may fit more closely, since no water sprays from the buckets through this half of the revolution.

The foundation may be made of such materials as timbers in a framework, masonry or concrete (so long as it fulfills the above requirements). The wheel and the machinery being driven may then be housed in any suitable, inexpensive shed.

It's not wise to dispense with a gate valve, which is used to cut off or to throttle the water supply to the wheel. Since a gate valve cannot be operated rapidly, it is the best type, eliminating the risk of dangerous water hammer in the penstock. It is also well suited for throttling because fine adjustment is obtainable through the long operating screw. In throttling, the gate valve should be used together with a tachometer or revolution counter connected to the wheel shaft to secure the optimum speed and horsepower for the stream condition and load. Either fasten a tachometer permanently to the shaft, or keep a revolution counter handy in the wheel shed.

Generally the head and volume of water flowing to the wheel will remain constant, resulting in a constant output. If the machinery driven by the wheel has a level power demand there will be little need for constant adjustment of the valve.

The requisite piping, pipe fittings, steel sheet and rod and the bolts, nuts and gaskets are available at building supply houses or steel distributors. Machine screws, lock nuts, bearings and the like may be purchased from good-sized hardware distributors or mail-order houses.

One final point to keep in mind in making your calculations: head is defined as the vertical distance between the water surface behind the dam and the tail-water surface at the wheel. For an impulse wheel, however, which cannot operate submerged, the available head is measured from headwater to the center line of the nozzle. As shown in the construction drawing, there is only 5 inches difference between the two definitions, but this can make some difference in output when working with the moderate heads for which this wheel is designed.

While many details can be altered, the reader should beware of any that will affect operating characteristics. Thus, stainless steel buckets and antifriction bearings would improve performance, involving only some extra work in building the wheel. Changes in the nozzle diameter, wheel radius or effective head, however, should be undertaken only after careful consideration of the probable effect on performance.

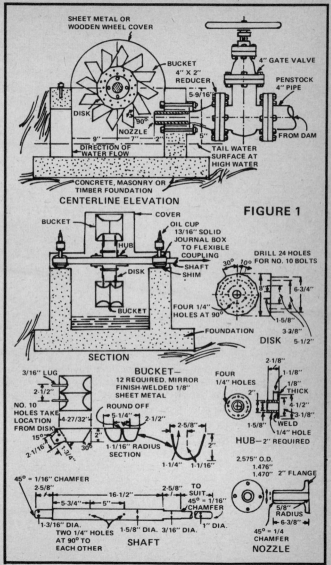

SHEET METAL OR WOODEN WHEEL COVER

BUCKET

4" GATE VALVE

4" X 2" REDUCER

PENSTOCK 4" PIPE

5-9/16"

DISK

90°

NOZZLE

FROM DAM

9"   7"   2"   5"

DIRECTION OF WATER FLOW

TAIL WATER SURFACE AT HIGH WATER

CONCRETE, MASONRY OR TIMBER FOUNDATION

CENTERLINE ELEVATION

FIGURE 1

COVER

BUCKET

OIL CUP

13/16" SOLID JOURNAL BOX TO FLEXIBLE COUPLING

HUB

SHAFT SHIM

DISK

DRILL 24 HOLES FOR NO. 10 BOLTS

30°   10°

BUCKET

FOUR 1/4" HOLES AT 90°

FOUNDATION

8"   6-3/4"

1-5/8"

3-3/8"

DISK   5-1/2"

SECTION

BUCKET—
12 REQUIRED. MIRROR FINISH-WELDED 1/8" SHEET METAL

3/16" LUG

2-1/2"

NO. 10 HOLES TAKE LOCATION FROM DISK

4-27/32"

15°

2-1/16"   1-3/4"   30°

ROUND OFF

5-1/4"   2-1/2"

2"

1-1/16" RADIUS SECTION

1-1/4"   1-1/16"

2-5/8"   2"

1-1/4"   1-1/16"

FOUR 1/4" HOLES

2-1/8"

1-1/8"

1/8" THICK

2"

4-1/8"

3-1/8"

1-5/8"

WELD

1/4" HOLE

HUB— 2" REQUIRED

45° = 1/16" CHAMFER

2-5/8"

16-1/2"

2-5/8"

TO SUIT

45° = 1/16" CHAMFER

5-3/4"   5"

1-3/16" DIA.

TWO 1/4" HOLES AT 90° TO EACH OTHER

1-5/8" DIA.   3/16" DIA.   1" DIA.

SHAFT

2.575" O.D.
1.476"
1.470"   **2" FLANGE**

5/8" RADIUS

6-3/8"

45° = 1/4 CHAMFER

NOZZLE

An impulse wheel converts the energy of falling water into useable work quite efficiently and you can build your own from these plans.

Dramatic contrast in wheel sizes. Top, a 25-ton job designed for installation in a 30,000-hp unit. It turns at 171 rpm and has a 1,008' head. Below, a 12" wheel with reducer and gate-valve throttle.

PART FIVE: BUILDING AN OVERSHOT WHEEL

Often seen beside a picturesque rural mill, an overshot water wheel possesses two excellent characteristics . . . considerable mechanical efficiency and easy maintenance. Many have remained in service for decades and now lend a nostalgic charm to their surroundings.

Operated by gravity, the overshot wheel derives its name from the manner in which water enters the buckets set around its periphery. Pouring from a flume above the wheel, the water shoots into buckets on the down-moving side, overbalancing the empty ones opposite and keeping the wheel in slow rotation.

Since such a wheel may be located near but not actually in the stream, it offers endless landscaping possibilities for a country home where a stream with sufficient flow is available. If a site on dry ground is chosen, the foundation may be constructed dry and the water led to the wheel and a tailrace excavated. With very little effort, the scene may be turned into an attractive garden spot, the wheel becoming both a landscaping feature and a source of power.

It should be noted, however, that an overshot wheel is practical only for a small-capacity output. How much power it will produce depends upon the weight of water the buckets hold and its radius, or lever arm. Expressed in another way, the output depends upon the weight of water transported and the height (or head) through which it falls while in the buckets. For maximum efficiency, the wheel must use the weight of the water through as much of the head as possible. Therefore, the buckets should not spill or sling water until very near tail water.

POWER INCREASES WITH WIDTH

Although of simple construction, an overshot wheel is cumbersome in size. For this reason, before attempting to build one, be certain you have the facilities to move and lift it into place when completed. Also allow yourself plenty of working

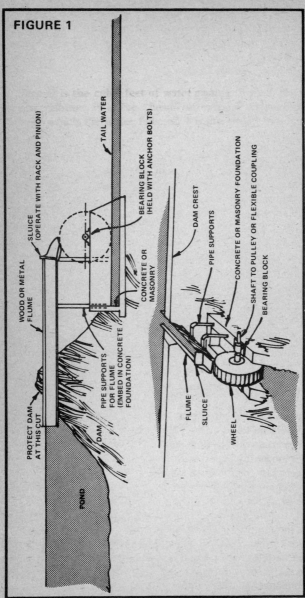

FIGURE 1

PROTECT DAM AT THIS CUT

WOOD OR METAL FLUME

SLUICE (OPERATE WITH RACK AND PINION)

TAIL WATER

BEARING BLOCK (HELD WITH ANCHOR BOLTS)

CONCRETE OR MASONRY

POND

DAM

PIPE SUPPORTS FOR FLUME (EMBED IN CONCRETE FOUNDATION)

DAM CREST

PIPE SUPPORTS

CONCRETE OR MASONRY FOUNDATION

SHAFT TO PULLEY OR FLEXIBLE COUPLING

BEARING BLOCK

FLUME

SLUICE

WHEEL

As the head of a water power system rises or falls, the sluice gate may be adjusted to meter the correct flow to the wheel.

floor space. It must be understood, too, that such a wheel is a sizable project and requires a lot of material and time. Extreme care in cutting and assembling the parts is not essential, however, because the wheel—operating at slow speed—need not be accurately balanced.

Accompanying this article are drawings that illustrate the construction of a small wheel suitable for a water head of 6' 3". The wheel itself has a diameter of 5 feet, leaving a flume head of 15 inches to propel the water into the buckets. As you will note in the table shown on page 107, you may build the wheel to give a power output ranging from 1/2 hp to 1 hp at 10 rpm. All dimensions remain the same except the width, the horsepower increasing as this is increased. For 1/2 hp the wheel should be 15-31/32" wide. For 1 hp it should be 31-29/32". Before deciding on the wheel size, you'll want to make a survey of the power available in the stream (refer to parts one and two of this article).

Virtually all large wheels are built with wood or steel arms (as in the drawing below) and have a shroud plate only around the outer edge, but you may find it simpler and more satisfactory to build the drum-type wheel described here. In this case, each shroud plate is a disk of 1/8" sheet steel. Each disk is braced by a 1/8" sheet steel soleplate to which it is continuously welded, by the buckets, by one of the two large-diameter 1/4" steel hub flanges to which it also is continuously welded, and by the long hub itself.

LARGE SHEET REQUIRED

If preferred the shroud plates may be made of wood. If so, care should be taken to bolt them securely to the hub flanges. Bushings pressed into the wood for the bolts will give the wheel a longer life expectancy.

Sheet steel for the disks may be ordered direct from several large steel companies in case your local supply house is unable to furnish it. Ordinarily, such steel comes in standard 48-inch widths, so you may have to weld together two or more sheets to get the required 5-foot diameter using either a butt weld or a backing plate. This will produce some distortion or ripple, as will the welding on of the numerous clips required. So long as distortion is local, however, and the main lines of wheel and shaft remain true, this will do no harm.

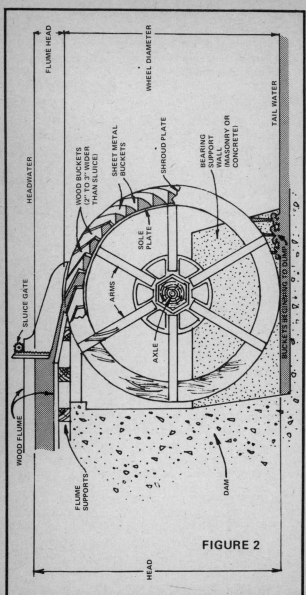

FLUME HEAD

WHEEL DIAMETER

HEADWATER

WOOD BUCKETS
(2" TO 3" WIDER
THAN SLUICE)

SHEET METAL
BUCKETS

SHROUD PLATE

SOLE
PLATE

BEARING
SUPPORT
WALL
(MASONRY OR
CONCRETE)

TAIL WATER

SLUICE GATE

ARMS

AXLE

BUCKETS BEGINNING TO SPILL

WOOD FLUME

FLUME
SUPPORTS

DAM

HEAD

FIGURE 2

For highest efficiency, the buckets of a water wheel must carry their load almost to tail water before beginning to spill.

After the sheet has been prepared, scribe a 5-foot circle on it and cut it with the cutting flame of a gas welding torch. With ordinary care, this method should give sufficient accuracy. Vent and drainage holes should be drilled as indicated around each disk to lessen corrosion with the drum.

GOOD BUCKETS IMPORTANT

The buckets are the most important element of the wheel. To give maximum efficiency, they must be formed so that the water enters smoothly at the top of their travel and remains in them until just before they reach the bottom. For this reason, the bucket form indicated on the facing page should be followed faithfully. Either sheet metal or wood is an acceptable material, but metal is better suited to cold climates since wood is damaged when absorbed water freezes. Because the buckets are subject to wear from the water and sediment that it carries along, you may want to install them so they can be easily replaced.

In laying out and making wooden buckets, follow these steps:

Using a common center, strike off two arcs, one with a 21-1/2" radius and the other with a 2' 6" radius. Then draw a radius line intersecting these arcs.

From the point where the radius crosses the inner arc, measure 2-3/4" farther along the line and mark the point *E*.

From the point where the radius crosses the outer arc, draw a chord 10-1/2" long and from the new point where this intersects the outer arc draw a line to point *E*. You now have the inner trace of the bucket.

Take a piece of the bucket stock and lay it along the upper edge of this inner trace, and you have a cross section through the bucket. Cut your stock accordingly, making the length equal to *B* in the table of dimensions.

STEEL BUCKETS REQUIRE JIG

Steel buckets are only slightly more difficult if you follow these steps:

Using a common center, strike off two arcs on a piece of plywood, one with a 21-1/2" radius and the other with a 2' 6" radius.

Draw a radius line and then a tangent to the inner arc.

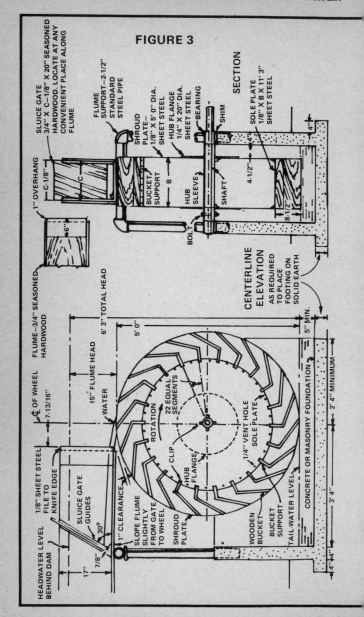

FIGURE 3

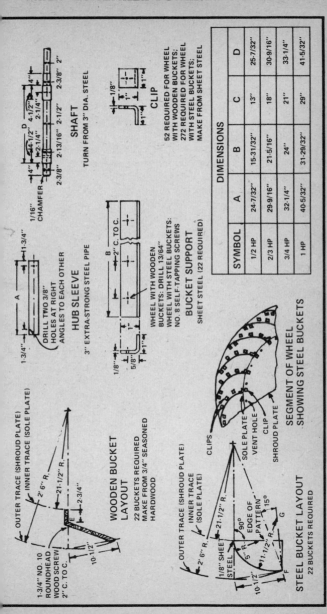

HUB SLEEVE
3" EXTRA-STRONG STEEL PIPE

DRILL TWO 3/8"
HOLES AT RIGHT
ANGLES TO EACH OTHER

SHAFT
TURN FROM 3" DIA. STEEL

1/16" CHAMFER

CLIP

WHEEL WITH WOODEN
BUCKETS: DRILL 13/64"
WHEEL WITH STEEL BUCKETS:
NO. 8 SELF-TAPPING SCREWS

BUCKET SUPPORT
SHEET STEEL (22 REQUIRED)

52 REQUIRED FOR WHEEL
WITH WOODEN BUCKETS.
272 REQUIRED FOR WHEEL
WITH STEEL BUCKETS;
MAKE FROM SHEET STEEL

SYMBOL	DIMENSIONS			
	A	B	C	D
1/2 HP	24-7/32"	15-31/32"	13"	25-7/32"
2/3 HP	29-9/16"	21-5/16"	18"	30-9/16"
3/4 HP	32-1/4"	24"	21"	33-1/4"
1 HP	40-5/32"	31-29/32"	29"	41-5/32"

OUTER TRACE (SHROUD PLATE)
INNER TRACE (SOLE PLATE)

2' 6" R.
21-1/2" R.
2-3/4"

1-3/4" NO. 10
ROUNDHEAD
WOOD SCREW
2" C. TO C.

10-1/2"

WOODEN BUCKET LAYOUT
22 BUCKETS REQUIRED
MAKE FROM 3/4" SEASONED
HARDWOOD

OUTER TRACE (SHROUD PLATE)
INNER TRACE (SOLE PLATE)

2' 6" R.
21-1/2" R.
1/8" SHEET STEEL
90°
5" R.
EDGE OF PATTERN
11-1/2" R.
15°
10-1/2"
F
G

STEEL BUCKET LAYOUT
22 BUCKETS REQUIRED

CLIPS

SOLE PLATE
VENT HOLE
CLIP
SHROUD PLATE

**SEGMENT OF WHEEL
SHOWING STEEL BUCKETS**

Increasing the width of a water wheel, while holding all its other dimensions the same, will boost its horsepower output.

making it vertical to the radius. From the point of tangency, measure 5 inches along the tangent. Mark this point.

Using this mark as a center, strike off an arc with a 5-inch radius. This is part of the inner trace of the bucket.

At the point where the original radius line (Step 2) crosses the outer arc, draw a chord 10-1/2" long, and at point *F* (where this chord intersects the outer arc) draw a new radius line. Also at point *F* measure off 15 degrees below the new radius and draw line *FG* 11-1/2 inches long.

Then, using *G* as a center, strike an arc with a 11-1/2" radius. This forms the rest of the inner trace of the bucket.

Cut the plywood along this line and along the lines that form a quarter ellipse. Using this as a pattern, cut several more quarter ellipses from scrap. Nail these to stretchers to make a bending jig around which the buckets may be formed.

WELD WHEEL PARTS

Welding of the various parts of the wheel produces an exceptionally strong construction. After getting together or making all the required parts, begin the assembly by welding four clips to each end of the hub sleeve. Then weld the required number of clips to the shroud plates for the soleplate, and weld the shroud plates to the clips on the hub sleeve. After welding both hub flanges to the shroud plates and the sleeve with a continuous weld, attach the soleplate to the clips on the shroud plates with No. 8 self-tapping screws. Also weld the soleplate to the shroud plates with a continuous weld, and the bucket-support angles to the soleplate.

Attach wooden buckets to the supports with 3/4" No. 10 roundhead wood screws, and then drill holes 2 inches from center to center through the shroud plates for 1-3/4" No. 10 roundhead wood screws. If you use steel buckets, rivet or screw 10 clips to each side of each bucket and attach the buckets to the angles with No. 8 self-tapping screws. Then drill holes through the shroud plates in the way of the clips for the same type of screws.

LUBRICATE BEARINGS WELL

Using locknuts and washers, fasten the hub sleeve to the shaft with two 3/8" by 4-1/2" bolts, placed at right angles to each other. Two bearing mountings having 2-3/8" renewable liners with shoulders should be bolted to the foundation. Place shims about 1/4" thick under the bearings.

Standard bearing mountings, variously called pedestals or blocks, may be bought complete with wick oiler or cup oil reservoir and with built-in self-aligning features. Standard bronze bearing metal liners or inserts likewise may be bought from any machine component supplier. Babbitt liners are equally satisfactory.

Although the wheel turns slowly, it is heavy and will be running almost constantly, so good lubrication of the bearings is essential. To this end, care should be taken to insure that the bearing liners are finished to the correct fit. Porous inserts or inserts containing graphite are excellent for this application, but may cost more than regular bearing inserts.

It is important that the foundation be carried deep enough so that water falling from the buckets will not undermine it. Avoid a long flume if possible, in order to keep the construction as simple as possible. Strengthen it along its entire length with an exterior frame and support it well from dam to wheel with pipe uprights.

SLUICE GOVERNS WHEEL

The sluice gate may be located at any convenient place along the flume. Since it is the governing mechanism of the wheel, its installation should be anything but slipshod. If it is installed at an angle as shown on page 106, water pressure will keep it at any desired position. If installed vertically, some mechanism (such as a rack and pinion) should be provided to keep it in place.

Adjust the sluice so that the buckets will run one-quarter full. This will give a wheel speed of 10 rpm. If the buckets are allowed to run more than one-quarter full, the efficiency of the wheel will drop for two reasons. Because of the increased speed, centrifugal force will throw water from the buckets. They also will begin to spill before approaching tail water. Although this practice does waste water, it may be profitably employed during a freshet to increase the power output, for at such times the excess water would be wasted anyway. ●

Some sources of water wheels and related equipment are listed in the bibliography at the back of this book (see Water, Hardware).

WILLIAM J. HEBERT: PERPETUAL MOTION FOR THE HOMESTEAD...

THE HYDRAULIC RAM PUMP

Are you planning to add a farm pond to your homestead, but bothered by the fact that the site you've selected is not naturally furnished with water year round? Or do you already have a pool which suffers from one or more of the maladies connected with a lack of sufficient incoming fresh water? Well —if your property contains a spring, creek, small stream or other source with a flow of at least three gallons per minute (gpm)—you can probably solve your problem easily and inexpensively with a hydraulic ram pump.

As I write this, it's been three months since we installed our ram pump in a nearby creek . . . at a total cost of under $200. All that time the device has been pumping clear, cool spring water up over a 25-foot hill—a distance of 150 feet—and into our farm pond, without the use of any fuel whatsoever. In short, we're getting about 500 gallons of water per day at an operating cost of zero . . . and we expect this to continue for ten years or more.

Prior to this installation, the water level of our 15-foot-deep, half-acre fishing and swimming hole dropped at least two feet each July and August, the pond's temperature rose to the tepid bathtub stage and the algae blossomed. Not so these days! The level remains constant, the water is clearer, cooler and more invigorating and the plant population has been drastically reduced. Even the largemouth bass and bluegills (now five years old) put up a stiffer fight when we hook them.

Although our own pump is used solely to replenish that pond, the ram is a versatile machine with many other possible applications. For instance, it can drive water to a storage tank in or near a house . . . with the overflow first diverted to a barn or watering trough for animals and then finally to a pool. Or the device can be used purely for irrigation.

Before this country's rural electrification program such pumps were in wide use, since they employ only water power for activation. In Japan, in fact, the ram still commonly serves to bring water from the mountains into villages a mile or more away.

These days, a revival of the hydraulic ram seems to be underway among back-to-the-landers . . . and you may be thinking about putting the water-current-driven pump to work on your own spread. Whether or not you can do this successfully depends on five important and interdependent conditions:

[1] The amount of water (gpm) available from the source.

[2] The length of the main pipe from the source to the pump.

[3] The drop in feet from the source to the pump.

[4] The height in feet that water must be lifted.

[5] The distance in feet that water must be delivered.

(See Don Marier's accompanying piece for a graphic summary of the relationships among these factors, and see the explanation that follows the diagram for a guide to how much water you can expect your pump to deliver.—MOTHER.)

Here's how we measured the first of these variables on our own place: We temporarily dammed up a creek a few feet downstream from its source (a spring) and inserted a pipe near the top of the dam. The water from the conduit was allowed to run into a gallon bucket while we timed the flow with a sweep second hand on a watch. During the dry month of August, the figure we obtained was three-and-a-half gpm.

Our next step was to construct a more permanent dam in order to form a small pool of at least 50 gallons. This reservoir would constantly be filled from the brook, and out of it would run our main pipe to the pump downstream. We began this project by building plywood forms across the creek in the shape of an elongated letter "U", with a base width of five feet and with two-foot arms extending back upstream. The walls were to be four inches thick and only two feet high.

After the forms were laid—but before the concrete was mixed and poured—we temporarily diverted the stream around one side of the plywood mold to permit the box's contents to dry without being diluted or washed away. We also inserted a one-foot length of one-inch pipe, threaded on both ends, through the walls of the form about six inches from its top and inclined downstream. The upstream opening of this tube would later be covered with a strainer, and the lower outlet would connect with the long steel pipe leading to the ram pump.

The position for the ram itself was selected with the knowledge that we wanted at least a five-foot "head" or "fall" of water . . . that is, a five-foot vertical distance from the pool's surface to the base of the pump. With the aid of a transit on a five-foot stand (a simple carpenter's level does just as well) we found that a distance downstream of 42 feet gave us a level sight with the top of the newly poured dam. At that spot beside the creek we built a simple concrete slab (2' X 2' X 8" thick) upon which we would later bolt the ram.

Next, two sections of one-inch black pipe—each a standard length of 21 feet—were joined together with nipples and then connected to the one-foot piece of pipe which pierced the dam. We used more nipples and a simple one-inch union to hook the waterline to the pump, and then attached the strainer (supplied by the ram's manufacturer) to the intake in the pool area. We completed our pipe-laying by running 150 feet of three-quarter-inch, flexible plastic tubing (the high-pressure type for durability) from the pump outlet up over a 25-foot hill to our pond.

Finally, we allowed the pool in the creek to fill by simply blocking up the temporary, diversionary stream around the side of the forms. Within ten minutes, and after a minor adjustment to the ram's release valve, the water rushing down the main pipe activated the device and commenced its "perpetual motion". Sure enough, a steady stream of water emerged from the plastic tubing into our pond. At first the flow looked disappointingly small . . . only after careful measurement did we suddenly realize that our swimming hole would be receiving about 500 gallons of fresh spring water each day. That amounts to about 15,000 gallons per month or 180,000 gallons per year!

As I've already suggested, the same system could just as easily be used to solve more sophisticated problems pertaining to the delivery of drinking water or to the supply of storage tanks, irrigation networks, dairy barn needs or livestock troughs. The higher and further water must be pumped, of course, the larger the ram required. All the same, we feel that the hydraulic ram offers a homesteader the most pollution-free and least expensive method of getting water from Point X to Point Y next to hauling it by hand in buckets . . . and it's a helluva lot easier. Happy swimming and fishing!

HOW IT WORKS

DON MARIER *(Reprinted from*
Alternative Sources of Energy, *No. 1, July 1971.)*

A diagram of a typical ram is shown in Fig. 1. Here's how it works: Water rushes down the drive pipe and escapes out the waste valve until enough pressure is built up to close that outlet. (The amount of this pressure increases with the "fall" or vertical distance from the source to the ram.)

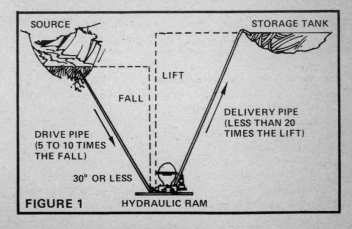

SOURCE

STORAGE TANK

LIFT

FALL

DELIVERY PIPE
(LESS THAN 20
TIMES THE LIFT)

DRIVE PIPE
(5 TO 10 TIMES
THE FALL)

30° OR LESS

FIGURE 1   HYDRAULIC RAM

The shutting of the waste valve forces water through the check valve and into the air chamber. The rushing liquid compresses the air enclosed in the compartment so that it pushes back like a piston. This action closes the check valve and forces water up the delivery pipe to a storage tank.

When the check valve closes, the water in the drive pipe rebounds for a moment and creates a partial vacuum that allows the waste valve to drop open again. The excess fluid which was not pushed up the delivery pipe thus flows out of the opening. At the same time, the vacuum draws a small amount of air into the ram through the air valve or "snifter" just below the air chamber. This gas—which is needed to replace the enclosed air because some is mixed with the water during each cycle—will be forced into the compartment when the incoming stream starts flowing down the drive pipe again. A small amount of water is lost through the air valve during each stroke of the pump, but the leakage is minute and serves to keep the opening clean.

The cycle just described is repeated about 25 to 100 times per minute . . . the exact rate depends on how much tension is put on the waste valve spring by adjustment of the screws. The slower the ram works, the more water it will pump. The ideal setting is for the minimum number of strokes per minute at which the pump will still operate. I had to rework the waste valve spring on my ram a couple of times until it lined up properly and had the correct tension; otherwise, the pressure failed to build properly and the machine wouldn't work.

How much water the ram will pump can be calculated from the following formula:

$$D = \frac{S \times F}{L} \times \frac{2}{3}$$

where,

D is the amount of water delivered in gallons per minute (gpm).
S is the amount of water supplied to the machine in gallons per minute.
F is the fall or vertical distance in height between the supply of water and the ram.
L is the lift or vertical distance the water is lifted from the pump to the storage tank.
The fraction of 2/3 represents the efficiency of the ram. Older models had efficiencies of about 40%.

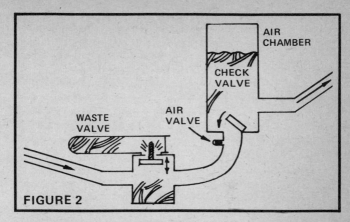

FIGURE 2

The minimum fall from which a ram will operate is 18 inches, and that's the vertical distance I had to work with. I measured the supply flow at 10 gallons per minute by catching the water in a pail and timing how long the container took to fill. The lift I used was 10 feet. Thus the amount of water I should have expected to be delivered was:

$$D = \frac{10 \text{ gpm} \times 1\text{-}1/2 \text{ feet}}{10 \text{ feet}} \times \frac{2}{3} = 1 \text{ gpm}$$

I actually measured about nine-tenths of a gallon per minute.

It sounds inefficient to use 10 gallons of water to pump one gallon, but remember that the ram works constantly (unlike a windmill) . . . so that one gpm adds up to 1,440 gallons per day. Besides, the nine gallons which go out the waste valve aren't really wasted since they can be returned to the stream or used for any convenient purpose.

Note that you can't pump the water to an indefinite height since pipe friction slows the flow down. This effect is reduced by using a sufficiently large water line and by keeping connections and bends to a minimum. It is much better to shape a long piece of pipe into a gradual curve than to use sections of tubing connected at a sharp angle. Garden hose is out of the question because all the kinks would produce too much friction. ◓

If you don't feel up to building your own hydraulic ram, you'll find manufacturers of the units listed in the bibliography at the back of this book. Look in the Hardware *section under* Water.

THOMAS OATES'
WATER
POWER!

The old water wheel—used in the United States for grinding grains and producing energy at the beginning of the Industrial Revolution—has declined in popularity since this country's rural electrification program was initiated in the early 1930's. There are, however, still individuals who refuse to give up the virtually free power source.

One such person is Thomas Oates of Route 74, Gerton, North Carolina. Sparkling, crystal clear water has splashed over his water wheel for more than four decades now . . . to provide his woodworking shop, office and home with electricity since long before transmission lines were installed in this one-time remote mountainous area of the Tarheel State.

Tom, an agile 71-year-old craftsman, owns and operates The Manual Wood-Workers—a crafts and souvenirs center— where thousands of people stop each year to sample sourwood honey and to buy handmade cedar churns, dulcimers or corn-shuck dolls made by the local mountaineers.

Although Oates doesn't depend on his current metal water wheel as completely as he relied on his first wooden one back in 1933, it—and quick-flowing Hickory Creek—still provides his business with standby power.

Tom—who was born and raised near Asheville, North Carolina—started his first hydroelectric project during the depression, "when I had plenty of time to think about things". Oates adds, "My brother sent me three direct current (DC) generators from New York City, and I had the water . . . so the two just fit together."

A total of sixteen woodworking machines and a battery of over fifty lights were hooked into that initial electrical system, to satisfy all of Oates' energy needs eleven years before commercial lines were run through his section of the country.

"Even after the power company put electricity in here,"

Tom chuckles, "I kept my generation unit going because it was more dependable. With the old utility company, the power was off more than it was on."

Because of this constant interruption of service, Oates wired his shop and home for both DC and Alternating Current (AC). "I kept every other light hooked up to DC and I still use the same setup today. I call it my security protection system because I can leave half the lights burning without them costing me a cent," Tom says.

The wheel Tom now uses is made of steel and measures 15 feet in diameter. It was manufactured in 1914 by the Fitz Water Wheel Company of Hanover, Pennsylvania (the firm is no longer in business) and was originally used for milling grains. The Greenville, South Carolina City Waterworks then bought the apparatus secondhand and ran a generator with it until the utility sold it to Oates 26 years ago. "It cost me $200 to buy the wheel and another $300 to fix it up and transport it to my site here on the edge of Bearwallow Mountain (elevation 4,249 ft.)."

While standing amidst the cluttered workshop that overlooks his hydroelectric plant, Tom describes how he funnels Hickory Creek's flow through a 136-foot-long sluice—an artificial channel for diverting water—to his water wheel. "It's lasted me a good long time," he says, "and I've never had a bit of trouble with it. All I've done is look after the sluice and make a few minor adjustments along the way. But this fall I think I'll have to build another one because the wood is finally starting to rot."

The sluice is 5 feet wide, 12 feet high and directs water over the wheel (making this an overshot system) to provide approximately 17 horsepower at 15 rpm. By stepping this rotational force through a series of belts, jack shafts and seven pulleys, Oates uses it to turn his electrical generator at approximately 800 rpm.

And that's where the bind comes in with most homebuilt hydroelectric systems: matching the setup's output to the amount of power needed. That is: A DC generator of a certain size will have to run at a specific speed to produce enough electricity to light, say, a 100-watt bulb. If you suddenly turn on two more 100-watt lights, however, all the bulbs will glow only weakly unless you also increase the rpm of the DC generator to meet the increased energy demand.

Oates overcame this problem by placing a sluice gate a few feet behind the spillway which regulates the amount of water-flow over the wheel. By means of pulleys, Tom can open or close this gate from his shop or home.

"It took a lot of experimenting," Oates recalls, "to get the system working right. One time when my daughter was a baby, she yanked on a pulley-cable and opened the sluice gate all the

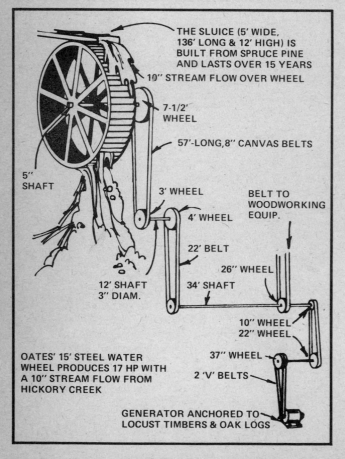

THE SLUICE (5' WIDE, 136' LONG & 12' HIGH) IS BUILT FROM SPRUCE PINE AND LASTS OVER 15 YEARS

10" STREAM FLOW OVER WHEEL

7-1/2' WHEEL

57'-LONG, 8" CANVAS BELTS

5" SHAFT

3' WHEEL

4' WHEEL

BELT TO WOODWORKING EQUIP.

22' BELT

26" WHEEL

12' SHAFT 3" DIAM.

34' SHAFT

10" WHEEL
22" WHEEL

37" WHEEL

OATES' 15' STEEL WATER WHEEL PRODUCES 17 HP WITH A 10" STREAM FLOW FROM HICKORY CREEK

2 'V' BELTS

GENERATOR ANCHORED TO LOCUST TIMBERS & OAK LOGS

Oates uses a series of canvas belts and nine drive pulleys to transfer power from his water wheel to a generator and other equipment.

way—making the water shoot full-blast over the wheel—and it blew out every dang light on the place." After that, Tom put in a safety mechanism to prevent a recurrence of the accidental power surge.

"It just took a lot of trial and error to hook up this operation. The pulleys are from all over and I doubt if you can find them very easily anymore. When my son and I rebuild the

Our inventive craftsman adjusts wooden "light switch" that regulates sluice gate which, in turn, controls flow of water to wheel.

sluice this fall, we'll be putting in another generator, but I'm getting a little old for this kind of thing now. The system has worked for me though, and it's been fun to play with."

Even when the water's low in Hickory Creek, the stream supplies enough power to create electricity. Tom uses a 5-horsepower, 220-volt DC generator which produces 110 volts at 800 rpm. This setup is capable of running 50 or more

Water streams over Thomas Oates' Fitz Wheel as access flow from his water power system's "race" is diverted by the sluice gate.

60-watt light bulbs . . . more than even enough to light Oates' office and run his shop and home.

"It's easy enough to do," says our country woodworker. "All it takes is a little figuring and some work." If you have a good stream of water flowing on your property, you might well look into the idea of harnessing it with your own hydro-electric plant. ⬤

The water outlet is positioned six inches above the wheel so that logs and other debris shoot out over the buckets, preventing damage.

A MONSTER ROCK TUMBLER AND...

There's nothing complicated or overly expensive about the gigantic rock tumbler Walter Thompson built up in Gold Bar, Washington back in the early 60's. The tumbling tank itself is a discarded "paper drying roller" and the wheel's buckets are old hot water tanks cut in two.

We found this fine example of "water power made easy" in the October 1964 issue of *Popular Mechanics*. The magazine reported that Thompson smooths off eight tons of semiprecious rocks in the rig at a time and that he then cuts the finished chunks of stone into slabs that are used for tabletops, bar counters, etc. At least he did back in 1964.

Whether or not Mr. Thompson still tumbles rocks with water power or not, however, is not the important point here. We've included mention of this contrivance in these pages just to point out that meaningful work most certainly can be extracted from moving water in a very simple and straightforward manner. With salvaged materials yet. ●

Old-timers back in the hills of the southeastern United States used to "shoot marvels" (play marbles) with stones that—amazingly enough—were perfectly spherical in shape. Flatlanders who happened across these wondrous pebbles always asked how they had been formed and, naturally enough, were treated to some rather farfetched explanations.

"Them little round rocks come out of mountain turkey gizzards," the wide-eyed visitors were told. "They's a hermit that nobody ain't never seen. He files them stones down with alligator teeth and leaves 'em out where folks can find 'em."

In actual fact, the "stone marvels" were smoothed down so perfectly by a very primitive—but very effective—use of water power. First, a hole was drilled straight down a couple of inches into a boulder just below a small drop in a mountain stream. Then a piece of hollowed-out stem or store-bought pipe was positioned so that a small but continuous flow of water would fall into one edge of the opening. After that, it was a simple matter of dropping a nearly circular pebble into the indentation . . . and then letting it spin over and over for days at a time until it had worn itself "jest as round as a fish egg and smooth as a baby's behind". ◓

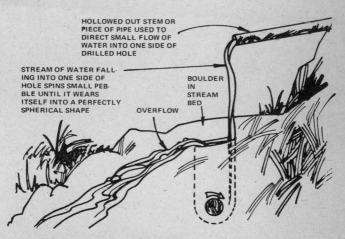

HOLLOWED OUT STEM OR PIECE OF PIPE USED TO DIRECT SMALL FLOW OF WATER INTO ONE SIDE OF DRILLED HOLE

STREAM OF WATER FALLING INTO ONE SIDE OF HOLE SPINS SMALL PEBBLE UNTIL IT WEARS ITSELF INTO A PERFECTLY SPHERICAL SHAPE

OVERFLOW

BOULDER IN STREAM BED

...A MINIATURE PEBBLE SMOOTHER

WIND
ENERGY FROM THE AIR

"Ah, but I may as well try and catch the wind." The words belong to Donovan . . . but the hardware that will do the job is being hammered together by hundreds of grassroots experimenters. From the Great Plains of Canada and the United States to the uplands of Costa Rica to the emerging nations of Africa to the Outback of Australia . . . the "windmill economy" is once again making a comeback.

Wind engines, you know, rank with water wheels as one of mankind's first major mechanical sources of energy. (Contrivances designed to harness moving air masses date back at least to the 10th century.) During the past 200 years, however, the devices have been almost completely replaced by steam engines, internal combustion powerplants, nuclear installations and other "more convenient" and "more reliable" prime movers.

Unfortunately, on the other hand, those "more convenient" and "more reliable" prime movers are also "more dirty" and "more nerve-racking". They pollute the air we breathe and the water we drink. They often make a lot of noise. They gobble up non-renewable resources at an alarming rate. In less than 200 years, in short, they've begun to overstay their welcome in a most noxious manner.

And so the farsighted among us are once again casting amorous glances at wind mills, plants, turbines, generators and chargers.

The following section of this book is mainly concerned with the harnessing of moving air masses for the production of electricity. It contains a brief but informative survey of the field, an interview with *the* pioneering giant of windplants, an explanation of how to calculate the size plant you'll need to produce a certain amount of power, tips on recycling used units and discussions of the fabrication of a couple of homebuilt wind-driven electrical generators. You *can* catch the wind . . . and transform it into usable power. ●

HENRY CLEWS' MIRACULOUS WIND-POWERED HOMESTEAD

What better way to kick off this section of the book than by introducing you to a young couple that not only uses the wind to produce all *the electricity they consume . . . but that now find themselves up to their ears in a business devoted to supplying* others *with windplants too!*

Hello! We're actually alive and well and living on (off?) the land in East Holden, Maine. We have 50 acres here that include an old orchard, a trout stream, large vegetable garden and our own 950-foot mountain. We built (mostly through last winter) a small house on the farm and moved in during the spring.

Bringing power to our homestead would have cost $3,000 or more (we're five miles from the nearest paved road) plus a minimum bill of $15.00 per month for the next five years . . . so, instead, we paid $1,800 and I spent many hours this summer setting up a complete and self-contained wind-generated electrical system.

The propeller and generator are from Quirk's in Australia and—to my knowledge—ours is the first large Quirk's unit to be installed in the U.S. It's a 2,000-watt, 120-volt, low-speed, geared alternator with a 12-foot-diameter full-feathering propeller mounted atop a 50-foot steel tower. Other components in the system include 20 six-volt, 180 amp-hour "house lighting" batteries with built-in charge indicators, an automatic transistorized voltage control and various rectifiers and inverters designed to yield 120 volts AC or DC.

APPLIANCES	Power in Watts	Current Required in Amps at 12V	at 115V	Time Used per mo. in hrs.	Total kw-hrs. per mo.
Adjustable Handsaw	1,000	83.5	8.7	6	6.
Air Conditioner (window)	1,566	130.	13.7	74	116.
Blanket, electric	177	14.5	1.5	73	13.
Blender	350	29.2	3.0	1.5	0.5
Broiler	1,436	120.	12.5	6	8.5
Clothes Dryer (electric)	4,856		42.0	18	86.
Clothes Dryer (gas)	325	27.	2.8	18	6.0
Coffee Pot	894	75.	7.8	10	9.
Dishwasher	1,200	100.	10.4	25	30.
Drill (1/4 in. Elec.)	250	20.8	2.2	2	.5
Fan (attic)	370	30.8	3.2	65	24.
Freezer (15 cu. ft.)	340	28.4	3.0	290	100.
Freezer (15 cu. ft.), frostless	440	36.6	3.8	330	145
Frying Pan	1,196	99.6	10.4	12	15.
Garbage Disposal	445	36.	3.9	6	3.
Heat, electric baseboard, avg.-size home	10,000		87.	160	1600.
Iron	1,088	90.5	9.5	11	12.
Light Bulb, 75-Watt	75	6.25	.65	120	9.
Light Bulb, 40-Watt	40	3.3	.35	120	4.8
Light Bulb, 25-Watt	25	2.1	.22	120	3.
Oil Burner, 1/8 hp	250	20.8	2.2	64	16.
Range	12,200		106.0	8	98.
Record Player (tube)	150	12.5	1.3	50	7.5
Record Player (solid st.)	60	5.0	.52	50	3.
Refrigerator-Freezer (14 cu. ft.)	326	27.2	2.8	290	95.
Refrigerator-Freezer (14 cu. ft.) frostless	615	51.3	5.35	250	152.
Sun Lamp	279	23.2	2.4	5.4	1.5
Television (B&W)	237	19.8	2.1	110	25.
Television (color)	332	27.6	2.9	125	42.
Toaster	1,146	95.5	10.0	2.6	3.
Typewriter	30	2.5	.26	15	.45
Vacuum Cleaner	630	52.5	5.5	6.4	4.
Washing Machine (auto.)	512	42.5	4.5	17.6	9.
Washing Machine (wringer)	275	23.	2.4	15	4.
Water Heater	4,474		39.	89	400.
Water Pump	460	38.3	4.0	44.	20.

POWER, CURRENT, & MONTHLY KW-HR CONSUMPTION OF VARIOUS HOME APPLIANCES

The above chart is representative of the information packed into the $2.00 information packet now being sold by Henry Clews. The handbook Henry publishes, although not really very large, is a quite definitive introduction to extracting energy from the wind. It's loaded with many other tables, tips, hints, ideas and facts.

And it all seems to work! Since our system was put into operation a month ago, we've had uninterrupted power for lights, shop tools, water pump, hi-fi and—yes—even television ... which is quite a change from candles and kerosene lamps!

We're so enthusiastic that we've formed a company to import Quirk's windplants and I'm now the official agent for the units in the northeastern states (which is all of New England and New York). Our company, Solar Wind, will eventually be expanded to produce and sell plans and kits for simpler, less expensive wind generators, solar heating units (hot water heaters) and other alternative energy devices for homesteaders and country folk.

If anyone wants to ask whether or not I'm enthusiastic about using the wind as a practical source of energy on a large scale, I *am*. The feeling of running a whole shop, lights and appliances (with the stereo blaring away in the background) on a totally invisible, non-polluting and *free* power source is nothing short of exhilarating. NOTE: This letter was typed on a SCM electric typewriter operating on 120 volts AC ... supplied entirely by our wind-driven rig!

EDITOR'S NOTE: The above mini-article was originally published in the November-December issue of THE MOTHER EARTH NEWS (MOTHER NO. 18, available for $1.50 from THE MOTHER EARTH NEWS, INC., P.O. Box 70, Hendersonville, N.C. 28739). It was followed by the suggestion that others interested in wind power might well encourage Henry to write a small handbook on the subject.

Well, that one small mention—it seems—put Henry Clews in business. He did write the booklet (now available for $2.00) and has since become an authorized agent for at least one domestic manufacturer of windplants (Dyna Technology, Inc., of Sioux City, Iowa) and another foreign producer of such equipment (Elektro gmbH of Winterthur, Switzerland).

Clews has become so associated with wind power in the Pine Tree State, in fact, that his "company" car now sports the special license plate shown in the accompanying illustration. And, by the way, that's a brand-new 6,000-watt Elektro unit behind the vehicle.

For the address of Henry Clews' company—Solar Wind—see the bibliography (look under Wind, Hardware*) in the back of this book.* ●

Most people are not aware of the great increase in electric power consumption that has occurred in the last 10 or 20 years and which is now leading to energy shortages and environmental disaster. The trend in power consumption is ever upward and fuel combustion, generating plants and utility lines increasingly mar the landscape in even remote and otherwise unspoiled parts of our land. We must curtail our energy consumption first, then turn to alternate sources of power—such as the wind—if we want to live in tune with nature on this planet.

Before considering the wind as a source of power for your domestic needs, however, you should take a look at the electrical appliances you now have and decide which you consider essential and which are just conveniences. Wind power can be useful, but a very large and expensive windmill would be needed to operate such greedy consumers of electric energy as clothes dryers, space heaters, hot water heaters, electric ranges and large, color TV sets.

If, on the other hand, you can live with reasonably modest

IT CAN BE DONE!
ED TRUNK TELLS YOU
HOW TO EXTRACT
FREE
POWER FROM
THE WIND

lighting, radios, shavers, a small black and white TV, a refrigerator and perhaps an oil burner motor and circulator . . . you may find that the wind can supply all or part of your electric energy needs.

Let me, however, point out some aspects of wind power that must be taken into account before embarking on any such home energy generation project. First and most obvious is the intermittent nature of this resource. Wind power is extracted from the kinetic energy of moving air and the power available from any mill at any given time is proportional to the cube of the wind velocity. Which is to say that if you can get, for example, 160 watts from a mill at a wind speed of 10 mph . . . then you can obtain 1,280 watts when the air velocity is 20 mph (if the generator has the capability), but only 20 watts at a wind speed of 5 mph.

Remember too that—depending on your location—you may find there are long intervals during which the wind will be relatively calm. If this is so, your wind generator will not put out any appreciable power for long periods, during which

FIGURE 1

FIGURE 2

you'll have to resort either to energy stored in batteries, or to a standby gasoline or diesel-driven generator. If you are fortunate in having a windy site, this will be less of a problem . . . but it cannot be overlooked.

Another aspect to be considered is that of excessive winds, such as a severe storm, hurricane or tornado. Provision must be made for feathering the mill's blades, tilting the attitude of the propeller so that the wind hits the ends and edges of the fan instead of the airfoil surfaces or applying some kind of brake or aerodynamic spoiler. Automatic as well as manual operation of such a device is desirable.

The intermittent nature of wind as an energy source makes it most useful for those applications where the effect or result is easily stored. Pumping water for irrigation or domestic use with power extracted from moving air is a natural. Windmills have been used for this purpose in the Low Countries for many centuries, and were commonly harnessed for the same work on this continent only a few decades ago. Today such American farm windmills (Fig. 1) are found mostly in Amish areas. Elsewhere the machines are often seen in a state of disrepair on abandoned or unused homesteads.

If you're interested in pumping water with wind power you

may be able to find an old American farm windmill and re-
furbish it with new vanes and mechanical parts. Or you can
purchase one brand new, as they're still made in a variety of
sizes from 6 to 16 ft. in diameter, mounted on steel towers as
high as 80 ft. tall, by the Aeromotor Company of Broken
Arrow, Oklahoma 74012. The manufacturer gives performance
in terms of pumping rate ranging from 100 to 3,000 gallons
per hour. Construction is sturdy, self-lubricating and the designs are dependable through many decades of experience in
production and usage. Dempster Industries of Beatrice,
Nebraska 68310 and the Heller-Aller Company, Napoleon,
Ohio 43545 are two other sources for these water pumping
windmills.

The most comprehensive description of a homebuilt windmill is contained in a report prepared for an organization
called Volunteers for International Technical Assistance (College Campus, Schenectady, New York 12308) by a Dr. Bossel
of the University of California (see *Low-cost Windmill for
Developing Nations* in Bibliography at back of this book). The
paper describes a 16-blade mill with a diameter of 4 meters (13
ft.). The machine employs an automobile rear axle and differential as both the shaft and support for the fan . . . and the
means for transmitting the mechanical energy to the bottom
of the tower.

Detailed descriptions of sheet metal blade construction and
regulating mechanism are given in Bossel's report and the only
tool required which may not be readily available to most
MOTHER readers is welding equipment. Any body and fender
shop or blacksmith (check the Yellow Pages) should have both
the necessary equipment and skill, however, or—in lieu of
welding—other fastening methods such as screws and nuts or
rivets can be used.

This mill is primarily intended for pumping water and doing
other mechanical duties rather than for generating electric
power. Its tower and elevated turntable platform (see Fig. 4)
are of wooden construction. The machine's output in a 10
mph breeze is 1/3 horsepower, it produces 1 hp in a wind of
15 mph and over 2-1/2 hp when spun by air moving 20 mph.

But what about electric power generation? Such energy is
not easily stored (a bank of automotive-type storage batteries
may supply a few hours' needs . . . but then you're either out
of power or you crank up a gasoline-driven generator). I would

strongly recommend such a gasoline-powered standby unit for any wind-driven generator if you want reliable power without tying into the utility line. At some future date, perhaps, the fuel cell will serve as the alternate source, thereby avoiding the noise and pollution problems of the internal combustion engine.

There is a wind-powered generator called the *Wincharger* available for about $400 from Dyna Technology, Inc., of Sioux City, Iowa 51102. It uses a 6-ft. two-bladed propeller with a patented air-brake governor to limit its speed in high winds, and comes with a 10-ft. steel tower. Although of small

FIGURE 3

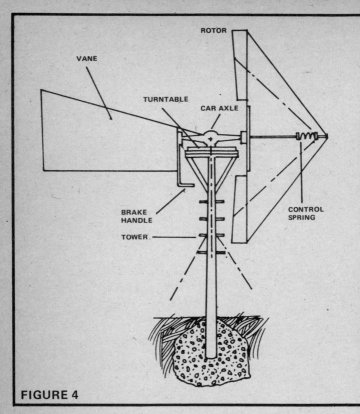

VANE

ROTOR

TURNTABLE

CAR AXLE

BRAKE
HANDLE

TOWER

CONTROL
SPRING

FIGURE 4

capacity (it produces 20 to 30 kilowatt-hrs. of energy per month and charges a 12-volt battery at rates up to 14 amperes), the unit is very reliable and has been produced for many years. A 7 mph breeze is sufficient to start charging, and full output is reached in a 23 mph wind. For a cabin, campsite, trailer, camper or boat the Wincharger would be adequate to serve the electrical needs of 12-volt lighting, radio, shaver and portable TV.

It should be noted that when 120-volt AC appliances are to be accommodated, an electrical device called an inverter must be used to convert a wind generator's 12-volt DC to the higher AC. The size and cost of this stationary converter depends on the maximum wattage of the various loads which may be con-

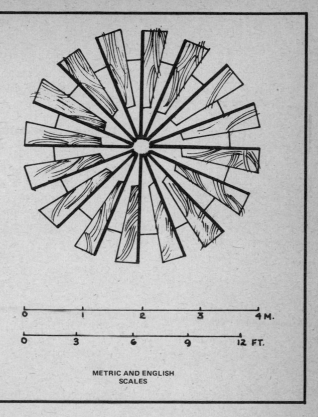

METRIC AND ENGLISH
SCALES

nected at any time and there is a certain loss of power in the inverter (typical efficiency being 80 to 90%).

If you're looking for a windmill which will serve needs up to a few kilowatts, you must consider larger machines. One source for them is Elektro gmbH of Winterthur, Switzerland. This manufacturer's units employ three-bladed propellers ranging from 3.5 to 5.0 meters in diameter with output ratings from 2,000 to 5,000 watts. The equipment produces 110-volt DC and, as usual, is employed in conjunction with a bank of storage batteries.

The Elektro units are of sophisticated design with blades which may be adjusted or "feathered" to compensate for varying wind speeds. The propeller shaft is coupled to the generator by gears running in an oil bath. As might be expected, the price of these machines runs to several thousand dollars, but— if you add up all your electric bills over a few years—that's not so unreasonable.

And what about building your own wind-driven electric generator? Well I'd advise that you first arm yourself with all the information you can get and ask yourself if your site is suitable. You might even record daily air velocities at your location with an inexpensive wind gauge (F.W. Dwyer of Michigan City, Indiana 46360 sells a small hand-held wind meter for about $9.00).

Figure that the mill should be situated at a higher level than any obstructions nearer than a few hundred feet. This may require a high tower, or running a line out to a hilltop location. Remember that the power you'll get is strongly dependent on average air speed, so make sure you pick the spot most exposed to prevailing winds.

Next, decide on the approximate-sized machine you need or can readily build, bearing in mind that power output varies as the square of propeller diameter (a 6-ft. diameter propeller yields four times as much power as one of the same design but only 3 ft. across). Construction costs also go up sharply with increased size. With 3 ft. or less, all you can expect to do is trickle charge batteries or carry very small loads such as a

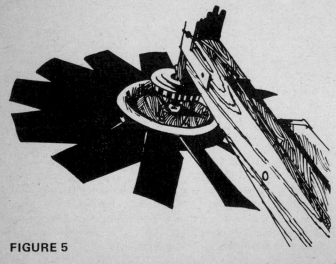

FIGURE 5

single radio or small light. Then again, building and operating a generator of this size might be worthwhile before undertaking a larger unit.

You'll find a 6-ft. diameter mill to be a good practical size if you can really limit your consumption of electricity. Even more useful is a 10- or 12-ft. diameter powerplant unless you find the difficulty and costs of construction prohibitive. I would not recommend fabrication of any larger units until some experience is gained with one of these smaller sizes.

Choice of propeller style and design has a strong bearing on the efficiency of a windmill. All modern electric generating mills have two or three very slender blades resembling aircraft propellers (see Figs. 2 and 3). Such designs feature a high *tip-speed ratio* which is a comparison between the velocity of the blade tips and the wind speed. Tip-speed ratios between 5:1 and 8:1 are not uncommon for efficient high-speed mills . . . as compared to ratios between 1:1 and 3:1 which are typical for the slower-running multiblade machines such as the American farm water-pumping windmill. On the other hand, although the latter design is less efficient, its higher starting torque and better performance at low wind velocities give it a steadier pumping action in light breezes.

Ideally, the propeller of a wind machine used for generating electricity should have a cross section resembling that of an aircraft wing . . . with a thick, rounded leading edge tapering down to a sharp trailing edge. It should be noted, however, that the most efficient airfoils for aircraft propellers, helicopter blades or contoured fan blades (all designed to move air) are not the most efficient airfoils for windmills (which are intended to be *moved by* air). An old airplane propeller, in other words, has neither the proper contour nor angle of attack to satisfactorily extract energy from the wind. If you have the ability and time to devote to carving a propeller from wood, however, you'll find good wind-charger designs to copy in *Proceedings of the United Nations Conference on New Sources of Energy* in the Bibliography at the back of this book.

The generator itself is of vital importance in any wind-electric system. Unfortunately, most generators which would seem to be suitable suffer from the requirement that they be driven at high speeds (most are built to be turned by gasoline engines at 1,500 to 3,600 rpm) and windmills, especially in

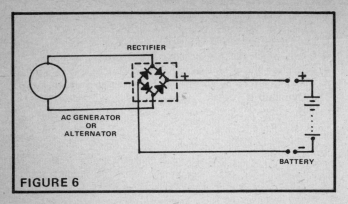

RECTIFIER

AC GENERATOR
OR
ALTERNATOR

BATTERY

FIGURE 6

larger sizes, seldom exceed 300 rpm. This means that one must either find special generators, or resort to step-up gearing to achieve the high rotational speed needed by the generator. Brushless permanent-magnet rotor alternators give reliable, trouble-free operation and require no electric power for a field winding but, unfortunately, are hard to come by. One possibility is to adapt an automobile alternator by replacing the field winding in the rotor with a permanent magnet.

On a much smaller scale, there is available at reasonable cost (about $11.00) a bicycle generator which will produce a useful output of one to two watts at low rotational speeds. This is the English-made Sturmey-Archer *Dynohub* generator, sold in this country by Raleigh of America, 350 Secaucus, Secaucus, New Jersey 07094. With a 2-ft. diameter propeller it can deliver its rated output without any modification. All that's required is the attachment of propeller blades.

Fig. 5 illustrates one unit constructed by the author. For charging a 6-volt automotive battery, a bridge rectifier such as the VARO W111, available from Allied Electronics, or the Motorola MDA 920-2 is used as shown in Fig. 6. Either costs about $1.50.

The propeller on the model shown in Fig. 5 is the modular construction "Multi-Wing" fan made in Denmark, and sold in the US by ILG Industries. In many respects the design is far from ideal as it is somewhat heavy, expensive and its minimum pitch angle of 30° results in a rather low tip-speed ratio. The Danish fan, however, is rugged, weatherproof, durable and develops plenty of torque—even in a moderate breeze—to overcome the slight cogging effect in the Dynohub generator.

The Dynohub unit is made for use as the hub of a bicycle front wheel and comes equipped with ball bearings and spoke holes . . . which make it possible to construct sheet aluminum or fiberglass blades and secure them to the hub at two points. At the perimeter a bicycle rim can serve as the supporting ring. The Dynohub is available in two models, with holes to accommodate either a 32- or 36-spoke wheel. One model is suited to a 4- or 8-bladed fan and the other to a 3- or 9-bladed propeller.

Practical applications of this design are limited to trickle charging batteries, such as for a boat at a mooring, or for a two-way radio at a remote campsite or cabin.

Inspiration for my Dynohub mill came from a wind-powered generator developed about 1964 by the National Bureau of Standards for use by the Navy or Weather Bureau on the MAMOS automatic weather reporting station. The *Tri-GEN* wind power units (Fig. 7) which supply power to this buoy, use three modified Dynohub generators on the shaft of the windmill to produce a three-phase output and reduce cogging effect. Both 30" and 36" 20-bladed mills are used to reach peak outputs close to 7 watts at wind velocities between 23 and 25 knots. Their low tip-speed ratio of 1.7:1 is typical of multibladed mills. The propeller blades are fabricated of sheet aluminum and are supported at their tips by a double ring and at half-span by a smaller ring.

The table below gives the theoretical power available from reasonably high-performance (70% efficient) mills such as those having two slender blades with a high tip-speed ratio.

Wind Velocity in mph	Diameter in Feet							
	2	3	4	5	6	8	10	12
5	0.6	1	2	4	5	10	15	21
10	5	11	19	30	42	75	120	170
15	16	36	64	100	140	260	400	540
20	38	85	150	240	340	610	950	1360
25	73	160	300	410	660	1180	1840	2660
Windmill Power Output in Watts								

The above figures are based on a formula given in the six-page section on wind power in Marks' Mechanical Engineers Handbook.

FIGURE 7

The design of a windmill involves decisions as to the size of the generator as well as the size and style of the propeller or rotor. Since there are no fuel costs, the cost of construction and maintenance are prime considerations and it's best to start with an electric generator of adequate power rating at relatively low speeds (a few hundred rpm).

Once a suitable machine is selected, a decision must be made as to what wind velocity will be necessary to achieve full output of the generator. If you decide to get full electric output at low wind speeds, you'll need a larger propeller ... whereas a small fan will be adequate if you want full electric output only in very high winds. The question to ask when designing a mill, then, is: How frequently do winds blow with a velocity greater than X mph?

Statistical studies made of wind records at Dayton, Ohio show that each month there is a well-defined group of wind velocities which predominate. These are called the *prevalent*, or frequent winds. There is also a well-defined group which contains the bulk of the energy each month called, appropriately enough, *energy winds*. Energy winds blow 2 out of 7 days; prevalent winds 5 out of 7.

Many working wind machines are designed to reach full output in air velocities of 20 to 25 mph, and deliver no appreciable output in breezes of less than 6 or 8 mph. At winds higher than those required for maximum output, governors or spoilers limit the rpm of the mill, thereby throwing away large quantities of energy but protecting the machine against damage. Lack of good performance at low wind velocities is not a serious drawback, since there is very little energy available from the wind at these calm conditions anyway.

Here are some average wind velocities at various locations:

	MPH		MPH
Albuquerque, N.M.	8.8	Mobile, Ala.	9.5
Bismarck, N.D.	10.8	Nashville, Tenn.	7.5
Buffalo, N.Y.	12.6	New York, N.Y.	
Chattanooga, Tenn.	6.3	(Battery)	14.5
Chicago, Ill.	10.3	New York, N.Y.	
Cleveland, O.	10.9	(Cent. Park)	9.5
Denver, Colo.	9.2	Philadelphia, Pa.	9.6
Detroit, Mich.	10.0	Portland, Ore.	7.8
Galveston, Tex.	11.1	St. Louis, Mo.	9.5
Jacksonville, Fla.	8.8	San Francisco, Calif.	10.4
Knoxville, Tenn.	7.4	Spokane, Wash.	8.4
Louisville, Ky.	8.3	Toledo, O.	9.5
Miami, Fla.	9.0	Washington, D.C.	9.4
		Mt. Washington, N.H.	35.4

It should be noted that wind velocity will vary considerably even in a local area, as the figures for New York City indicate.

At any rate, figures and tables aside, nature has free power available for you to use, without polluting Mother Earth or consuming her resources. Think about harnessing the wind and give it a try . . . you'll like it! ◗

If you'd like to build or install a wind-powered energy system of your own, you'll find several sources of equipment listed in the bibliography at the back of this book (see Wind, Hardware*).*

On June 2nd and 3rd, 1973 a Wind Energy Conversion Workshop was held in Washington, D.C. The gathering was sponsored by the National Science Foundation and implemented by the National Aeronautics and Space Administration.

Well sir... conferences and symposiums and workshops and all the other fancy meetings held to "study" a problem are all right, I suppose. But a fellow sometimes wonders if they're worth the trouble it takes to organize them.

This particular assembly was no exception. For, we're told, after nearly two days of absorbing reports and addresses from people who've experimented with and used wind power... many of the "experts" and "engineers" there still didn't have what you could call a grasp of the energy source's potential. "You mean you really run all your lights and appliances and a typewriter and stereo and TV on electricity produced by a windplant? You mean you're doing that right now?" one incredulous engineer asked Henry Clews. "I mean, if this thing actually works we should find out if it's practical enough to put into production."

MEET THE MAN WHO INVENTED THE MODERN WINDPLANT: MARCELLUS JACOBS

It was then that an authoritative-looking 70-year-old gentleman rose to his feet in the audience and said, in effect: "Why, you young whippersnapper. You're trying to reinvent the wheel. Not only will windplants work . . . not only can they be put into production . . . and not only can they be manufactured and sold profitably . . . but I personally built and marketed approximately 50 million dollars' worth of the units from the early 30's to the mid-50's. We were already in full swing before you were born."

Now I hasten to add that genial, polite Marcellus Jacobs didn't address the young and well-meaning (but somewhat ignorant) engineer quite so abruptly. Mr. Jacobs did, however, leave no doubt that windplants could be made to work. And he should know: Marcellus Jacobs is the man who almost singlehandedly invented the first practical wind-powered electrical generating system. He's the man who originated nearly all the noteworthy advances in the field from 1930 to 1956. And he's the man who dominated this specialized mini-industry until the day he decided to move on to other interests.

Marcellus Jacobs hasn't manufactured a windplant since

1956 . . . but people who know still fight to find one of his old second or third hand units. Why? Well, Admiral Byrd set up one of the Jacobs systems at the South Pole in 1933. On June 17, 1955, Richard E. Byrd, Jr., wrote a letter to Mr. Jacobs in which he said:

> I thought it might interest you to know that the wind generator installed (by my father) . . . at the original Little America, was still intact this year after almost a quarter of a century . . . The blades were still turning in the breeze (and) show little signs of weathering. Much of the paint is intact.

Marcellus Jacobs, in short, designed good windplants. He built 'em good too . . . and he built 'em to last.

Mr. Jacobs now lives and works on other environmentally oriented projects in Florida and Steve Weichelt recently visited him there. During the course of their conversation, Steve asked Jacobs to describe the development of his plants and to comment on the future he sees for wind power.

PLOWBOY: Mr. Jacobs, when and where were you born?

JACOBS: I was born in 1903 in Cando, North Dakota . . . up near the Canadian border. Then dad moved to a ranch in Montana south of Wolf Point . . . thirty miles from the Fort Peck Dam on the Missouri River. Wheat and cattle country.

PLOWBOY: Where did you go to school?

JACOBS: Everywhere. I didn't graduate from any university but I went to school in several different places. After I left high school I took one year of electrical training in Indiana and a special six-month course in electricity in Kansas City. Most of my education, though, just came from studying on my own. I got the books and picked up what I could from them, and thought the rest out for myself.

PLOWBOY: Which came first? Did your interest in electricity lead you to find that you could produce this form of power from the wind . . . or did you set out to do something useful with moving air masses, and end up harnessing them to electrical generators?

JACOBS: It was a little bit of both. When I was still in high school I built and sold little peanut radios that operated on storage batteries . . . and pretty soon we wanted motors and welders and drill presses and what have you that operated on current. At the same time, I had always been intrigued by the wind. It was natural, I suppose, to put the two interests together.

PLOWBOY: I take it then that you used the wind to produce the first electrical power you generated?

JACOBS: Oh no. Our ranch was 40 miles from town and in them days, of course, there wasn't any Rural Electrification Administration lines running all over the country. We—there were eight children in our family—had to make do with kerosene lamps and so on . . . but we soon got tired of that. So we rigged up an old secondhand engine to run a little DC generator. But it fluctuated every time the load changed so we hooked the generator up to some old car batteries to balance the system some and that worked pretty well. Along about then, though, we started a hand forge and put a motor on that and we needed more current than our engine-driven generator would produce. This was about 1922.

PLOWBOY: And that's when you began experimenting with windplants.

JACOBS: Yes. I first tried to use a fan off one of the regular water-pumping windmills we had there on the ranch. I took a Ford Model T rear axle and cut the side shaft off where one of the wheels was supposed to go and I put the big fan on instead. Then I mounted the tail vane out where the other wheel should be . . . and I extended the drive shaft down to the ground where I had my generator. I just locked the differential with a pin so that as the wind turned the fan it would drive the shaft.

PLOWBOY: Did it work?

JACOBS: Oh yes, after a fashion. But there were several things wrong with the setup. It wasn't efficient, you know . . . there was no real gain. One of those big water-pumping windmill wheels is designed to catch all the wind in its diameter right at the start. Otherwise it'll never go. It'll just sit there. Unless the pump has lost its prime, the wheel has to lift water right from the instant it begins turning. It needs a lot of starting torque . . . and that's why it has so many large blades.

Once the wheel gets up some speed, however, about 80% of those blades get in each other's way. They begin fighting each other. In fact, a water-pumping windmill needs all the power it generates just to run *itself* in an 18 or 20 mph wind. You can pull the pump rod loose and the wheel won't run away. It can't. The force of the wind during a storm may blow the wheel into the tower and push the tower over . . . but the fan won't over-rev and tear itself apart.

The wheel we finally came up with for a windplant, now, is altogether different. There's no load on it at the beginning, you see . . . just the very slight drag of two ball bearings. The three little blades sticking out of the wheel's hub are all you need to start the thing turning in a two mph breeze. And those narrow blades are also all you need to catch every bit of air that moves through the wheel's diameter when the wind blows 20 mph. They'll do it better than all those sails on a water-pumping windmill's fan too. A three-bladed windplant propeller may develop between six and eight horsepower in an 18 mph wind, while an ordinary windmill wheel of the same diameter sitting right beside it won't produce much over two.

PLOWBOY: How long did you experiment with the old water-pumping windmill fans before you gave up on them?

JACOBS: Well, we messed around for three years or so. We even made a governor that turned every one of the blades—to feather them—on such a wheel . . . but there were just too many other factors working against the design. To put it very simply: If you can catch all the wind that moves through a certain diameter with three blades, there's no need to have fifty of them hanging out there. The extras just get in the way.

PLOWBOY: But why *three?* Why not two blades? Or four?

JACOBS: We tried them. We tried those other numbers. See, I learned to fly in 1926 or '27 and that gave me the idea that an airplane-type propeller was what we wanted. Most of those props, of course, had only two blades so that's what we used.

PLOWBOY: You took one right off an airplane?

JACOBS: No. They didn't have the right pitch. But we made some windplant propellers that were quite similar to the ones used on aircraft. We didn't stay with them long, though. I discovered—very early in the game—that a two-bladed propeller has vibration problems that a prop with three blades doesn't have.

PLOWBOY: But we're still using two-bladers on airplanes!

JACOBS: Not always. When Curtiss-Wright developed some of that company's first really big engines at the start of World War II, they found that the powerplants tore themselves right out of their mounts when the planes were kicked into an abrupt turn. I won't go into a long, confusing explanation of why this happens. It's enough to say that the Curtiss-Wright engineers and test pilots wrecked a bunch of aircraft before they finally solved the problem by going to three-bladed propellers . . . something I had done years earlier with my windplants.

See, this potentially destructive situation always exists with propellers that have two blades. It's always there but most of the time it doesn't give airplanes any trouble. I mean . . . when you make a turn with a plane, how large a curve do you usually fly? A quarter mile? Half mile? That's not nearly sharp enough to cause a problem. But a windplant supported in its center on a bearing whips right around, doesn't it? There just isn't any way to make a two-bladed wheel hold up on a windplant. Sooner or later—and probably sooner—it'll snap off at the hub . . . or one of the blades will let go.

PLOWBOY: But a three-blader won't.

JACOBS: No.

PLOWBOY: OK. Why wouldn't four blades be better yet?

JACOBS: Well, there'd be no object in going to four.

Look. It doesn't matter if you have one blade or a dozen . . . if you design them right you can make that wheel catch all the wind that comes through it. You can stand behind those spinning blades and strike a match and it'll hardly blow out. You're catching all the wind, you see, and slowing it down and changing its direction. One blade is just as good as four or five or more.

The only trouble with one blade, however, is that you can't balance it . . . and two blades have the vibration problem I've mentioned. A wheel with three blades nicely solves both these problems and you'd be foolish to add any more.

PLOWBOY: Why?

JACOBS: Because the tips of that wheel are moving through the air at 125 mph and every time you put on another tip you're adding unnecessary drag. It takes a lot of energy to push something through the air at 125 mph, you know. That's a waste of power.

There's another factor involved too. We wanted our windplants—which had 15-foot-diameter propellers—to develop their maximum charging rates in a wind of, say, 20 mph . . . but we didn't want their tip speeds to exceed 125 mph. A three-bladed prop met these requirements admirably.

PLOWBOY: All right. This takes us up to about 1927. What happened next?

JACOBS: Well, once we had the propeller design worked out, we still had two main problems: speed and pressure. If you want to get as much power as you can from a light breeze, you've got to have a propeller of large diameter. But when you have a large diameter, you've also got something you can't control in a high wind. You need some way to regulate your propeller's speed and you want to be able to take the pressure of the wind off your blades during a real gale.

So I developed the fly-ball governor. I mounted weights on the hubs of our propellers so the centrifugal force of higher speeds would twist all three blades identically, see, and change their pitch. This automatically feathered the propellers in high winds. It both slowed them down and relieved the pressure against them.

PLOWBOY: There's another kind of governor, you know . . . made by the Zenith Corporation.

JACOBS: They call that a governor! It's like holding the throttle down on your car while you step on the brakes to slow down! Their blade is fixed, you see, and when you apply a brake out here the way they do, you only slow down the propeller. You don't relieve the pressure of the wind blowing against those blades. I've replaced hundreds of those windplants when storms just pushed their blades right into the towers.

PLOWBOY: Your plants never had that trouble?

JACOBS: Never. We set the centrifugal controls so our blades couldn't receive more than the pressure for which they were rated. We've had winds of more than a hundred miles an hour on our plants down there at the South Pole. No problem. We've had plants scattered all over the West Indies and on the Florida Keys, and we've never had one go down in a hurricane yet.

PLOWBOY: Did you patent your governor . . .

JACOBS: Yes, but Curtiss-Wright stole it from me on a technicality.

PLOWBOY: . . . and did you start putting it on windplants?

JACOBS: Oh yes. We built about 20 or 25 plants out there in Montana from 1927 to 1931. They all had our new propellers and governors on them and we sold them to ranchers in the area.

PLOWBOY: What did you use for generators?

JACOBS: We bought our generators from Robbins and Myers and we built both 32- and 110-volt DC systems. I think we got

·our towers from the Challenge Windmill Company in Batavia, Illinois. The towers, you know, were actually meant for water-pumping windmills. Nobody else was making windplants. We invented the business in North America . . . I guess the world. A few others were playing around with ideas but we were the first to manufacture a practical machine.

In 1931 we sold our ranch holdings—my brother was with me at the time—and I formed a Montana corporation, sold stock and really set up to make windplants. Later, of course, I moved the operation to Minneapolis.

PLOWBOY: Did you go right into production on an assembly line basis back there in 1931?

JACOBS: No, we spent about a year or better designing and building a big generator. There wasn't one available at that time that would produce 2,000 watts of power at our working range of 225 rpm. You couldn't buy one anywhere, so we designed and built one just for our propeller.

Now this was quite important for a couple of reasons: Number one, there's a lot more to good propeller design than most people realize and, number two, the best propeller in the world isn't worth much if the generator it turns isn't exactly matched to the prop.

See, the whole idea of high-speed propeller design is to throw the wind that hits the blades . . . the whole idea is to throw it out quickly. You don't want it to drag all the way along the back of the blades. That's a tremendous amount of friction—a tremendous force—and you want to eliminate it. Sometimes a very little change—a 64th of an inch—in the curve on the back of a propeller can affect its power output a seemingly immeasurable amount.

Well forty years ago, I designed a special machine that would let me determine just how efficient a blade design might be. I had a test stand made up that extended out two feet past the end of a propeller and at each foot along the arm we mounted a separate wind pressure gauge. We checked a lot of blades on that stand until we knew exactly how to design a propeller that was as efficient as we could make it.

PLOWBOY: And then you built a generator to match the prop?

JACOBS: Yes. We had to balance the generator's load to match the efficiency of the propeller. If your blades work best at a certain rpm in a 7-1/2 mph breeze, they should turn exactly twice as fast when the wind blows 15 mph, shouldn't they? They won't catch all of that 15 mph wind unless they do, will they?

OK. The trick is to design the generator so that its load increases just fast enough to allow the propeller to double its rpm as the force of the wind doubles. And that's what we did . . . right up to the top speed we wanted, which was 18—20 mph.

Now this wasn't easy, because a conventional generator doubles its output when its speed increases by only something like 25%. Obviously that wasn't a very good match for our propeller . . . so we tried several things until we finally came up with a special alloy for the field poles in the generator. We finally got a combination that made the load of the generator fit the output power curve of the propeller over the entire range of windspeeds up to 22, -3 or -4 miles an hour . . . where the blades were set to feather out.

It was a lot of trouble, but it was worth it. Wincharger, for instance, didn't take the time to balance the components of its plant in this manner and that unit was only one-third as efficient as ours at higher windspeeds.

PLOWBOY: Wow. You really took pains to design and build the best possible windplant, didn't you?

JACOBS: Oh yes. I've only told you a part of it. We came up with our own special brushes in the generator, you know.

It's not too hard to set up a big DC generator and run it with a stationary engine, see, because you've got a fixed speed of operation and you can adjust everything so it's working the best for that rate of output. Now I'm particularly thinking of the commutator arm and its brushes which slide from one wound coil to another inside the generator. Every time those brushes move from coil to coil, you know, they want to throw a spark. When you break DC you get an arc . . . and those flashes will burn little rust spots on the commutator and then it'll just grind the brushes off in a matter of months.

What you look for, of course, is the neutral zone . . . the one small area where your brushes will throw the least spark as they leave one coil and go to the next. This isn't too hard to find and when you've got a fixed speed on your engine and generator you can set everything just right to make use of it.

A windplant isn't like that, though. It's set to kick its generator into operation at about 125 rpm and it reaches full output—3,000 watts or whatever—up around 225 rpm. Now that's OK . . . but every time the rpm varies—and it can change a thousand times a day—the neutral zone shifts. No matter how you adjust your commutator, then, your windplant's brushes are going to be set to throw a much bigger spark than you'd like as they move from coil to coil during the greater part of the plant's operation.

Everyone in the business faced this problem, of course, but none of the others ever licked it. We did. I developed a brush made up of a layer of graphite, then carbon, then graphite, then carbon. This gave us a brush with a high cross-section resistance. The DC current would practically quit flowing before the brush made its jump from one coil to the next and that was just what we wanted.

We tried to get National Carbon to make these special brushes for us but they weren't even interested enough to send a man out to see us. Stackpole couldn't understand what we wanted either but they did build the brushes to our specifications and that licked the commutation problem. We've had plants run ten or fifteen years on their original set of brushes.

That's unusual. Ask anyone who's operated other manufacturers' windplants.

PLOWBOY: Didn't you also make some noteworthy breakthroughs in the way you regulated the voltage of your units?

JACOBS: Yes. That's another tough situation you have to face with DC. To change the irregular power generated by the wind into a steady flow of current for use, you have to go through batteries. The only trouble is that you can't let your generator feed the same amount of electrical energy to the batteries all the time or you'll burn the storage cells out. As a charge is built in a battery—as the battery becomes more nearly "full"—you want to charge it at a slower and slower rate.

Well, Wincharger and all the others tried this and that but they never came up with the voltage regulators and cutoffs they needed to solve the problem. That's why you always had to get up at two o'clock in the morning or some other unhandy hour and shut those plants off to keep them from burning out their storage banks.

We had the only windplant that didn't have this trouble because ours was the only one which was completely voltage regulated. Our control—we called it the Master Mind—inserted a resistance into the generator fields to weaken their output as the batteries filled up.

Now that was a problem in itself because the Master Mind contained a set of points that had to open and close thousands of times a week. This meant thousands of arcs and flashes. Eventually the points would stick and make the generator begin to run like a motor as soon as the wind died down. That wasn't good, you know, because it would soon drain all the energy stored in the batteries.

We licked that one by developing what we called our "reverse current relay". We ran a little bit of direct current—opposite in polarity to the main flow—right back through the points to make them open with one quick flash instead of just hang there, floating, until they'd burned themselves out. It was a little shunt circuit, actually, that opened and closed the main cutoff with one clean action just when we wanted it to.

PLOWBOY: How long did it take you to figure all this out?

JACOBS: Well, from the time we started fooling with windplants . . . about ten years. Our most important work was done in less than two years . . . from 1931 to 1933. By '33 or '34 we were in pretty good swing. We came up with a few improvements as we went along, of course . . . but after 1936 or '37 we ran for 20 years without making any basic changes in our design.

PLOWBOY: I suppose you brought in an expert from time to time for consultation.

JACOBS: No, because back then there weren't any experts on slow-speed electrical generation. There were no experts on voltage regulation and nobody had ever heard of making an airplane-type propeller for a generator. There were no books on the subject . . . nothing to go by. I developed my own expertise. When you have a problem, you know, you just stick with it until you find a solution. That's how I wound up with more than 25 patents. Every one of those patents represents a problem that we solved.

PLOWBOY: Well it seems that there's more than just problem solving involved here. People who know say that yours are still absolutely the finest windplants ever manufactured by anybody anywhere in the world. You must have had strong feelings about the quality of any equipment that bore your name.

JACOBS: Oh sure. I'm kind of a freak, see. I want things to work forever. I built my plants to last a lifetime.

I've had battles with manufacturers all my life. When I started looking for bearings to put in our windplants, I found out that what the companies that made them called "permanent" . . . would last about two years. The bearings themselves were pretty good, see, but the seals around the races would dry out and let the grease inside get away after a few years. What I did was take some of the bearings used in the rear axle of a car, mount them in a special compartment with a special lubricant and then put my own seal over them. They'll last 20 years that way . . . and 20 years is closer to a lifetime than two.

We've had plants that have run 25 years with no lubrication. I talked to a rancher out in New Mexico last July and he's been using his for *over* 25. He's still using it and he's never done much more than climb up once a year and tighten a few bolts and whatnot.

The brushes on most windplants, as you know, go out all the time. They don't last long at all. Well I got a letter about a year ago from a mission in Africa. The people there bought their plant in 1936 and that letter was their first order for replacement brushes. They've used the generator all that time. Same thing with our blades.

PLOWBOY: Yes! I wanted to get to that. Tell me about the construction of your propellers. Did you make them of metal?

JACOBS: Oh no. Solid metal—even aluminum—would have been too heavy. Too much centrifugal force. The, more fly-wheel effect you get, see, the more trouble you have shifting the plant around and that means more strain on all the component parts.

We did stamp out some hollow aluminum blades once, but they weren't at all satisfactory in the north country. They had a tendency to sweat. Frost would form on their insides and throw them out of balance . . . and that could shake a plant completely apart.

No. Our old standby was aircraft-quality, vertical grain spruce. Sitka spruce from the West Coast. I used to go out and select the lumber personally and have carloads of it shipped back to the factory. During the war, I had a little trouble getting the quality I wanted.

PLOWBOY: And how did you turn the raw lumber into blades?

JACOBS: We rough-cut the airfoils first—from 2 X 8 planks— on a special machine. Then we put them aside in the kiln-dry rooms for several weeks to make sure they were completely set and weren't going to warp. After that we made our final cuts.

PLOWBOY: Did you hand-sand them?

JACOBS: No, we had a great big sanding machine that worked down both sides of a blade. It was set up like a planer or a duplicating lathe, you know. You clamped your raw blade into mounts on one side and then you ran a set of feeler rollers over a perfectly finished blade that was always mounted on the other side. This guided the application of power sanders to the unfinished airfoil . . . and you could smooth it right down to the exact contours of the master very quickly, easily and automatically this way.

PLOWBOY: How did you finish the blades?

JACOBS: With an asphalt-base, aluminum paint.

PLOWBOY: And that's all?

JACOBS: That's all they needed. Propellers we built 25 or more years ago are still going strong.

PLOWBOY: I notice that you never put a brake on your plants.

JACOBS: No, our tail vane was enough. We had it hinged so we could lock it straight behind the generator or swung away off to the side. It would remain streamlined to the wind either way, of course, so when it was in the second position it pulled the generator and propeller right around edgeways to the moving air. This took most of the wind off the blades and they'd sit up there and just idle during violent storms.

PLOWBOY: But other manufacturers could swing the tail vanes on their machines to the side too.

JACOBS: Yes, but most of them did it the wrong way. They fastened the vane straight behind the generator with springs and you had to use a line from the ground to pull it around to the side. If that line broke during a gale, there was nothing you could do about it. The windplant would run away and tear itself all to pieces . . . unless you had a brake that you could apply . . . and brakes, for some other reasons, weren't a good idea either.

We set our spring up the other way, see. It always wanted to hold the vane to the side and you had to use a line to pull the tail straight back. This way, if the line broke, the vane would pull the propeller around and make it idle. Ours was designed to protect itself if anything went wrong.

PLOWBOY: So you never used a brake?

JACOBS: We tested some when we were still experimenting out in Montana, and very quickly found that they're a source of trouble. The brake bands freeze up and you have to climb the tower with a hammer and knock them loose. Besides that, it's not very smart to completely stop a windplant propeller. The ice mostly freezes on the lowest blade and that'll wreck your plant if you turn it loose. It's much better to let the propeller swing around a little bit during a winter storm. What ice or frost it collects will be distributed evenly that way and won't give you any trouble.

PLOWBOY: Fantastic. You really checked out all the angles, didn't you? What did this translate to in business?

JACOBS: Oh, I don't know exactly. We must have built about 50 million dollars' worth of plants in 25 years.

PLOWBOY: Wow! What was your biggest year?

JACOBS: I can't remember . . . but I think we had 260 employees at one time. We could produce eight to ten plants a day working one shift and during the war we ran three. We ran around the clock in Minneapolis and I even bought another factory in Iowa and ran it for a few years. We didn't build windplants out there but we manufactured similar equipment . . . electrical and magnetic hardware for the Army and Navy. Gear that protected our ships from the Germans' magnetic mines . . . stuff like that.

PLOWBOY: I've heard you once came up with another protective device. Something to do with pipelines.

JACOBS: Yes, I'm quite proud—I'd say justifiably so—of the cathodic protection system I devised in 1933. I don't know if you're familiar with the problem or not, but when you put big pieces of metal in the ground—things like pipelines—they just waste away. They don't rust . . . but the metal is carried into the dirt by electrolysis. It's just eaten up and carried away. The earth, in effect, is electroplated at the expense of the pipeline.

I found that this action can be stopped by putting a little negative direct current—only 3/10 of a volt—on the metal and a little positive DC into the surrounding soil. This discovery has saved the pipeline companies millions upon millions of dollars. All the big bridges are now protected this way too. Every very large steel structure.

PLOWBOY: Have you developed anything else that the ordinary individual would find more directly related to your windplants?

JACOBS: Well we used to sell everything you'd need on the ranch—fans, motors, electric irons, toasters, percolators, freezers, refrigerators, whatever—all built to run on 32-volt DC. Hamilton Beach manufactured them for me to my specifications. I even had a freezer that was so well insulated you could unplug it and it would keep ice cream frozen for four or five days. All this equipment could be powered by our windplants, of course.

PLOWBOY: Do you think those days will ever come back? What future do you see for windplants?

JACOBS: There'll always be a small, scattered market for individual plants—especially in the more remote areas of the world—but the Rural Electrification Administration has pretty well killed the demand for self-contained DC systems in this country. AC is just too readily available everywhere. Alternating current is all over the place . . . often at artificially low prices. That's a tough combination to beat and I quit trying to fight it in the 50's. I could see the handwriting on the wall back around '52, '53, '54 . . . and we closed the factory in 1956.

PLOWBOY: But conditions *are* changing. There *is* an energy crisis now, you know. That AC is going to get more and more expensive and we're going to have to tap some power sources—such as the wind—that we haven't really thought a lot about in the past.

JACOBS: Yes, but I still feel that the individual DC plant is largely a thing of the past. If I were building windplants today, I'd go AC. And I wouldn't concentrate on the small units . . . I'd think about larger ones that could feed directly into the distribution grid that's already set up.

As a matter of fact, I proposed just that idea to Congress back in 1952. The power companies, you know, already have a great number of steel towers set up to carry their transmission lines across the country. I added to this the fact that AC generators require almost no maintenance at all . . . and I came up with an idea: Put windplants right on top of the towers.

Pick a stretch—I took Minneapolis to Great Falls for an example—and install a thousand AC windplants on the towers in between. It doesn't matter what the wind does, at least some of the generators will be producing all the time. Just let 'em feed supplemental power into the grid whenever the wind blows.

The beautiful part of this plan is the fact that the wind blows strongest and most steadily when we need it most . . . in the winter. I've talked to the men who manage the power grid and they tell me electric heat has become so popular that they're now forced to keep thousands of dollars' worth of standby diesels on hand . . . just to handle the winter overload.

PLOWBOY: OK. But let's say that someone who reads this doesn't agree with you. Let's say he wants to go into business right now manufacturing essentially the same windplant you produced for 25 years. What happened to your old dies, the old tools? What about your patents?

JACOBS: The equipment is all gone. I stopped in at the factory a while back and it's used for something else now. None of the original setup is there at all. As for the patents . . . quite a few are public property now.

PLOWBOY: All right. Let's get even more basic. What if an individual wants to go out and build his own windplant the way you put your first ones together . . . with materials he finds in junkyards and other odds and ends?

JACOBS: Well I haven't been active in the field for 15 or 18 years now. There's a lot of new stuff I'm not familiar with . . . but I'd say that some of the AC generators and the rectifiers now available should make that pretty easy.

PLOWBOY: You're not actively engaged in windplant work of any kind at this time?

JACOBS: No, I have other interests now.

PLOWBOY: You mean you don't think about wind-driven generators at all?

JACOBS: Well . . . I did buy one of my old plants out in New Mexico this summer . . . and I've still got quite an assortment of DC equipment and appliances packed away. I'm doing it mostly for my son, you know . . . but I imagine I'm going to have a little fun setting that windplant up and running it this winter. ◆

NEED A LITTLE CLEAN ENERGY? JAMES B. DE KORNE SAYS THAT THE ANSWER IS BLOWIN' IN THE WIND

A little over a year ago, I wrote a short article for *Organic Gardening and Farming* magazine. In that piece, I described our life on a small New Mexico homestead . . . and how we planned to utilize non-polluting sources of energy such as methane gas, solar heating and wind generators.

The response to the article was nothing short of amazing. I received correspondence from all over the United States, Canada, France and the Philippines . . . and most letters requested further information about the alternate energy sources I had named.

It didn't take long for me to realize that my optimistic enthusiasm for my subject was a bit naive and premature . . . I

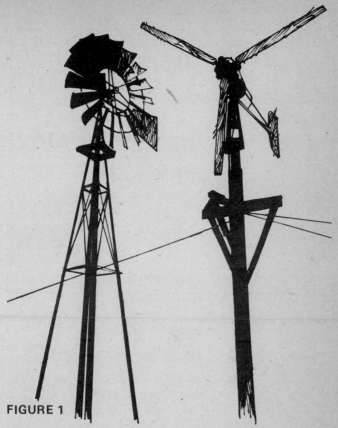

FIGURE 1

didn't really know any more about alternative sources of energy than the folks who were requesting further information, yet I was being regarded as an expert in the field!

I answered the letters as best I could, then set out to learn as much as possible about the subject . . . which has now become almost an obsession with me. Through the generosity of the Verde Valley School of Sedona, Arizona, I was able to make an 8,000-mile trip this spring with six students . . . a trip during which we traveled across America seeking out information from the people who *were* experts in alternate sources of energy. The story of that journey, and the information we gathered, will—we hope—soon be published as a book. Until

NOMENCLATURE

Although people still refer to wind generators and wind pumps as "windmills", the differences between windmills, wind pumps and wind generators are obvious when you think about them.

A windmill is technically a machine powered by the wind for the purpose of grinding grain into flour. The old Dutch windmills were generally used for this purpose.

The commonly-referred-to "windmill", found on farms and homesteads all over America, is actually a wind pump, since its purpose is to pump water. Bona fide windmills are actually very rare in this country.

To call a wind generator a windmill is equally erroneous, since the only thing the two have in common is that they're powered by a moving air mass. One may as well confuse motorcycles with chain saws because each makes use of a similar gasoline-powered engine.

then, I'd like to share with MOTHER's readers some of the information we gathered about wind generators.

NANSEN WAS FIRST

The first wind generator, as far as I'm able to discover, was built by the Arctic explorer Fridtjof Nansen in 1894. Ice-bound in the polar sea, Nansen rigged up a Holland-type windmill to drive a dynamo which charged batteries. He was enjoying electric lights in the vicinity of the North Pole when the houses of New York and London were still illuminated with kerosene and gas.

Sometime around 1935 or '36, the Wincharger Corporation of Sioux City, Iowa began production of wind-electric plants for use by farms and homesteads far from powerlines. Wind generators were then used extensively in some rural areas and continued to be up until the early fifties, when the Rural Electrification Administration at last brought power to most of the country. The Wincharger Corporation finally ceased production on all models except a small 200-watt unit in 1953 and the Jacobs Company of Minneapolis, Minnesota—another manufacturer of such equipment—stopped building its wind generators in 1956.

With the energy crisis and air pollution becoming problems of concern (most electricity these days, in the Southwest at least, comes from coal-fired generators which are saturating our once clean skies with tons of filth), more and more people are looking for alternative sources of power. Do wind generators offer a valid solution? The answer is both yes and no. To understand such a seemingly ambivalent reply, we first must understand some basic facts of electricity.

VOLTS, AMPS AND WATTS

The three most important units of electrical measurement which concern us are: volts, amps and watts . . . and the first two are often confused.

The easiest way to remember the difference between amps and volts is to think of amps as "current" which is measured in much the same way as the volume of water in a pipe. And, if amps are volume, then volts can be thought of as "pressure" or the amount of push behind the volume of water. This is an important distinction: There's a world of difference between the flow of a swift mountain brook (high voltage, low amperage), and the flow of sluggish water in a large, slow-moving river (high amperage, low voltage). The analogy is not perfect but it gives you the idea.

Obviously, the relationship between amps and volts is very important . . . and the combination of the two when multiplied together is the total amount of electricity available. This total is measured in *watts*. Volts times amps, in other words, equals watts. *The very first thing that should concern us when we consider the installation of a wind generator is: HOW MANY* **WATTS** *DOES IT PRODUCE?*

WATTS ARE THE KEY

The answer to the question: do wind generators offer a valid solution to the electrical needs of folks concerned about pollution, the energy crisis and self-sufficiency—then—hinges on the number of *watts* required by the user. A 200-watt generator might well serve a couple living simply in a small dome or one-room cabin, but would hardly be adequate for a family homestead which wants electric lights *plus* a deep-freeze, arc-welder and power tools.

The easiest way to visualize the output of any given generator is to imagine the number of 100-watt bulbs it will fully light at one time. A 200-watt generator will handle two 100-watt bulbs; a 3,000-watt unit will simultaneously power thirty 100-watt bulbs. To find out how much capacity you need, just add up the total wattage of all of the light bulbs and appliances you plan to use . . . and tack on a few more for good measure.

WHAT DOES THE MARKET OFFER?

What kinds of wind generators are available today and where can a person get one which will fulfill his energy requirements? There are three ways to go: [1] you can buy a new wind generator, [2] you can buy a used one, or [3] you can build one yourself from automobile components.

Since Wincharger ceased production of its high-wattage machines, and Jacobs went out of business entirely, the only source I know of for a new wind generator that produces more than 1,000 watts is the Quirk's Company in Australia.

I recently (three months ago) wrote airmail to Quirk's and requested information on their machine (I even enclosed return postage and offered to pay for any data they might send). To date, I've received no reply . . . so it appears that the firm is not overly interested in the U.S. market. Henry Clews —of East Holden, Maine—is said to be the American agent for this wind generator. I wrote to him at the same time I sent a letter to the Australian firm and, again, have received no reply. It's beginning to look as if the Quirk's machine is not easily obtainable in the States.

(NOTE: Between the time this was written and press time, I received a most informative packet of information from Henry Clews' Solar Wind Company. Clews is the dealer for several models of high-wattage machines from Australia and Switzerland. Anyone even slightly interested in wind generators owes it to himself to send $2.00 to the Solar Wind Company, RFD 2, East Holden, Maine 04429, and request Henry's publication, Electric Power From the Wind. *This pamphlet is probably the definitive guide to wind electric plants to date.)*

Dyna Technology, Inc., Box 3263, Sioux City, Iowa 51102

FIGURE 2

now handles the only Wincharger still produced in the U.S.
... a 200-watt machine which sells for around $400. The
folks at that company were most helpful people, and kindly
gave me permission to publish some of their literature. The
20-page instruction manual (Fig. 2) for their 200-watt unit is
full of valuable information about wind generators in general.

If you need no more than 200 watts and aren't into building your own generator, the Dyna Technology machine might
be just what you need. Most of them are presently being sold

in Latin America and the Pacific Islands for the purpose of charging radio batteries.

For three dollars, the Bucknell Engineering Company, 10717 East Rush Street, South El Monte, California 91733, will sell you information about a 250-watt wind generator. They also offer the completed unit for $1,082.

Unless you have a lot more money than I do, such low-wattage new wind generators are out of the question. And, until someone goes into production on a high-wattage machine at a reasonable price, most people will have to buy a used unit or build their own.

USED WIND GENERATORS: WHERE THEY ARE AND WHAT THEY COST

Just about anywhere in the rural Great Plains States, wind generators were common sights on farms during the 1930's and 40's. When the REA finally strung its wires to these localities, the machines were often taken down and sold for scrap. Occasionally, however—after a lot of backroad driving, and many conversations with farmers old enough to remember them—one can still find a few of these generators still standing. (Usually they weren't taken down because most folks aren't into the hair-raising job of working with upwards of 400 pounds of machinery while tied onto the top of a high tower . . . an experience roughly analogous to removing an engine from an automobile at an altitude of 45 feet!)

The two most common wind generators were the Wincharger and the Jacobs . . . respectively the Chevrolet and Cadillac of homestead wind-electric plants. The Wincharger came in several models, from 6 to 110 volts and from 200 to 1,200 watts. The Jacobs, a much heavier machine, was built in 32- and 110-volt configurations and ranged from 1,500 to 3,000 watts. The 32-volt models of both makes were the most popular in their day, and of the two, Wincharger is the brand you're most likely to encounter now. The Jacobs is currently quite rare, but a real find if you turn one up in reasonably good condition.

Almost any old wind generator you may locate is more likely than not in need of extensive restoration. It's unusual to find one that still has usable propellers . . . these, being made of wood (with the exception of some later models of the

Wincharger, which had aluminum props), are the first parts to
deteriorate. After all, the machine has probably stood
untended for well over 25 years of summer thunderstorms and
winter blizzards! It is even rarer yet to find a generator that
still has the original control box, though one can be made up
by most any electrician worth his salt.

Is it worthwhile to try to restore one of these old wind-
electric plants? Most definitely yes! If you're selective, and can
locate a machine that doesn't have unrepairable damage—such
as broken castings or missing major parts—a little bit of enjoyable restoration will reward you with up to 3,000 watts of
"free" electricity. Anyone who has rebuilt a Model A Ford or
likes to fool around with old cars will feel right at home tear-
ing into a 1940-vintage wind generator. It is my opinion that
this is a better route to go than to construct a generator out of
automobile components . . . an endeavor which can result at
best in no more than 600 watts. (Remember, that's enough
juice to light only six 100-watt bulbs . . . not a very impressive
yield for your time and money.)

My main need for electricity on our one-acre homestead in
New Mexico is for power to operate a deepfreeze . . . almost a
necessity for folks who raise their own food and are shooting
for total self-sufficiency. Some foods can't be dried satisfactorily . . . and while canning is certainly one solution to that
problem, fresh-frozen food retains even more of its vitamin
content and just plain tastes better.

Someone may prove me wrong, but I don't think you can
run a deepfreeze on a 600-watt wind generator adapted from
automobile parts. (Not and have enough juice left over for
lights and power tools.) If you're interested in more than lighting a few bulbs or running a low-wattage stereo set, think in
terms of something greater than a thousand watts of power.

OK. After from a few days to several weeks of bumpy
roads and elderly farmers who think you're mildly insane for
wanting a 30-year-old piece of "junk", you've finally located a
wind generator that looks as if it could be made to work again.
There it is, 45 feet up in the air . . . a glorious piece of rusted
cast iron with a splatter of .22 holes leaking light through the
tail vane. What's it worth?

You may be so overjoyed that you've finally found one,
that you'll be willing to shell out whatever the farmer asks for
the wind generator. ("Well, I paid over two thousand dollars

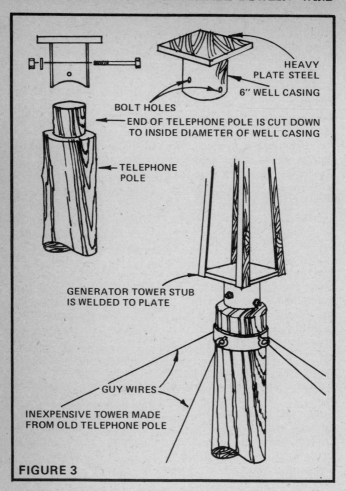

HEAVY
PLATE STEEL

6" WELL CASING

BOLT HOLES

END OF TELEPHONE POLE IS CUT DOWN
TO INSIDE DIAMETER OF WELL CASING

TELEPHONE
POLE

GENERATOR TOWER STUB
IS WELDED TO PLATE

GUY WIRES

INEXPENSIVE TOWER MADE
FROM OLD TELEPHONE POLE

FIGURE 3

for the whole system back in 1943 . . . would you give me
$150 for it?")

That may not sound like much money, but bear in mind
that the "whole system" included the batteries, which 999
times out of 1,000 were sold to a scrap dealer back in 1949
when the REA came in. Also, the generator has endured torna-
does, been struck by lightning six or seven times, and is all but
rusted into one solid chunk of cast iron and copper wire. Add

to that the fact that YOU are the one who has to take it down from that 45-foot tower, and the price rapidly drops to something like $20.00 or $30.00. (This for the generator alone . . . "tower included" raises the price.)

The most I ever paid for a wind generator was $100 for a Jacobs (the best machine made) that put out 2,500 watts, was *complete* with no busted parts, and—moreover—had been carefully removed from its tower in 1949 and stored ever since in a nice warm barn.

The reason I offer these price guidelines is because I'd hate to see the cost of used wind generators inflated to beyond their true value, like everything else seems to be these days. Also remember that you're going to have to put considerable time and money into making the thing work again.

On a recent trip out on the plains I managed to scrounge up seven old wind generators: four Winchargers and three Jacobs. Out of the seven, only three are complete enough to be usable. (In learning by experience I made a few mistakes and bought some junk.) I only purchased one tower, mostly because all those generators constituted an overload for my truck and trailer, and towers are readily available in my part of the country. (Any windmill stand works just fine and support for a generator can be made from an old telephone pole for very little money . . . see Figs. 1 and 3.)

AND ONCE YOU'VE GOT
YOUR RIG . . . THEN WHAT?

So you've bought the generator—you're satisfied, the farmer's satisfied—now how do you get the blamed thing down? Believe me, unless you're a telephone lineman or a circus tightrope walker, working on top of a tower is a scary proposition. Once you've tied yourself in with a safety belt, it isn't so bad . . . except when the wind starts blowing and the generator wants to move around with it! (Even with the vane turned "out of the wind" so that the tail is horizontal with the plane of the propeller, the mechanism will still want to turn when the breezes get gusty.)

Do not, I repeat, DO NOT delude yourself into thinking that the tower can be lowered safely with the generator still in place! I made this mistake on the very first machine I took down . . . and completely destroyed it (see Fig. 4). I don't

FIGURE 4

know much about some of the principles of physics, but it seems to be a law of nature that an object which weighs 400 pounds on top of a vertical tower will come to weigh more than a ton as the structure leans toward the horizontal.

In the case of our infamous first adventure, we tried to lower a tower and generator with a line tied to the back of my pickup truck while two men "steadied" the assembly by hold-

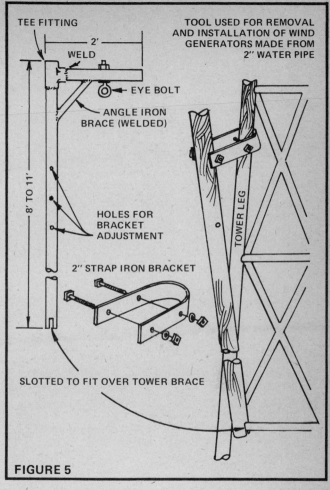

TEE FITTING

TOOL USED FOR REMOVAL
AND INSTALLATION OF WIND
GENERATORS MADE FROM
2" WATER PIPE

2'

WELD

EYE BOLT

ANGLE IRON
BRACE (WELDED)

8' TO 11'

HOLES FOR
BRACKET
ADJUSTMENT

TOWER LEG

2" STRAP IRON BRACKET

SLOTTED TO FIT OVER TOWER BRACE

FIGURE 5

ing lines perpendicular to the lowering line. Fig. 4 was made
from a photograph which was taken only an instant before the
rig got out of control and crashed into the ground . . . bending
the tower, breaking the cast-iron generator housing and gear
box in several places and plowing a big hole in the soil. It was a
lesson that could have been tragic . . . anyone struck by the
falling tower would have been killed instantly.

FIGURE 6

All right then: how do you get wind generators down? After talking with farmers who remember putting them up, and having the rare good fortune of obtaining an operating and installation manual for an old Wincharger, we were able to construct a device from two-inch water pipe which served the purpose (see Fig. 5).

This device is *securely* bolted to the tower with enough

room above the generator to lift it free of its mounting with a block and tackle. Remove the propellers, vane and any other easily removable parts *from below* with the help of an assistant on the ground who handles the block and tackle. The generator itself will, of course, be the last and heaviest load.

Bear in mind that many of the nuts and bolts you'll be working with are likely to be quite rusty. A can of Liquid Wrench or a similar product will help considerably in loosening them. Be most careful of parts under tension . . . it's a hair-raising experience to have a spring-loaded tail vane pop loose on you when there's no place to duck! Wear a hard hat in any case: I wish I'd had one when I was up there (see Fig. 6 and learn from my mistakes).

You'll also find that a carpenter's tool pouch, or a pouch such as telephone linemen use, will be a good investment. It's most inconvenient to have your pockets bristling with screwdrivers, wrenches and hammers . . . and a constant bother to have to worry about the possibility that a tool may fall from your pocket and brain your buddy on the ground.

GET IT DOWN AND TAKE IT HOME

Once the generator is off the tower you're ready to haul it home and tear it down to see what makes it tick. If you didn't buy the whole tower, be sure you take the "stub" . . . the top five feet or so which contains the generator's pivoting mechanism and the all-important slipring collector. (This is the device which allows the generator to turn in any direction without twisting the wires which lead to the battery bank.)

Be double sure to ask the former owner for any wires and control boxes which go with the generator. If you're fortunate, he'll have them stashed away in the toolshed . . . if not, you'll just have to have an electrician make up a control box for you (see the wiring diagram—Fig. 7—reproduced from an old Wincharger manual). If your generator is a 32-volt model, and you don't plan on installing a device which converts 32 volts DC to 110 volts AC, remember to ask the seller if he has any old 32-volt DC motors lying around. He'll have no more use for them but you'll certainly find them handy for powering tools, etc.

I now have a 32-volt (1,200-watt) Wincharger, and a 32-volt (2,500-watt) Jacobs . . . both of which I will install on my

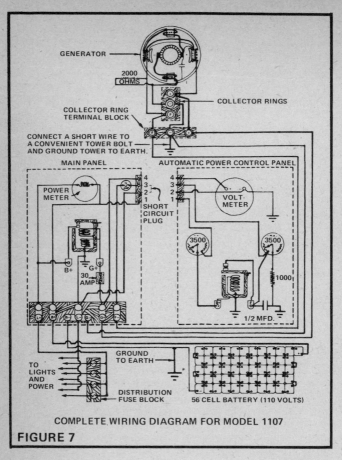

COMPLETE WIRING DIAGRAM FOR MODEL 1107

FIGURE 7

homestead to give me 3,700 watts of power. The Wincharger should be up and working by the time this is published. It now only awaits brushes, a rebuilt prop and a control box.

REBUILDING A RIG

Brushes for the Wincharger are, of course, no longer manufactured, but they may be purchased on special order (custom made) from the Becker Brothers Carbon Company, 3450 South Laramie Avenue, Cicero, Illinois 60650. The cost is

FIGURE 8

$35.00 for ten brushes. (Although a generator only needs two brushes, you should buy extras . . . they eventually wear out and must be replaced.) Send Becker Brothers an old brush when you place an order so they'll know what to make up for you.

What about rebuilding, or in most cases, *making* a propeller? I haven't tackled that one yet, but am not worried about it. LIFESTYLE! NO. 3 has an article (see pages 198–203 of this book) on how to construct a wooden prop, and the November 1972 issue of *Popular Science* describes a propeller

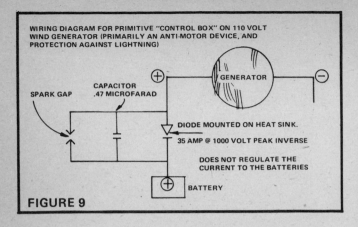

WIRING DIAGRAM FOR PRIMITIVE "CONTROL BOX" ON 110 VOLT
WIND GENERATOR (PRIMARILY AN ANTI-MOTOR DEVICE, AND
PROTECTION AGAINST LIGHTNING)

SPARK GAP

CAPACITOR
.47 MICROFARAD

⊕

GENERATOR

⊖

DIODE MOUNTED ON HEAT SINK.
35 AMP @ 1000 VOLT PEAK INVERSE

DOES NOT REGULATE THE
CURRENT TO THE BATTERIES

⊕ BATTERY

FIGURE 9

FIGURE 10

made of expandable paper and fiberglass. Actually, a wind
generator prop is not as difficult to make as it may seem at
first. A friend of mine crudely hacked one out of an old 2 X 4
in a few minutes . . . and it turned up a storm when held faced
into the wind (see Fig. 8).

The control box poses my third problem. What goes into it,
and how is it constructed? Knowing as little as I do about

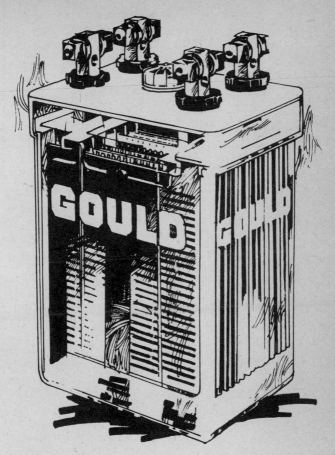

FIGURE 11

electricity, I'm going to entrust that one to a qualified electrician. With the help of an old wiring diagram from the 32-volt Wincharger manual, we should be able to put one together without much trouble. A "control box" of sorts can be as simple as the one in Figs. 9 and 10, which really amounts to an anti-motor device and protection from lightning. (A DC *generator* will act as an electric *motor* if the current is

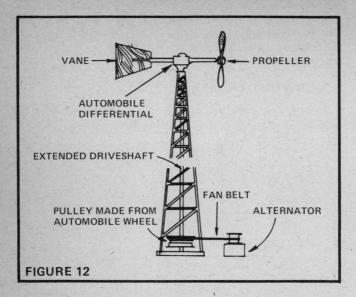

VANE → PROPELLER

AUTOMOBILE
DIFFERENTIAL

EXTENDED DRIVESHAFT

FAN BELT

PULLEY MADE FROM
AUTOMOBILE WHEEL

ALTERNATOR

FIGURE 12

reversed. Without an anti-motor device, the juice from the batteries will "motor" the generator when the wind isn't blowing . . . and this will eventually discharge the storage units completely.)

And what about batteries? What kind are best? You can get a lot of different opinions on the subject, but the kind of storage cells used by the old-timers I visited out on the plains were large industrial-type 2-volt units connected in series to add up to the voltage of the generator. (Nine times out of ten, that was 32 volts . . . or sixteen 2-volt cells hooked up to make one big 32-volt battery.)

These units are still available from the industrial division of any battery manufacturer. The flyer shown here is from Gould, Inc. (Fig. 11), but Exide, Delco and others offer similar units. They're heavy (upwards of 70 pounds each), and expensive (several hundred dollars for a set) . . . but in the long run probably the most efficient and economical way to go. Some units have a life expectancy of 25 to 30 years . . . and if you prorate their initial expense over that period of time, your costs are really very reasonable when compared to what you'd otherwise be paying for Reddy Kilowatt's pollution-producing electricity. Probably the minimum capacity you'll want to

consider for efficient operation is 180-amp-hour batteries.
(The 110-volt Wincharger manual speaks of batteries in the
240- to 424-amp-hour range.) If you can't afford the big units,
golf cart or diesel truck batteries will be a better bet than
ordinary automobile units.

. . . OR YOU CAN BUILD FROM SCRATCH

Perhaps you can't afford a new wind generator, can't locate a
used one in restorable condition and really don't want electric-

FIGURE 13

FIGURE 14

ity for much more than a small stereo set and a few 25-watt light bulbs. In that case, if you're a do-it-yourself type who enjoys tinkering with mechanical devices, you can build your own wind generator out of automobile parts. I've seen several homemade units now (and perhaps it was only coincidental that none of them were working at the time of my visit).

About the most output you can expect from a wind generator made from car parts is 600 watts. I must confess that I can't get very excited about putting in the necessary time, energy and money for such a small return . . . but I'll try to withhold my prejudice while I tell you what I've managed to learn about home-constructed rigs.

The November 1972 issue of *Popular Science* magazine has an article with detailed plans for building a wind generator. While the design is very interesting, and the concept for making the propellers is downright brilliant, please notice that *nowhere in the article does it tell you how many watts the machine will produce.* I visited the commune in Wisconsin where that generator was built and—while the designer, Hans Meyer, wasn't there on the day I visited—one of the residents showed me where the generator tower was lying in the weeds

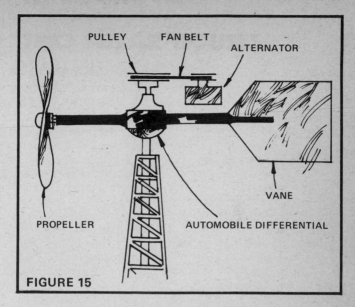

PULLEY   FAN BELT   ALTERNATOR

VANE

PROPELLER   AUTOMOBILE DIFFERENTIAL

FIGURE 15

at the back of a pasture. He told me that the unit hadn't produced enough watts to be practical and had been abandoned.

Pages 186–197 of this book contain an article by Jim Sencenbaugh which describes a 500-watt wind generator. The piece includes an offer to sell detailed plans for building the rig and—from the tone of the article and the photographs and drawings which accompany it—the machine looks like a good one. If you don't need any more than 500 watts, Sencenbaugh's design could be the unit to go for.

Eugene Eccli—co-editor of *Alternative Sources of Energy*, and an instructor at New Paltz College in New York—built a wind generator, with the help of his students, from one of Hans Meyer's designs (Fig. 13). The concept is ingenious and uses an automobile differential to transfer rotation from the horizontal plane of the propeller shaft to a vertical plane perpendicular to it (see Fig. 12).

The "drive shaft" of Eccli's setup is lengthened to accommodate the high tower, and an ordinary automobile wheel is attached at the bottom to provide a "pulley" which runs a fan belt to an automobile alternator (see Fig. 14). The main difficulty with this arrangement is that it generates considerable friction, and the unit will only put out usable amounts of energy in extremely high winds. Also, gear oil tends to leak from the differential housing because of the unusual angle at which the unit must be mounted on the tower.

One solution—which solves most of the friction problem and stops the oil leakage—is to mount the differential so that the drive shaft stub (with pulley and generator attached) points *up* instead of down (see Fig. 15). The New Alchemy Institute in Woods Hole, Massachusetts thought this idea up, and it seems to work. Their generator was down for repairs when I visited them, however, so I have no photograph of the unit. This solution, of course, requires that the generating unit be mounted at the top of the tower, and that means periodic forays "up there" for routine maintenance. (You may as well face it: If you plan on getting into wind generators, you'll have to get used to climbing towers!)

The New Alchemists are also experimenting with a wind pump made from 55-gallon drum halves (Fig. 16). This is based on a design that the Amish have used for years to pump water, and my feeling is that if the device were geared up properly it could be used to generate electricity. Complete plans for this machine are available for about $2.00 from:

> Brace Research Institute
> MacDonald College of McGill University
> Ste. Anne de Bellevue 800
> Quebec, Canada.

Ask for Do-It-Yourself Leaflet No. L-5, entitled: *How To Construct a Cheap Wind Machine for Pumping Water*. (I'm not absolutely certain of the price of this publication, but if you send them $2.00 you'll probably be OK.) The machine is most impressive to see in operation, and it could probably be easily geared up with a bicycle chain and sprockets for the production of electricity.

TO SUM UP THEN . . .

To date, the above is the extent of what I've learned about generating electricity from the wind. I have not yet installed my own two wind generators, so I cannot offer any information about what that will entail. All signs, however, seem to

FIGURE 16

indicate that wind generators are a very practical solution to the energy, pollution and self-sufficiency problems of individuals living on the land.

I don't hold much hope that wind-driven generators will ever be able to solve the power needs of New York, Chicago or Los Angeles . . . but living as I have for the past three years I've come to feel that New York, Chicago and Los Angeles will get just about what they deserve. When the Red Cross is providing disaster relief to the denizens of Megalopolis, I'll be eating fresh-frozen peas from my garden . . . peas which were preserved in a deepfreeze powered by the wind! ●

JIM SENCENBAUGH:
I BUILT
A WIND CHARGER FOR $400!

Intrigued—as many folks are nowadays—by the idea of free, non-polluting electrical energy, I set about constructing (with a little help from my friends) a wind charger of my own design. The research, planning, blueprinting and building consumed a little over a year's worth of spare time . . . but the months of work seemed well worth the investment the first evening we enjoyed stereo music and fluorescent lighting powered by our self-contained system.

The total cost of my homebuilt unit was a little over $400 and—now that I've pioneered the design—I'm sure you can duplicate the rig for from $300 to $350, depending on your choice of batteries. I'm also reasonably confident that you should be able to construct a wind charger like mine in any ordinary home woodworking shop. Everything but the blades can be made with hand tools and an electric drill. If you're exceedingly clever and determined, I suppose you might even fabricate the propeller with a 14" band saw and hand sand them . . . but I recommend that you figure on using a tilting table saw and belt sander for building the three airfoils.

My complete wind-driven electrical system consists of five main parts: [1] the fan, which is rotated by the wind and which—in turn—drives [2] the unit that generates direct current, [3] a tower that supports the first two components, [4] batteries and [5] an inverter that changes the direct current to alternating current.

THE ROTOR ASSEMBLY

The fan on my wind charger is a wooden, three-bladed, variable pitch (constant speed) propeller ten feet in diameter. The prop is made of *clear* white pine and is sealed and protected by an epoxy resin compound called Envirotex.

I chose the three-blade design because my research indicated that such an arrangement provides the best balance and highest efficiency. The "Clark Y" airfoil that I used was picked because it gives high lift at low speeds.

For optimum efficiency, it's quite important that a windplant's entire prop-rotor assembly be very carefully balanced so that all loads are equally distributed along the blades at high speeds. Otherwise the rotor vibrates as it turns, performance falls drastically and the whole unit can be endangered.

This balancing can be done statically—that is, with the fan at rest—by placing the completed and painted prop assembly on a free pivot at the hub's center point and using a level to compare two planes 90 degrees to each other on its face. *(Statically balancing a windplant's fan will, indeed, improve its performance . . . but really technically oriented experimenters may well want to dynamically balance—true up the prop assembly while it rotates at speed—a rotor that is designed to turn at higher rpm's. This is a much more difficult operation, however, and is hardly worth the trouble for any prop assembly that is intended to spin at ordinary windplant speeds.—MOTHER.)*

We used a simple string level line placed directly on the flat surface of the rotor hub to statically balance our wind machine's fan. Small lead weights were placed about the hub until it was level in both planes and the weights were then secured to the hub with screws. After the operation the rotor assembly began turning in a wind 5 mph slower than before, accelerated to maximum speed faster and produced almost no vibration on the input shaft. Balancing is very important!

This summer, after school is over, we plan to experiment with an entirely different kind of windplant prop called a *sailwing.* It's currently being developed at Princeton University (see *Aviation Week and Space Technology,* November 13, 1972, page 47) and is a foldable, lightweight, flexible wing with a high lift-to-drag ratio. The concept is both unique and exciting in that the airfoil actually twists as rpm increases . . .

thus creating a very efficient angle of attack at all windspeeds. Stay tuned to MOTHER for news of our work with the idea.

I planned, from the beginning, to install my windplant in a remote area and took pains to design the machine to be both reliable and—equally important—self-regulating.

To prevent propeller overspeed (and potential disaster), I fell back on a device used in 1908 by Kenwood Manufacturing, a maker of prairie windmills. This is a *pilot vane* (or air governor) placed at right angles to the main vane (or tail) which holds my machine's fan into the wind. As developed by Kenwood, a pilot vane is generally between 50—70% as large as the total area of the main tail (the determining factor being the prop size and tip speeds of a windplant's fan). The idea, of course, is that as wind velocity approaches a critical level, the pilot vane will increasingly counteract the main tail and turn the fan further and further away from directly facing the moving air mass.

The pilot vane is a simple and effective device . . . when winds are steady. During gusty and outright violent conditions, though, it's sometimes better to completely shut down a windplant. One of the easiest ways to do this is by designing the main vane to fold into position alongside its little brother so that—as it continues to streamline itself—it safely faces the prop out of the blasting flow of air. During normal operation the big tail is held in its regular position by spring tension and

The Sencenbaugh O_2 Powered Delight gets boosted into the air.

folding is initiated from the ground by the use of a rope and pulley system. The foldable main vane was popular among homebuilders in the 1920's and 30's and is quite effective.

In addition to the pilot vane and folding main vane that I've put on my windplant to prevent overspeeding, I've added yet a third device that accomplishes the same end. This is a mechanism that automatically feathers the propeller (lessens the angle of attack of its blades) as the fan starts to over-rev, thereby spilling off lift and maintaining a safe prop rpm.

This system is activated by centrifugal force (and you know what that is if you've ever tied something to a string, swung it in a big circle, let go of the twine . . . and watched the object travel off in a straight line). By placing a lead weight on a lever arm attached to the bases of the three propeller blades so that the lever depitches the airfoils as the centrifugal force generated by increasing rpm's tries to throw the lead weight "out", the fan will regulate its own top speed quite effectively. The blades, of course, are held at the maximum effective angle of attack for slow speed operation by spring tension and they're kept from depitching too much by stops that limit their travel in that direction.

Actually, this latter technique for controlling propeller overspeed is probably the most effective of all. We've retained the pilot vane on our windplant, however, as a measure of insurance and kept the movable main vane as a simple and effective means of completely stopping the fan whenever we desire.

By the way, we initially tested these various mechanisms by attaching our windcharger's whole rotor assembly to the front end of my old Porsche and driving up and down the street. Our neighbors at first thought we were experimenting with the flight characteristics of German autos, but soon dismissed our actions as normal nonsense.

THE ALTERNATOR

We chose to mount an automobile alternator on our windplant for the production of electricity for good reasons: such a unit is now readily available in junkyards for little or nothing and it produces usable current at lower rpm's than a generator.

An alternator is simply an AC (alternating current) generator with its cycle unregulated and its output rectified through a diode bridge so that the unit yields fullwave DC (direct

The Sencenbaugh O_2 Powered Delight is up and almost ready to go.

current). The main advantage of DC over AC, of course, being that direct current can be stored in batteries for use when the wind isn't blowing.

Due to the fact that an alternator creates electrical energy by inducing a field current into the rotating field of an armature, we did have to overcome one problem before we could satisfactorily drive such a unit with an irregular source of power like the wind. An alternator will generate AC (which, changed into DC, can be stored in batteries) only as long as the armature spins and cuts across the field current's lines of electromagnetic force. If the field current is left on while the armature is at rest, however, the unit will slowly drain any batteries to which it's connected.

The obvious solution to this hang-up is to build a device that will turn the alternator on only when the wind is blowing strong enough to generate power. Our approach was to use a vane (another vane!) dampened with a spring (another spring!) to operate a relay capable of switching on and off the alternator's three amps of field current. We call this our "wind sensor" and we set it to turn field current into the alternator when the breeze reaches a velocity of 8 mph. It works beautifully.

The alternator is coupled to the windplant rotor with standard go-cart chains and gears so that the generating unit turns faster than the prop (if you build a system like mine, the suggested ratio of alternator to rotor rpm's should be somewhere between 7:1 and 9:1). I used two sets of chains (see view of generator assembly) to minimize any stretching and derailing tendencies and when our prop turns over at 100 rpm in a 12 mph wind, the alternator spins up fast enough to produce electricity at a medium charging rate.

THE TOWER

The structure which supports the rotor-alternator combination is 22 feet high and fabricated of 2 X 2 Douglas fir. Although my choice of lumber may seem to be somewhat on the light side, the tower has steadfastly withstood the rather large loads imposed upon it. The secret is in the framework's careful design and construction.

Please note—in the accompanying illustrations—the tower's lattice design with opposing diagonals on each side. The structure is reinforced with internal bracing at its top where the rotor-alternator support pipe anchors . . . it's strengthened again halfway down by a horizontal 3/4-inch plywood plate . . . and it's reinforced once more at the bottom by a plywood storage cabinet. All joints are secured with galvanized nails and

Resorcinol, a waterproof marine glue. The wood is sealed with three coats of outdoor sealer and painted with two coats of Sears "Sky Blue" latex house paint.

There's a built-in ladder up one side of the structure and the tower is guyed at four points and anchored to 2 X 2-inch angle iron embedded three feet deep in a 4 X 4 X 3-foot-deep concrete foundation. The whole plant is hinged on two of the angles and can be pushed upright by four people (just make sure the shortest fella is closest to the pivot point). A brush arrangement built into the support bracket on top allows power to be transferred down the framework to the cabinet at the bottom while the rotor-alternator assembly remains free to weathercock through a full 360 degrees.

BATTERIES AND THE INVERTER

The cabinet at the base of the tower houses several surplus 70-amp/hour nickel-cadmium aircraft batteries, a regulating system and a solid-state DC-to-AC inverter that produces 500 watts of 60-cycle, 110-volt AC (typical house current).

The batteries and inverter are located close to the generator for a very important reason: the dome that my windplant was set up to power is 125 feet away from the tower and DC transmission through a conductor of that length would result

The wooden, three-bladed, variable pitch propeller on Sencenbaugh's windplant is ten feet in diameter and made of clear white pine.

in an unacceptably large voltage drop. AC transmission losses, on the other hand, are very low . . . so, by converting the DC to AC as soon as possible and then making the long run with alternating current, our whole system becomes much more practical.

If you try to duplicate my wind-powered generating station you may be tempted to save some money by substituting new or used automobile lead-acid batteries for the nickel-cadmium batteries I've used. If you do, be sure to include a regulator between the generating unit and the storage units to protect the batteries from being overcharged. Overcharging lead-acid batteries can warp their plates, severely damage them in other ways and make them worthless.

Lead-acid electrical storage units have additional disadvantages. They can lose up to 50% of their capacity in cold or freezing weather, they do not dissipate heat well when under high-current stress, they contain acid that can violently burn the flesh, they're large, bulky and heavy and—sooner or later—they deteriorate internally. Why do we use them? Because they're economical to produce and they work well enough when installed in a car or truck.

Nickel-cadmium aircraft batteries make far better electrical storage units. They're virtually indestructible (broken cells are repaired with epoxy), smaller, lighter and retain 100% of their capacity in cold weather. Ni-Cad batteries also charge faster, high currents can be drawn from them without damaging the units internally and their electrolyte (an alkaline) is less hazardous than acid. Since N-C batteries cannot be overcharged, you can omit the voltage regulator when you use them. (The alternator—unlike a DC generator—will not pass reverse current through itself because of its diodes . . . and will charge only to the load it "sees". If it sees a fully charged N-C battery, the alternator will produce just a minimum amount of current . . . which will not bother a nickel-cadmium storage unit.)

The only real drawback to N-C batteries is their cost. New, they are *very* expensive . . . BUT, given proper care, they're considered by many mechanics to be true lifetime batteries and they can be obtained through surplus houses for just about the cost of new lead-acid storage units. Write to ESSE Radio Company, 368 South Meridian Street, Indianapolis, Indiana 46225 and ask for their price sheet on Ni-Cad batteries and you'll be surprised at the bargains you find listed.

For converting my system's 12-volt DC into usable 60-Hz (cycle), 110-volt AC, I picked a Heathkit Model MP-14 solid-state inverter from the Heath Company, Benton Harbor, Michigan 49022. The unit will produce 400 watts of 110-volt AC continuously or 500 watts intermittently at 80—85% efficiency. This is enough alternating current to operate fluorescent lights (which consume much less power than incandescent lamps), phonographs, electric razors, TV's with transformer power supplies, drill motors and almost anything else within its design parameters. In other words—with the exception of ridiculously gluttonous electrical appliances such as room heaters, stoves and air conditioners—the little Heath inverter supplies more than enough AC power for almost anything you'd care to operate electrically in a dome or small cabin.

Once the "juice" developed by my wind-driven system is converted to AC, it's carried to the dome via underground outdoor cable. There, on a master control panel in the building, we can monitor AC output and battery charge (respectively) on a combination AC-DC voltmeter. By flicking a switch on the panel, we can either charge the batteries at the normal rate or—during winds of short duration—fast charge the storage units by changing the field windings of the alternator from their usual 12 volts DC to 110 volts DC.

Another panel switch controls a relay which turns the inverter on and off at the base of the windplant. This relay, it should be noted, requires about .25 amps of 12-volt DC for its operation . . . which is nothing compared to the electrical loss that would take place if we tried to bring direct—instead of alternating—current to the dome.

ADDITIONAL TIPS AND HINTS ABOUT COMPONENTS

The Heathkit inverter dented my pocketbook $130 but I think it was worth it . . . especially since it has a built-in provision for remote control (which I use every time I turn the unit on or off from the dome 125 feet away) and its output transformer secondary taps can be switched to compensate for low battery voltage input or AC voltage drop due to load changes.

The only drag about this particular inverter is that—even though it's available directly from Heath's home office and the company's big city dealers—it doesn't seem to be a stock item (at least it doesn't appear in the Heath catalog). But never

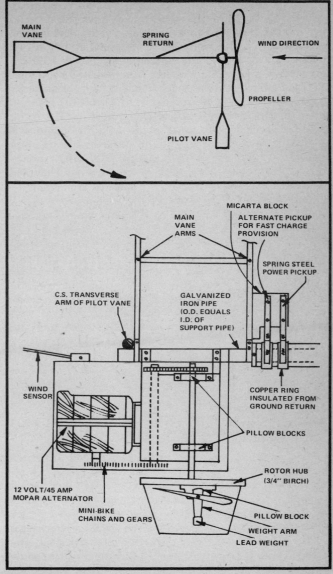

MAIN
VANE

SPRING
RETURN

WIND DIRECTION

PROPELLER

PILOT VANE

MICARTA BLOCK

MAIN
VANE
ARMS

ALTERNATE PICKUP
FOR FAST CHARGE
PROVISION

SPRING STEEL
POWER PICKUP

C.S. TRANSVERSE
ARM OF PILOT VANE

GALVANIZED
IRON PIPE
(O.D. EQUALS
I.D. OF
SUPPORT PIPE)

COPPER RING
INSULATED FROM
GROUND RETURN

WIND
SENSOR

PILLOW BLOCKS

ROTOR HUB
(3/4" BIRCH)

12 VOLT/45 AMP
MOPAR ALTERNATOR

MINI-BIKE
CHAINS AND GEARS

PILLOW BLOCK

WEIGHT ARM

LEAD WEIGHT

Basic schematic layout of the Sencenbaugh O_2 Powered delight.

A view of the fully assembled windplant standing above the dome which it furnishes with power in the mountains of California.

mind. Any comparable inverter can be substituted, I suppose, provided a relay is added for the external control.

The Dodge Dart alternator I adapted to my system goes, used, for $15.00–$20.00 out here on the West Coast . . . but I got three absolutely free from a mechanic who said that he didn't want them lying around anymore!

I spent a little better than $70.00 for my bank of Ni-Cad

batteries and I'd advise you to lay out the cash to assemble yourself enough storage units to total a minimum of 100 amp/hrs . . . more if your local winds are very sporadic.

The bearings, pillow blocks and shafts for my light plant all were obtained by mail from Sears and the remaining mechanical odds and ends came from neighborhood hardware and electronics dealers. I also got my lumber from local sources and, like the hardware, it varied in price a good deal from one outlet to another. Shop around!

If you're careful how you spend your money you should be able to build a copy of my system for $300–$350 . . . which isn't bad, considering that one U.S. firm wants $500 for a windplant that was designed 40 years ago and which produces nothing but DC. The only alternative worth considering is Quirk's fine gear which, at $1,800 or more, is out of reach for most people with limited funds.

Nor are there any other good homebuilt designs being widely circulated. None, at any rate, that I know of. In researching this project I found much information on mechanical theory, but little on the actual construction of a practical wind-driven powerplant for the small homestead. Most articles with plans for such equipment were published before 1940 (and are now outdated). The only recent respectable attempt in the field that I've run across was featured in the November '72 *Popular Science* . . . and that unit is somewhat impractical for continuous use since it exhibits no facilities for autoregulation or DC conversion.

I have decided, therefore—upon the urging of John and O'Malley Stouman (the people for whom I built this plant), Henry Clews (the authorized Quirk's agent for the U.S.), my parents and friends and the folks at MOTHER—to produce a complete and highly detailed set of plans for the *SENCEN-BAUGH O_2 POWERED DELIGHT*. The format of these drawings is similar to homebuilt aircraft plans and all components and specifications, parts substitutions, addresses of suppliers, etc., are given. ●

_____

Jim's complete and highly detailed plans for the construction of his windplant are now available and, in fact, have already been updated once or twice. If you'd like to find out how you can order a set, you'll find Jim's address listed in the back of this book. Look in the bibliography under Wind, Hardware.

WINNIE RED ROCKER:

HERE'S HOW I BUILT A WIND GENERATOR

Here's a nice little wind generator that was pretty easy to put together . . . and works good, too! It starts to charge in a fairly light breeze (5 to 10 mph), and puts out maybe 12 to 15 amps (12-volt system) in a stiff 25 mph wind. I figure that with sufficient storage, say 150 to 200 amp-hours worth, and with our local 10–15 mph average wind conditions, this machine will give us at least 600 to 700 watt-hours a day, wind or no wind. This is not something to run big power tools with, but for us it means being able to play our stereo any time we want, without having to start our gasoline-fired generator. Also, there will be a few electric reading lights thrown into the deal, so we'll be burning less kerosene. And maybe we can even put a light inside our propane refrigerator! The machine consists mainly of:

[1] Some parts (stand, brake, slip rings, and governor) from a couple of old Dyna Technology Winchargers *(NOTE: "Wincharger" is the trade name of wind-powered generators manufactured by Dyna Technology and should not be confused with the term "wind charger" applied to wind-driven generators in general.)* which I got for the asking from some farms around here.

[2] An American Motors alternator a friend laid on me.

[3] A 7-foot-diameter propeller based on the plan from the LeJay Manual which I made from a redwood 2 X 6 I bought from a lumberyard for $2.35.

Now, if you want to build something like this, don't get freaked out because you can't get hold of all the nice Wincharger parts as I did . . . you don't need them. The same basic machine can be built using scrap iron and junked car parts. The basic idea is that there is a gear-up via a V-belt from the prop to the alternator (a ratio of 1 to 3-1/2 in this case). The prop turns on a shaft which is just the armature of an old (not working) car generator with good bearings. The way all these components are put together and mounted on a stand depends entirely on what kinds of materials you have around or can get easily.

The brake in our case is a level and drum assembly made by Dyna Technology . . . but you can easily construct a swinging vane type of brake as in the LeJay Manual. Or skip the brake and just tie the thing up in bad weather!

For slip rings, I'm using the ones that came on the old Wincharger with new brushes I got from Dyna Technology. They still make a wind generator that's essentially the same as 30 years ago. But you could more easily use a length of heavy-duty multistranded lamp cord and just let it get twisted up! According to the LeJay Manual, you shouldn't have to replace it for at least two years.

The governor could be skipped, too . . . I've had mine free-wheeling in a pretty stiff wind. It's scary, but it hangs together. If you want a governor, you could build one on the same principle as the Wincharger model (centrifugally acti-vated air brake), or you can buy one exactly like the one I'm using—except about 30 years newer—from Dyna for $13.31. It's Part No. 8830.

I decided to use an alternator because I thought it would

put out at lower rpm's than a generator and because it was modern and had diodes in it. But I'm beginning to think that there is no problem using a regular DC car generator. In fact, there are some definite advantages: they are cheaper, they *don't* have diodes in them, and you can use a cutout relay to take the battery out of the circuit when the wind stops. With an alternator, you have to rig up some kind of wind- or centrifugal-force-activated switch to accomplish this.

Now, about the propeller. This is really the heart of the thing . . . and if nothing else, the main point of this article is that a wooden propeller of this type is *easy* to build with almost no woodworking skill and very little money. The plan I used is from the LeJay Manual and I've included step-by-step instructions which I hope anyone can follow to make a prop, using a good piece of wood, a drawknife, a rasp and some sandpaper. If you've never seen a high-speed prop going in the wind, by all means try building this one. Mount it on an old generator or something and set it up in the wind. Don't hold it in your hands! I almost lost my head that way. It'll blow your mind when you get a feeling of the power that this thing produces!

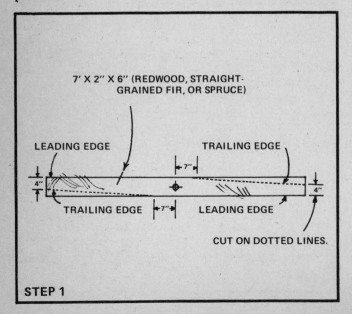

DRAW DOTTED LINES ON EDGES (FIGURE FOR
STEP 2 SHOWS RIGHT-HAND EDGE OF FIGURE
IN STEP 1).

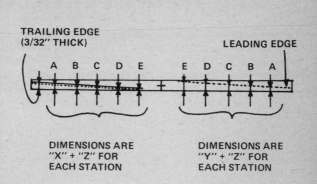

TRAILING EDGE
(3/32" THICK)

LEADING EDGE

A B C D E   E D C B A

DIMENSIONS ARE
"X" + "Z" FOR
EACH STATION

DIMENSIONS ARE
"Y" + "Z" FOR
EACH STATION

STEP 2

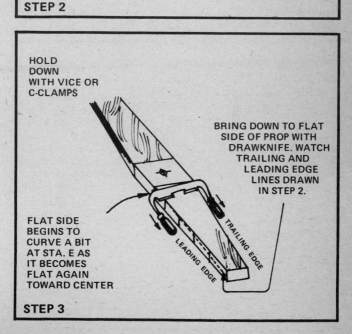

HOLD
DOWN
WITH VICE OR
C-CLAMPS

BRING DOWN TO FLAT
SIDE OF PROP WITH
DRAWKNIFE. WATCH
TRAILING AND
LEADING EDGE
LINES DRAWN
IN STEP 2.

FLAT SIDE
BEGINS TO
CURVE A BIT
AT STA. E AS
IT BECOMES
FLAT AGAIN
TOWARD CENTER

TRAILING EDGE

LEADING EDGE

STEP 3

**DRAW CROSS SECTIONS FOR EACH STATION
FULL SIZE ON CARDBOARD AND CUT OUT
WITH RAZOR TO MAKE TEMPLATE**

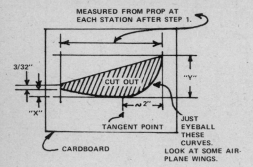

MEASURED FROM PROP AT
EACH STATION AFTER STEP 1.

3/32"

CUT OUT

"Y"

"X"

~2"

TANGENT POINT

JUST
EYEBALL
THESE
CURVES.
LOOK AT SOME AIR-
PLANE WINGS.

CARDBOARD

STEP 4

GENERAL CONSTRUCTION TIPS

Start at tips bringing wood down on airfoil side of prop with drawknife (or rasp when it starts getting close) until template for station A will fit on prop in the right place (7" from tip)—then go to template B until it fits (7" from A)—and so on toward the center. The flat side made in Step 3 is your reference for positioning the templates.

Sand well, varnish (several coats), and balance both horizontally and vertically. Balancing can easily be accomplished by adding small weights to the edge (vert. balance) and front (horiz. balance).

NOTE: This prop can be made 10 feet long by extending the distance between stations from 7" to 10", making the 3" x 4" sections both 5". All other dimensions, the same. ⬤

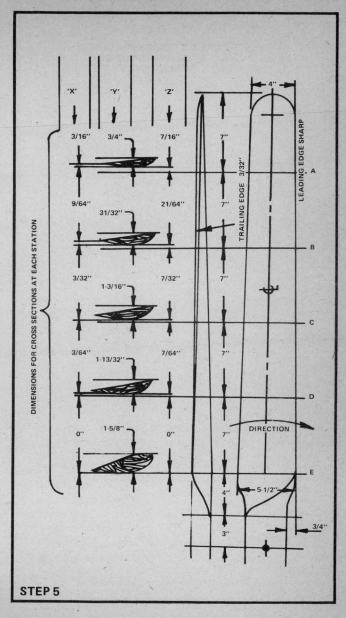

DIMENSIONS FOR CROSS SECTIONS AT EACH STATION

'X' 'Y' 'Z'

LEADING EDGE SHARP

4"

TRAILING EDGE 3/32"

DIRECTION

3/16" 3/4" 7/16" 7" A

9/64" 31/32" 21/64" 7" B

3/32" 1-3/16" 7/32" 7" C

3/64" 1-13/32" 7/64" 7" D

0" 1-5/8" 0" 7" E

4" 5-1/2"

3" 3/4"

STEP 5

SOLAR
HARNESS THE SUN

In his book, *The Coming Age of Solar Energy*, D.S. Halacy, Jr., states that the Homo sapiens population of the world consumed about 90 trillion horsepower-hours of energy in 1972 . . . while—during the same 12-month period—Ole Sol lavished 1.5 *MILLION trillion* horsepower-hours of sunlight on the planet.

Interestingly enough, only a tiny fraction of one percent of this natural force (about 40 billion kilowatts) is converted by green plants into all the food and timber and other vegetation that grows on earth. And, of course, only a further fraction of this growth eventually (over hundreds of thousands of years) turns into the fossil fuels we've been squandering so recklessly.

In short: All the energy we use comes from the sun in the first place and trying to capture that power by first changing it into fossil fuels is a long, involved and very inefficient process. Why not just rig up our mechanical devices, heating systems and blast furnaces to run directly off solar radiation in the first place?

Why not indeed? The next 72 pages will introduce you to just a few of the hundreds (perhaps thousands!) who are now doing exactly that in the United States.

There's Dr. E.A. Farber, for instance, whose magnificent array of sun-powered hardware should convince you that virtually *anything* can be run directly on Ole Sol's energy. And don't be surprised if the incredible simplicity of Steve and Holly Baer's solar-heated house inspires you to construct a similar system of your own. Or, if you prefer to begin your sunshine experiments on a more modest scale, you can flip directly over to D.S. Halacy's plans for a solar-powered cooker, oven and water heater . . . *that really work*.

And that should inspire you to start digging into this book's bibliography for more information about what will surely be one of the major direct energy sources of the future. ●

Parabolic collectors, sun-powered steam engines, solar stills and other equipment at the University of Florida's Solar Energy Lab.

"The energy crisis is really nothing new," says Dr. E.A. Farber, Director of the Solar Energy & Energy Conversion Laboratory at the University of Florida in Gainesville. "We were already running short of fossil fuels—our so-called 'conventional' sources of power—40 years ago. It just hadn't come to the public's attention at that time."

Maybe not . . . but the world's supply of energy and its relationship to the development of nations most certainly *had* already come to the attention of a few farsighted individuals back there in the early 1930's . . . and Austrian-born Erich Farber was one of them.

Four decades ago, while still a high school student, Farber observed that the countries and civilizations which controlled the most energy—and used it—were the nations and cultures that also advanced most rapidly. Young Erich further noted that the power providing this advantage came mainly from the fossil fuels—gas, coal and oil—which obviously (to him, at least) would one day be exhausted.

"This led me directly to solar energy," Dr. Farber says. "I thought of the planet's human population as a family trying to live off its savings (fossil fuels) which were stored in a bank (underground) and which were being steadily depleted. This, of course, cannot go on indefinitely. Sooner or later that family has to begin living on its income . . . sooner or later we have

DR. E. A. FARBER: SUNSHINE SUPERMAN

to make do with the amount of renewable, incoming energy we receive. After mulling over the possibilities of wind, geothermal, tidal and other sources of power—all very good when the conditions are right for their use—I realized that the sun alone offered the resource I was seeking. Solar energy is readily available, well distributed, inexhaustible for all practical purposes and does not pollute the environment when converted and utilized."

Farber developed his ideas as he received the major part of his education in Europe and during the time he studied at the Universities of Missouri and Iowa. He further honed his keen interest in solar power while teaching at the Universities of Missouri, Iowa and Wisconsin. By the time he moved to Gainesville—20 years ago—to instruct at the University of Florida, Erich was quite possibly the planet's most enthusiastic and knowledgeable authority on the subject. Little wonder that the University of Florida's Solar Energy Lab is one of the largest and most advanced facilities of its kind in the world.

The UF solar energy installation is especially interesting because of its emphasis on working hardware. Ever think of building a solar energy collector or sun-operated water heater, stove or still? How about a solar turbine, steam engine, refrigerator or air conditioner? Or an electric car which has its batteries recharged by the sun? Or a "solar gravity" motor? Or a

This solar heater (which warms a house with hot air) is made up of overlapping aluminum plates that are painted black (to absorb heat).

sewage treatment plant that uses Ole Sol's rays to double its processing capacity? All old hat to Farber, his staff of ten and the students who attend the three classes conducted by the Solar Energy Lab.

And don't think you can't duplicate UF's success just because you live in Minnesota or British Columbia. Farber believes that, "Florida isn't any better than many other areas of the earth for solar energy collection. Look at the Weather Bureau's data and you'll be surprised at how evenly this source of power is distributed. Pick practically any point on the face of the planet and, if people live there, the chances are very good that the surrounding region receives meaningful amounts

A collection of parabolic solar cookers. The unit actually being used here collapses and folds up as compactly as an umbrella.

of sunshine."

Yes but is it *practical* to try to utilize the sun's rays to heat our houses, drive our engines, cook our food and otherwise power the industrialized society in which we live? "It depends on what you mean by 'practical'," says Dr. Farber. "What's practical to one man is not practical to another.

"We now know how to use the sun to provide all the forms of energy which we need in our daily lives. We can warm a house, heat water, air-condition buildings, produce electricity and so on. We've already done these things. We've even converted a Corvair automobile to run on batteries which can be charged by solar cells. Theoretically, at least, we could replace

This Corvair has been modified by the UF Solar Energy Lab to run on electricity . . . and that "juice" is furnished by the sun!

our present fossil-fueled transportation system with a sun-powered electrical system. Instead of gasoline stations, you'd drive your car into solar-battery-charging stations. The attendants there would lift out your discharged batteries, give you a freshly charged set and you'd drive right on.

"Now this would be a very 'practical' way of doing business if you started it from scratch. It's pollution-free and it makes use of a virtually inexhaustible energy resource. But the point is that we're *not* starting from scratch. We're already set up to power our personal transportation with gasoline . . . and as long as we have gasoline and the government doesn't ration it, I'm sure we'll find it more 'practical' to keep right on using

A small steam engine, quarter-horse closed cycle hot air engine and half-horse closed cycle hot air engine in operation at the UF lab.

gasoline until we run out."

Maybe so. But in the meantime, Dr. Farber and his staff and the students in the classes conducted at the University of Florida's Solar Energy Lab are going to continue right on developing and *operating* sun-powered hardware of many kinds. The illustrations accompanying this article will give you a small idea of the scope of their work. ◓

A paper entitled Solar Energy Conversion Research And Development At The University Of Florida Solar Energy And Energy Conversion Laboratory *briefly describes approximately 50 of Dr. Farber's experiments. See bibliography at back of book (*Solar, Publications*).*

EVERETT CARLSON, JR.:

TWO WAYS TO HEAT A HOME WITH SUNSHINE POWER

Sunshine Power—heating a home by harvesting the energy which flows freely down from above—is a relatively new concept for the homestead. However, reams of money and heavy brainwork over the years have gone into sophisticated solar-power projects and that research can now be turned on to light—or rather, heat—a place in the outback.

In the past, most buildings which have successfully utilized solar heat have been costly experiments aimed at proving an adaptability for suburban homes. This meant working within the limits of traditional suburban architecture to a large degree. Back at the homestead, outside of this genteel strait-jacket, the subtle art of sunshine power can be more properly exploited. If your place is away from it all, and you like the idea of a cheap heating plant which isn't helping to use up the last of our fossil fuels . . . the sun may be for you!

The basic principle of solar heating, long used for building greenhouses, is that the transparency of glass is greater for visible light than for the infrared part of the light spectrum. Early attempts at the solar house relied extensively on this single principle. The first models, developed in the early 30's by Professor F.W. Hutchinson, were almost conventional structures save for their oversize windows on the south side. They were fine so long as the sun was shining . . . but eventually used more fuel than conventional homes because—soon after nightfall—the large area of exposed glass lost all the heat which had been gathered during the day. A heating system which goes into reverse at sunset and never starts up at all on cloudy days is obviously not much competition for the fossil fuel burners.

There are ways to change this situation for the better, however. Insulated glass has solved the reversal problem and interior shutters which close over the windows at night provide an additional barrier against heat loss. Even in a normal house, with regular single-pane windows, interior shutters can cut heating bills by 30%. This was shown in a number of test houses situated between latitudes 40—43 degrees (e.g., New York—Nebraska) . . . not the warmest of winter's zones. Incidentally, well-sealed double-pane windows or insulated glass can reduce heat loss by an additional 20% (same ordinary homes, same area).

Our first design principle then is: USE LARGE SOUTH-FACING WINDOWS WITH SOLID INTERIOR SHUTTERS TO BE CLOSED AT NIGHT.

These windows need not be conventional, or expensive. As Rex Roberts points out in his very useful *Your Engineered House* (M. Evans and Company, Inc., 1964), a window does not also have to be a ventilator (it needn't open), so a simple homemade unit can offer large windows at low prices. Roberts points out that you can make a wall out of glass as easily as from anything else. A simple design from his book is shown with this article (see Fig. 1).

The framework is a simple box of 1" boards as wide as the thickness of the wall. Narrow strips are nailed on to form channels for the glass, which is set in at an angle. These holding channels can be made fairly tight, so that a little caulking

COMPARISON CHART FOR

DOVER

SIZE OF HOUSE
Five rooms and bath.

COST OF SOLAR-HEATING SYSTEM
$1,855 (in 1949).

COLLECTOR
Blackened metal sheets behind double plates of glass; air circulated in space behind metal sheet (720 square feet).

STORAGE
Solar heat from the roof collector reaches hermetically sealed tanks containing crystallized Glauber's salt by way of air circulation in a duct system (see diagram).

Glauber's salt (sodium sulphate decahydrate or $Na_2SO_410H_2O$), also called "crazy water crystals", is capable of storing 8.5 times more heat than water of the same volume when the temperature rises from 77 to 98 degrees F. Any of several hydrated salt compounds of sodium and calcium is suitable. Cost/Ton: $9.00 in 1949.

VOLUME OF STORAGE
470 cubic feet: 21 tons Glauber's salt sealed into five-gallon cans, stacked in columns to allow air circulation.

TOTAL HEAT-STORAGE CAPACITY
4,700,000 Btu (estimated 12 days' heat for this house).

STORAGE PRINCIPLE
Heat of fusion.

STANDBY HEAT
None.

DISTRIBUTION OF HEAT IN HOUSE
Warm air circulation.

TWO SOLAR HOUSES

THOMASON

SIZE OF HOUSE
Six rooms.

COST OF SOLAR-HEATING SYSTEM
$2,000 (in 1959).

COLLECTOR
Blackened sheets of corrugated aluminum under one layer of polyester film and one layer of window glass, installed over insulation on existing roof. Heat transferred by water flowing over metal (840 square feet).

STORAGE
Solar heat from roof collector is carried by water to tank in basement, surrounded by rock heat storage.

VOLUME OF STORAGE
1,600-gallon water tank fitted inside a bin 10 feet by 25 feet by 7 feet holding 50 tons of fist-sized rocks.

TOTAL HEAT-STORAGE CAPACITY
Not available.

STORAGE PRINCIPLE
High specific heat of rock.

STANDBY HEAT
Oil Furnace (average cost of oil to heat house for one full year, $6.30).

DISTRIBUTION OF HEAT IN HOUSE
Warm air circulation.

rather than a lot of putty will make a windproof seal. An added advantage is that the sills are now on the outside, and so is the dust that settles on them. One less chore to do!

You could use insulated glass for the angled, sun-catcher panels . . . but a cheaper and quite adequate solution would be to hang a sheet of heavy-duty clear plastic over the entire window wall for the winter.

You *will* need ventilation, but not through the windows. Roberts suggests simple screened openings, fitted with solid (heat barrier) doors that can be closed when needed. Unlike windows, these vents can be located solely to take advantage of the best cool airflow in the summertime. (Take a look at Roberts' book . . . his ideas on door construction alone seem worth the price.)

So, once the sun has shone in, it *can* be locked up for the night. The problem remaining is what to do in a cloud-ridden area that receives no sun at all for a week at a time. Somehow you must capture the heat when you can get it . . . to use when and where you need it. And these three requirements are the key to true solar-house design.

A modern solar-heating plant consists of three parts: a collector of solar energy, a storage capacity and a distribution system . . . big windows alone can't do the job.

Solar plants have proved most efficient in areas below 45 degrees latitude (e.g., south of New York—Nebraska), but the incidence of clear, sunny days is the real criterion. Local cloudiness makes nonsense of any hard and fast rule; so even if you're in the North, don't give up on the idea of solar heat yet. Cutting the use of traditional fuels by 75% in, say, northern New York State is not an unreasonable goal.

Energy from the sun is usually measured in terms of "horizontal incidence" . . . that is, the amount of energy falling on a horizontal surface. For 40 degrees latitude, the yearly average is 500 Btu per square foot per day. You can improve on this by tilting the collector(s) of your system up from the horizontal toward the south (and the sun). An angle equal to the latitude (i.e., 40 for 40) decreases summer insulation by 18% but increases the mid-winter intake by a whopping 130% . . . an annual overall improvement of 25%.

Some further juggling is possible. Increasing the angle by 23 degrees over the latitude (63 at 40) favors the winter solstice; a lesser amount of tilt favors the center of the cold season,

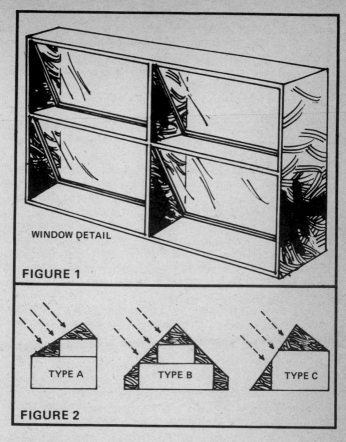

WINDOW DETAIL

FIGURE 1

TYPE A   TYPE B   TYPE C

FIGURE 2

which comes about one month after the solstice.

A good workable average seems to be latitude plus 15 degrees (55 degrees angle for latitude 40).

A vertical collector (like a billboard) might seem easier to build but it gives away 10–15% to tilted collectors during December, January and February . . . and even more during the rest of the year.

So, a tilted collector it must be and, ideally, tilted at the angle of latitude plus 15 degrees.

In the past, however, such ideals have been compromised. To understand the part compromise has played in collector design, look at Whillier's comments on the design of the 1953 MIT house: The home was planned for 1,100—1,200 square feet and its design cost was $12,000—$18,000 *exclusive* of heating system. Hardly a bargain, even in 1953. And—for appearance—the architect was allowed the range of 45 to 75 degrees collector angle. I suppose we should be thankful that, at least, the collector was to face south ... some solar houses in suburbs have been aligned to the streets rather than the sun! No wonder there are now only about twenty solar-heated homes (in spite of a "reliable" forecast of 13 million units in the United States by 1975!).

One useful thing (to you) to come out of the MIT study was the general shape of a solar house. Four designs were considered, three of which are shown here (see Fig. 2). The fourth included a curved wall, rejected on a cost basis.

The final package arrived at was TYPE A. Type A is a two-story house with the collector oriented to the south. The east-west dimension of Type A is about 20% greater than the north-south dimension. These figures are close to the optimum of minimum cost and heating load for the floor area and the shape is well worth considering for the homesteader. Here the collector serves as a major portion of the roof (which saves material) and allows room beneath it for south-facing windows.

A house of this pattern is theoretically impractical for total solar heat in a climate as harsh as upper New England and a 600-square-foot collector would require auxiliary heat (about 20% of total). A collector of twice the area would still require some additional heat. On the other hand, the MIT house used the south-facing windows ... and on sunny days in winter the extra heat trapped required excessive ventilation. So you'll have to work out a balance. The lower efficiency of a home-brewed unit should preclude the danger of having much excess heat to throw away, anyhow.

Our second design principle: USE THE MIT PACKAGE SHAPE A, AS SMALL AS PRACTICAL.

What about the design of the collector itself? The least expensive approach is to absorb the sun's energy with a black surface. Expensive focusing collectors (as used for solar cooking) are not needed in house heating because the collector surface is large and the desired temperature change—compared to cooking—is not great. One of the simplest designs (and owner built) was that used by Harry E. Thomason in Washington, D.C. His two houses were pictured and described in the February 1965 *Popular Mechanics.*

Thomason converted an existing roof into a collector by first laying down insulation, then blackened sheets of corrugated aluminum and finally . . . 840 square feet of glass! *(Possibly Thomason would today cut costs by substituting black plastic sheeting—the composter's friend—for the sheets of aluminum in the sandwich—MOTHER.)*

To transfer the heat down into storage—water tanks surrounded by bins filled with 50 tons of fist-sized rocks—Thomason installed a perforated pipe along the apex of the collector/roof. A light downward flow of water from the pipe and across the metal was sufficient to move the heat.

Another oft-quoted design is The Dover House by Dr. Maria Telkes (architect, Eleanor Raymond). The sun-trap sandwich chosen in this case was blackened metal sheeting overlaid by double plates of glass. Circulating air behind the metal carried

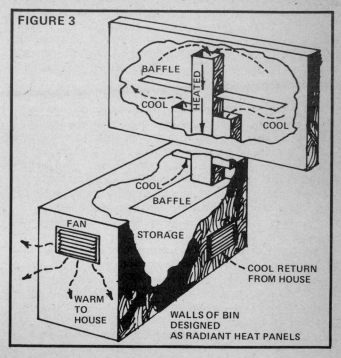

FIGURE 3

BAFFLE

COOL

HEATED

COOL

COOL
BAFFLE

STORAGE

FAN

WARM
TO
HOUSE

COOL RETURN
FROM HOUSE

WALLS OF BIN
DESIGNED
AS RADIANT HEAT PANELS

the heat off to storage and distribution (see Fig. 3).

In these two designs we can see many of the contrasts possible (and practical) in solar-heat design. Let's look at them in more detail (see Dover vs. Thomason comparison chart).

Each of these plans has some advantages. The Telkes plant had no running costs, except electricity for the fan. Neither system produces smoke, soot or fumes. There is no stoking, refueling, cleaning or repair, and no wasting of valuable fossil fuel. A further advantage is that air (used in the heat transfer) can't freeze; several water-based systems have had to add anti-freeze substances.

On the other hand, Thomason's water-storage system could undoubtedly be cheaper (especially if you have labor at hand to do the digging, and you're into gathering stone like Scott Nearing did). A small commune or large family could probably gather 50 tons of rocks eventually . . . and it'd sure make plowing a lot easier.

A possible compromise to consider would be the use of a hybrid of both these methods . . . a smaller amount of Glauber's salt than the Dover house, within a larger bin of crushed rock. You should get some of the advantages of both and, undoubtedly, some of the disadvantages. It's better than burning all that oil, though.

If you're going to use heated air to warm the house, you might as well use air all the way because—if you use water— you'll need expensive pumps. Although both the Thomason and Dover houses use electricity to drive fans, etc., it might be possible to arrange a "no moving parts" system of heat "chimneys" to move the air . . . just as the Model T Ford cooling system moved water. The idea has been used for cooling desert houses; perhaps it can also be used to move heating air. In any case, if you must use a fan, the electricity doesn't have to be bought from a high-pollution generating plant. Wind-powered and methane gas-powered generators can be set up on the homestead. Ken Kern shows solar-tempered houses in which wind-powered generators provide the fan power.

All right. Let's see what your solar-heated homestead house might look like (see Fig. 4): As small as practical, it should probably be based on the MIT Type A design with a roof collector oriented to the south at the angle of latitude plus 15 degrees. The structure would have large south-facing windows with interior shutters; no windows or doors on the west (to

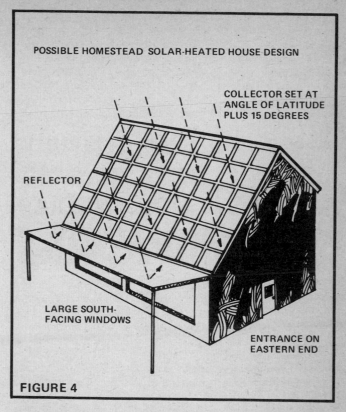

POSSIBLE HOMESTEAD SOLAR-HEATED HOUSE DESIGN

COLLECTOR SET AT ANGLE OF LATITUDE PLUS 15 DEGREES

REFLECTOR

LARGE SOUTH-FACING WINDOWS

ENTRANCE ON EASTERN END

FIGURE 4

shield against the coldest winds); entrance on the eastern (most sheltered) end; and relatively small, well-sealed windows on the north.

You might also try a reflector at the base of the collector. It would, of course, increase the collector's efficiency and—on the "A" design—shield the large windows during summer heat.

Materials and construction techniques—of both the house and the solar-heating system—are free choice . . . but, whatever you choose, never forget to insulate the structure well. Once you've caught the sun, you can't afford to throw it away! ●

Booklets/sets of plans for building both a model and full-size Thomason solar-heated house are listed for sale in the bibliography at the back of this book. Look under Solar, Publications.

AN INTERVIEW
WITH STEVE AND
HOLLY BAER OF
ZOMEWORKS

During the late 60's, a group of "dirty hippies"—as they were then known—dropped out of consumerist America's mainstream and began settling in the arid reaches of this country's Southwest. There, they usually eked out a living by raising organic gardens, doing odd jobs, selling craft products . . . and just plain scrounging.

Well, undoubtedly, some of those dropouts really were the ne'er-do-wells that their parents thought they were. But others in the crowd were genuine visionaries, philosophers, social critics and Renaissance men . . . and women. Steve and Holly Baer certainly fit into the second category.

The Baers, as so many of us have done since the mid-50's, did some rambling from one school and occupation to another and saw a little of the world before they came to rest near Albuquerque, New Mexico in the last half of the 60's. Steve was especially restless. He was capable enough to make a way for himself and his family wherever he went . . . but he couldn't seem to convince himself that he belonged in any of our culture's neat little pigeonholes.

The answer, of course, was simple (whether the Baers knew it at the time or not) . . . they'd just have to start building a new culture. Which they, and some others, proceeded to do.

The Baers—in alliance with a few of the Southwest's young

communes—began by showing the world that very inexpensive dome housing could be fabricated from the tops of junked automobiles (Steve's out-of-print manual, Dome Cookbook, is still the classic reference on the subject).

Steve then moved on to develop zomes (open, airy buildings that offer much greater structural flexibility than domes). At almost the same time, he plunged deeply into make-it-work-on-a-practical-basis solar energy research. Eventually, with two friends, Steve founded Zomeworks . . . a company that designs and manufactures zomes, solar water heaters and other imaginative hardware that springs from the fertile brains of Baer and the young innovators that are drawn to him.

Holly has stood close beside Steve during his struggle to develop his ideas. She has made many meaningful contributions to his work and done much valuable work of her own. Together, they make an impressive team.

Cass Wester visited Zomeworks and the Baers' new home (a solar-heated zome constructed largely of aluminum sandwich panels) in early June of 1973. At Zomeworks, Steve told Cass something about where the Baers have been and where they're headed . . . and Holly took her on a tour of the couple's unusual house.

PLOWBOY: Steve, let's begin at the beginning. How did you actually get into this whole thing?

STEVE: That question is hard to answer because I'd have to go back and explain all my childhood and my parents' childhoods and about my friends and everything. That's really difficult . . . so I'll just give you the outlines of what I've been doing for the last ten years or so.

I went to Amherst College in Massachusetts for a couple of years and I went to UCLA for a year or two and then I went back to Amherst . . . and I never quite fit in to that whole college thing. Then I joined the Army in 1960 and got married and Holly and I went to Germany for three years. I learned to speak an approximation of German and, after I got out of the Army, I went to school in Zurich.

PLOWBOY: You must have liked it over there.

STEVE: Zurich is really a neat town. I worked part time as a welder in a metal shop while we were there and it was fun living in Zurich and fun going to school there. But I began to see that I wasn't going to get a degree or become a conventional engineer or any of those things, so I just kept trying to get my education my own way . . . the way I wanted it and the way I saw it, rather than the way people were trying to tell me—probably quite wisely—it should be.

Along about then I began thinking of building a house, and I studied the geometry of polyhedra to see if I could figure out some simple ways of building such forms. And I did begin building them in the shop where I was employed. The people there were really generous. They let me work on these things on Saturdays and in the evenings and I designed and fabricated joints for structures and just got very involved in the whole idea.

PLOWBOY: But why polyhedra? Did any one person or book inspire you to begin experimenting with such forms?

STEVE: No . . . well, actually Holly had some little kid's toys made from polyhedra and she built one of these things and I started looking at it and I just blew my mind and that was kind of the starting point. Then I went out and found some mathematics books that described the geometry of polyhedra and convex figures. This wasn't too difficult since I had always

STEVE BAER

been fascinated by math. It was the subject I had spent the most time on in school and, as a matter of fact, was what I was studying at the time.

PLOWBOY: And?

STEVE: Well, next we left Zurich and came back to the States and moved to Albuquerque where I worked as a surveyor and welder. I was welding trailer frames for Fruehof and Holly had a job and we didn't spend much of what we were making. On top of that, Holly had some inherited money that had been accumulating while I was in the Army and pretty soon we had a good deal of cash. After a while I sort of gave up trying to make a living in Albuquerque—it's hard getting jobs here—and said, "We've got this money and I'm just going to spend it and study and do what I think I can do" . . . and I began to experiment more and more with structures.

I built a kind of shed in back of our house in Corrales and then I found out that the people at Drop City were building domes and I went up there and helped them for a while. Then they came down and helped me. We kind of inspired each other and really got the creative juices flowing. We built the first structures from car tops. We chopped the tops out of over a thousand cars and I think I chopped over 700 automobiles myself. It was a lot of fun.

PLOWBOY: Did you get the car tops for free?

STEVE: No, we paid 25¢ apiece for them. They're a good building material in a way, except that getting stuff from junkyards like that is very bad for your whole mentality. You basically become a parasite on something you criticize all the time. You can't help it when you're chopping cars apart . . . you can't help noticing how poorly they're made. Still, you're depending on them. You're feeding on something you hate. It really doesn't work out, although I think it's a fine thing to do for a few years.

Well, anyway . . . so we built buildings from car tops at Drop City and people from Drop City came down and stayed with us in Albuquerque. We built and did solar heating experiments . . . solar heated a dome in 1967 with a big chimney—a rock storage bin—down the side of a hill. Many of those first things didn't actually work very well. I didn't know what I was doing.

PLOWBOY: Wait a minute. You were recycling car tops into domes and zomes and all of a sudden you started trying to heat the buildings with solar energy. That seems like a rather big jump . . . how did you make it?

STEVE: I had always been fascinated, kind of indirectly, with solar energy. I used to do things like take a thermometer and measure the temperature of streams, for example, and I'd find that some streams—according to their exposure to the sun—would be about ten degrees warmer than others. That was very interesting to me.

Then in the fall of 1967—maybe it was '66—I read this book of Farrington Daniels', *Direct Use of the Sun's Energy*, and it just lit up my brain. The book is so beautifully written and so clear and just makes you *see* that solar energy is a power source that must be harnessed.

PLOWBOY: Wow. This subject really seems to excite you.

STEVE: It does, it does. When you start experimenting with, say, solar heating by covering collectors with glass or plastic and feeling the warm air blow out of them . . . well, it's so exciting that you just get hooked and can't stop.

There's so *much* energy all around us that we overlook, you know. It isn't apparent . . . but we can gather it so easily. And it's surprising . . . it's simply surprising when you take these dead materials—this glass and metal and insulation—and place them together in very simple, easy-to-build forms and—suddenly! in the middle of winter!—there's *warmth*. From no place, so to speak, because the energy wasn't apparent until you made the equipment to collect it and then it's *there*.

PLOWBOY: And once you know it's there, it probably seems logical to use it.

STEVE: Right. Solar heating just seemed like the obvious thing to do around here . . . and pretty soon all these things were happening. We were building solar-heated domes and zomes with the people from Drop City and Manera Nueva and so on and so forth.

Then, in the spring of '69, Barry Hickman and Holly and I organized the Alloy Conference in Alamogordo and we invited people who were working on all kinds of things. We just wanted to mix it all together and kind of see "what was on the other side of the mountain range". It was our ambition to try and find out or talk about what *could be* . . . rather than just continue to go along as we were more or less supposed to go along.

PLOWBOY: And then you started Zomeworks.

STEVE: After that conference we started Zomeworks. Barry Hickman and Ed Heinz and I issued stock like a corporation and got a lawyer and all of that . . . and it was quite an abrupt change from just casually working together on a project the way we had before. Organizing what we had been doing for fun and excitement into a business put a hell of a lot of strain on all of us at the beginning . . . but that's a long story and we won't take the time to go into it.

PLOWBOY: Did you start manufacturing zomes at the very beginning . . . or do research work . . . or what?

STEVE: We started making playground climbers—using the 31-zone truss which is a new geometrical structural system that's explained in the *Zome Primer*—and at the same time, we were working on solar heating experiments.

Right after we started Zomeworks, Day Chahroudi came out from California. He'd read the *Dome Cookbook* and he came walking up the road one afternoon with a rucksack on his back. I talked to Day that evening and, when he started telling me his ideas about how things worked—physics, etc.—I was so impressed by his whole approach to engineering problems that I persuaded him to stay and work with us. He did and pretty soon he developed a solar tracker—a mechanism that would keep a collector pointed at the sun as it traveled across the sky—that was very simple and easy to build. We've published a paper about it.

PLOWBOY: I know. You got some publicity about that . . . and about your buildings and solar heaters and the other things you were doing at that time.

STEVE: Yeah. Well, we learned a few things from that exposure. We had a lot of stories done about us and people were coming to see what we were doing and we were talking all the time about how great we were and how great all these ideas were. But now that I look back on it I can see that we were really nowhere at that time, because so many of those ideas were good ideas and they worked . . . but they couldn't *keep* working. Some of the first buildings we put up weren't good buildings because they leaked. Many of those first solar heaters weren't really very good solar heaters.

PLOWBOY: Maybe not, but they were a starting point . . . and you've come a long way since then.

STEVE: Yes, and I think we'll go a lot further . . . but on a real scale we still aren't anywhere. Some of our hardware is getting pretty good, but it still doesn't make economic sense for most people. All too often our zomes and heaters and so forth do not yet compete on a dollar basis with their conventional counterparts. It's very exciting intellectually to work with these ideas but their validity will not really be proven until they start to replace the things they're meant to replace.

PLOWBOY: You must be thinking about your playground climbers.

STEVE: That's a good example. We made these *beautiful* climbers with aluminum joints and steel pipe frames, all using this new 31-zone structural series which is a fascinating innovation in geometric spatial systems . . . and I was excited by it and everybody working at Zomeworks was excited by it and we thought the *whole world* would be covered by these structures. But we haven't had the money that would allow us to tool up to manufacture the parts for the playground climbers on a competitive basis. The people who come to us and want these things simply can't afford to buy them. I still very much want to build the climbers, but they just can't hold their own in the market and so we're not building them anymore.

PLOWBOY: But you *are* manufacturing and marketing other products?

STEVE: Yes. Things like the Skylid, which is a ventilator that's activated by the sun and automatically opens and closes itself to help maintain a constant temperature inside a building.

PLOWBOY: Can you tell us how the device works?

STEVE: It's pretty simple actually. The Skylid has no switches or wires or motors to go haywire. Instead, the unit contains a series of louvers. Each panel is supported and balanced so that it hinges easily around its center and all the louvers are connected with a tie rod so they'll open and close simultaneously.

Now, mounted on one of the panels are two canisters—one on the outside and one inside—and the containers are connected by a length of tubing. When we seal some Freon—which is a gas with a very low boiling point—into this system, we find that we can expand the Freon in one canister and make it condense in the other with a temperature difference of as little as 1° F. This shifting of the Freon's weight will open and close the finely balanced louvers, of course, and the rising and setting of the sun—even the shade of a cloud—produces more than enough temperature variation to boil the Freon from one container to the other.

PLOWBOY: It must work sort of like those toy birds that have a little bit of Freon that moves around inside them to make them dip their heads to "drink" water, then bob back up, then dip down again and so on . . . although I assume your Skylids ordinarily open themselves once in the morning and then close again just once at dusk.

STEVE: Right . . . and they have a locking chain that allows you to secure the panels anywhere from full open to full close whenever you want to override the automatic mechanism.

PLOWBOY: That seems to be a very simple, straightforward arrangement and I would think that one of your Skylids should operate indefinitely with little or no trouble at all.

STEVE: Well that's what Zomeworks means to me . . . that's what I'm personally trying to do. I want to build buildings and design systems that are beautiful and simple and that really work. We've taken this very basic approach in the planning and construction of the solar-heated house in which Holly and I now live. It's not very exotic or earthshaking to fill 55-gallon drums with water, paint them black and place them in the walls of a home for use as solar collectors . . . but it works. It's a very low-technology idea that almost anyone can understand and use and it works. This is the kind of real innovation that actually makes organizations function and keeps people happy . . . rather than the grandstand plays made by the Atomic Energy Commission or the National Aeronautics and Space Administration.

PLOWBOY: Would you care to expand on that last thought?

STEVE: I just don't think we can depend on General Motors or the Pentagon or NASA to produce the things that we really want and need. The people who work at places like that are fine human beings that care for their dogs and children, as we all know . . . but, somehow, the philosophical tactics and whole approach taken by the giant corporations and large power groups miss the point entirely.

It's like this tape recorder we're using. A pencil can break on you and you can sharpen it with your thumbnail and go right on . . . but if a circuit board or a resistor or condenser quits somewhere inside this recorder, we're stopped and there's probably not a lot we can do about it. That makes me queasy sometimes and I think other people feel the same way . . . yet we increasingly use tape recorders instead of pencils.

OK. It's the same thing when it comes right down to how the system works in this country. At one time an individual could pretty much fix everything in his life with his thumbnail or his teeth. But now the big corporations and organizations have so much to do with everyday life . . . and we know that they want to build things like nuclear bombs and missiles. People begin to feel spooky and hesitate—quite rightly—to put their faith in that kind of technology and I really don't think it's necessary. I believe the ground rules can be transformed so that technology simplifies life instead of continually complicating it.

PLOWBOY: Many of MOTHER's readers, of course, feel exactly the way you do . . . and often find themselves accused of wanting only to "go back" to some primitive level of subsistence. You're not talking about "going back", are you?

STEVE: No, I don't think that building everything out of stones and living in animal skins is necessarily the mark of a healthier civilization than the one into which we seem to be headed. I'm saying that—no matter where we are at the moment—life can be much more satisfying for an individual if he feels that *he* is in control of his destiny at that point and at that time. Society, and the tools of society, should be organized to give each one of us that feeling.

PLOWBOY: That's a simple enough goal.

STEVE: Well the theory is simple, but putting it into practice isn't so easy. Take those barrels in the walls of our house, for instance. I used them because I didn't want to be dependent upon more sophisticated solar energy collectors ... yet the machinery that *makes* the 55-gallon drums is probably as complicated as anything I'd care to imagine. It's a quandary, you see. Any way you turn you're caught this way unless you do forget the whole thing and go back to living with just animals.

PLOWBOY: But it's a quandary of your own making. In effect, you want the best of both ... the simplicity of living in a primitive, technology-poor society plus the wealth and ease made possible only by a highly organized, technology-rich "establishment". What makes you think this is possible?

STEVE: It all started back in high school, where I was very good in mathematics and physics. I was good in those areas but I was dissatisfied with the way in which I saw the knowledge in those fields used. Then when I was about 18 I started to read the writings of Lewis Mumford and I could see that we didn't have to have this "either-or" choice. We *could* have the best of both ... we could have a science and technology that could be understood and controlled by the individual instead of the other way around. I found the idea very exciting and I've been trying to crack the crap in science for 15 or 16 years now. I don't claim to have gotten anywhere but I'm trying.

PLOWBOY: Has anyone else influenced your thinking as profoundly as Mumford?

STEVE: I've already mentioned Farrington Daniels. Then there's Peter van Dresser, who built a solar heater here in New Mexico in 1956 or '58. We published his book, *Landscape for Humans.* One of the greatest forces of all, of course, has been Harold Hay from California.

PLOWBOY: I've never met Harold but I just talked to him on the phone and he was fascinating.

STEVE: Harold is extraordinary ... just an extraordinary guy.
I first heard him in '68 at the Solar Energy Conference. I had been working with a design for a solar heating system and I had had some modest success with it and thought I was doing pretty well ... until Harold got up and showed everyone these absolutely dead-simple methods of doing the same job. He just

completely changed my whole head around on how best to attack these problems.

The only trouble was that, except for me, nobody seemed to be listening to Hay. None of the engineers have ever been interested in Harold because what he's saying is so simple. The guys with the degrees are afraid to try his ideas. They're afraid people will laugh at them and say, "What? You're a Ph.D. and all you're doing is opening and closing those doors?"

So it was a really big thing for me just to know Harold and to talk to him, and we've worked together a lot since then trying to bring some reforms into the Solar Society.

PLOWBOY: Reforms?

STEVE: Yeah. The Society has been taken over by scientists and, as a group, I'm terribly suspicious of scientists because I don't think they practice science. I think they're practicing _power._ They're trying to keep technology for themselves and manipulate it as if they had some divine right to do so . . . no matter what the consequences. It's as if the captain of the Queen Mary is steaming straight ahead into a pier and, even after the timbers begin to break, he continues to pour on the coal because, "When I left London they said 'head west' so I'm heading west." It's crazy.

PLOWBOY: And you're going to change all that.

STEVE: Yeah, well . . . I don't have such great ambitions any-more for making big changes in organizations and mass move-ments. I still have the ambitions but I'm not so sure the changes will take place. I'm most interested now in taking small steps . . . in developing individual pieces of equipment and hardware that really work and that really make economic sense. And even this is not an easy thing to do . . . it's just not easy.

PLOWBOY: But you _are_ doing it. You've introduced the zome concept of construction and you've developed things like the Skylid and you've built a very simple solar-heated house that works . . . or I _think_ it works!

STEVE: Yes, it works . . . and that was a great surprise. This structure has a lot of experimental features and, when you're experimenting, about 80% of the ideas you try are failures that you have to wade through. But we put all these concepts together and they performed the first time.

Then again, we *had* pretested most of the ideas we incorporated into this home. We'd never used aluminum-skinned, honeycomb-cored structural sandwiches and—as far as we know—no one had ever fabricated a complete building from the material before we began . . . but every architectural and engineering book mentions the possibility of using such panels for the building of houses, even though it's expensive in small quantities. The 55-gallon, water-filled drums with which we absorb energy from the sun could also be considered an experiment . . . but we had tried the idea ahead of time and knew the amounts of energy that such containers could pick up.

I guess you'd have to say that the house was an experiment, but not a complete experiment . . . and it does work and we're happy with it.

PLOWBOY: Do you see it as the prototype of a whole new generation of living units?

STEVE: Not especially. One of our people, Dick Henry, is now working on a solar-heated house that's going to look very conventional. It's going to have adobe walls and a pitched roof and some of the individuals who follow our work are shocked that Zomeworks is doing something like this.

The point is that we're trying to do what makes sense to us rather than to pursue some particular direction—remember that steamship captain I mentioned?—because we want to build buildings that really work. And sometimes zomes work and in other cases another design does the job better. It all depends on what somebody wants and what fits the particular situation. We've never said that *everyone* should live in a solar-heated house.

We feel the same way about wind power. We have a windmill and it pumps water, but we don't advocate that everybody pump their water with a windmill. Sometimes it's better to hook up with the city water supply.

It's so easy for these things to become cults, you know. Like domes have become a cult in the counterculture . . . and wind generators . . . and so many things. And once they do, people become blinded to design. They look at a piece of hardware and they don't see the equipment's design, and demand that the design make sense for their particular region and circumstance . . . they see only something that's "groovy" for right now.

PLOWBOY: That's a very levelheaded approach . . . and I assume that the government and the large corporations must be showing a lot of curiosity in your work.

STEVE: Some in the field of solar heating, but not a lot. The National Science Foundation bought me tickets to this workshop they had on solar heating a few months ago . . . but all they wanted to discuss at the conference were projects that will cost ten million dollars before any heating or cooling gets done. And that's not necessary . . . it's just not necessary. The work they want to do has already been done.

We've organized things in this country so that we're like a millionaire who's going bankrupt and only his gardener knows how to pull him out. But the voice of salvation *can't* come from the gardener . . . it's gotta come from the millionaire's uncle or brother or friend next door.

PLOWBOY: And you're the gardener.

STEVE: Zomeworks and a lot of other groups that have practiced thriftiness and sensibleness and innovation since the country was founded are the gardeners. We may not have the final answers but we've already been down the road that the economy at large now wants to travel and we have something important to contribute. We're just not allowed to do so.

It's painful for us here at Zomeworks—now that we've labored so long to make things that work—to realize we'll probably never get much funding from a government that's trying to develop what we already have. We just don't smell right to the guys who control the purse strings, you know, and that's very frustrating.

PLOWBOY: Give me an example.

STEVE: An example?

PLOWBOY: Yeah. An example of a solution you already have that the government will probably spend ten million dollars rediscovering.

STEVE: Well there's Dave Harrison's bead wall. I teach some classes at the University of New Mexico and Dave was one of my students and he came up to me one day and said, "Hey, I've got this idea for building a wall out of two panes of glass. During the day the sunlight can go through the glass and you can blow styrofoam beads between the panes at night to insulate the wall."

I said, "Yeah, that's a good idea" . . . and then, while driving home that night, I thought, "WOW! That's a *great* idea!" Here's a problem that people have lived with for 80 or 100 years and nobody has thought of a way to solve. I've tried to find a solution and I know Harold Hay has tried to find a solution and so have a lot of others . . . and Dave Harrison has the answer!

Dave has come up with a fairly low-tech—I'd say—answer that's simple, that's easy to understand, that a heating and ventilating man in any small town can fix . . . and that works. It really works.

PLOWBOY: Have you tested it?

STEVE: We've built a number of the panels with beads that blow in and out and they really do the job. We never have the money to pay people what standard businesses can pay in a situation like this, of course, but we've made a deal with Dave so that he'll get a big part of any royalties we realize and we're now promoting the idea by building a greenhouse that will be insulated with the styrofoam beads. I think the idea is going to have a big impact.

PLOWBOY: But not with the government.

STEVE: Probably not with the government or the large corporations. Not for a while. Maybe 30 years from now the country will be ready to let us put all these concepts together and build an entire city based on different geometries and solar energy and the other innovations that we're trying to simplify. That would really be fun . . . but it just doesn't seem that the time is right for us to get a lot of help in pulling all these things together at this point.

PLOWBOY: But you do keep trying.

STEVE: I can't see anything else to do. It's better than sitting in a university writing abstract reports about the changes that are needed while you draw your paycheck from taxes levied on businesses and people that keep on doing things in the old way.

Damn it, if you want change you have to make it . . . and one way is to develop the tools of a new way of life and start small businesses to sell such equipment and put the whole thing on a paying basis and thereby show others that you have a viable alternative. That's what we're trying to do at Zomeworks. You have to make the change yourself or you have to shut up about it.

PLOWBOY: And?

STEVE: I think we've already shown that this approach works.

PLOWBOY: You've proven that the shoestring method can produce results which are just as good as the projects funded by ten million dollars.

STEVE: Yeah . . . and it's going to be fascinating to see which direction society takes during the next ten or twenty years. It's really going to be fascinating.

HOLLY BAER

PLOWBOY: Holly, I'm sure that most people who see this house for the first time find it to be quite an unusual structure. The building's shape, the materials from which it's made, its heating system . . . almost everything about your home must seem new and strange to the average person. Let's start with the house's shape: It looks a little like a dome . . . but, then again, not like a dome at all.

HOLLY: It's a zome, a structural system originated by Steve. The word was coined by combining "zonohedron" and "dome", although—unlike a dome which is basically limited to a more-or-less spherical shape—a zome can be stretched out asymmetrically or joined to other zomes to make very complicated and satisfying free-form buildings.

PLOWBOY: Just what is this "zonohedron" on which the zome is based?

HOLLY: A zonohedron is defined, I think, as a geometric shape which has parallel zoning running through it. If you look at this house, you'll notice that each room is basically hexagonal in floor plan and you can see which walls are parallel and which ones follow the ceiling.

PLOWBOY: What are these walls made of?

HOLLY: The main vertical panels are big sandwiches consisting of two aluminum skins laminated to a cardboard honeycomb core. Insulating urethane foam has been blown into each section from both sides and an inch of dead-air space left in the center of the panels.

PLOWBOY: A cross section, then, would consist of aluminum skin/urethane foam/dead-air space/urethane foam/aluminum skin . . . with the two layers of foam and the air space contained within the cardboard honeycomb.

HOLLY: Right. The panels are pop-riveted together with aluminum strips at their joints and there's no interior structure or ordinary framing in the house at all.

PLOWBOY: I see some adobe in here.

HOLLY: Yes. Once the exterior walls were up, we lined some of them with adobe and we used adobe for the interior walls and dividers.

PLOWBOY: You've even shaped it into a couch!

HOLLY: The couch is just an extension of the wall. That's not unusual in Mexico and New Mexico, by the way. When you build with adobe you can really sculpture with it . . . just pile it up and make a bench or sofa or whatever you choose.

PLOWBOY: Why did you and Steve decide to construct your home in this shape and largely of aluminum and cardboard honeycomb panels?

HOLLY: The longer Steve built zomes the more it seemed we ought to live in one. Almost all the zomes he designed were for communities and they were sort of big buildings and none of them was really a house. We wanted to see if he could use his structural ideas to make a little middle-class home.

PLOWBOY: Did he design this place?

HOLLY: Yes, and we worked together on the plans.

PLOWBOY: Did you have any help building it?

HOLLY: Oh, we had lots of help. We had to. We built about seven or eight zomes that summer—this was in 1971—and we were so busy putting up other people's zomes that we had to hire most of the labor that went into this one.

PLOWBOY: Just how long did it take to construct the house?

HOLLY: About a full year. We started leveling the site and drilling a well in May of '71 and then we ordered the aluminum and honeycomb and had the panels laminated. It was the last week in September before we began putting up the first wall. We continued construction through Thanksgiving and then were stalled again and didn't get back to work on the place until the following January. We moved into the kitchen and gave the kids their rooms at about that same time—in January of '72—when there was no bathroom in the house and some of the walls were still bedspreads and canopies. Finally, in March, we got the place sealed so the wind couldn't come through and we moved into the rest of the rooms during late July and August.

PLOWBOY: Could you have built this home in less time?

HOLLY: It could have been done in much less time . . . a *lot* less. We've constructed a two-zome house of aluminum sandwich panels in Houston in three days, for instance. This building is 11 zomes clustered together, of course, but we still should be able to put it up in just a couple of weeks . . . instead of the weeks and weeks and weeks we used. We've learned a lot.

PLOWBOY: Did you keep figures on cost?

HOLLY: Our house covers 2,000 square feet and cost us $20.00 a square foot.

PLOWBOY: What about zoning laws and building codes? Did you run into any trouble there?

HOLLY: No, it's still pretty loose around here. We had to follow the state codes for framing and footage and things like that and we had to have electrical and plumbing inspections, but that was about it. There are no rules against solar heat, you know.

PLOWBOY: Yes! Tell me about the ways in which this house uses solar energy.

HOLLY: Well the whole structure was designed to make efficient use of the sun. This concrete floor stores heat, for example. So do the adobe partitions and the barrels of water built into the south walls. When it gets cold outside, it takes a long time for it to cool down inside.

PLOWBOY: The barrels are something that you don't ordinarily expect to find built into the walls of a house. Can you explain how they work?

HOLLY: Yes, these are ordinary 55-gallon drums and each one contains 52 or 53 gallons of water. We didn't fill any of the containers completely full because the water will expand a little as it absorbs heat. There are 90 of the barrels stacked up in racks in the south walls of our zome. The ends of the drums that face out are painted black—for more efficient heat absorption—and the ends that face into our living area are off-white.

Just outside each wall of barrels is a pane of glass and just outside that is a big door made from the same sandwich panels that are used for the rest of the house's exterior surfaces. On winter days, we lower the doors and the sun shines through the glass and heats the water in the drums. When we close the doors at night, the water just radiates warmth into the rooms.

PLOWBOY: I see some containers above your head. Do those contain water too?

HOLLY: Right. They're honey cans and they're filled with water. There's a skylight above them that is closed right now, since it's summer. In the winter, however, when that skylight is open, the sun comes in and warms those canisters. Heat from the kitchen stove also collects up there and the cans then radiate it back, gradually, throughout the night.

PLOWBOY: That sounds like a really neat idea. Does the sun provide enough energy to heat your home completely in the winter, or do you need a backup system of some kind?

HOLLY: Only wood. Last winter we had fireplaces in just the children's rooms and the north end of the house. We'll have an additional fireplace in the living room this year to provide one really warm spot there. When the temperature gets down to 63 or 64 degrees, you know, it's too chilly to sit and read . . . but if you have a hot spot right in front of you, it's pleasant.

PLOWBOY: Have you found that your solar heating system has any drawbacks?

HOLLY: Actually, we should empty the overhead cans during the summer. They work to a slight disadvantage in warm weather because they hold excess heat that would otherwise dissipate. But they do so much good in the winter and it's so much trouble to empty them that we're willing to live with that minor flaw. Especially since it's offset by the fact that the barrels in the other part of the house act as a heat sink. That is, when the temperature in the rooms is hotter than the water in the drums—as it is every day during the summer—the water just sops up the difference and the rooms stay cool. The barrels only heat up a degree or so in the process but they really cool the rooms. It's a natural form of air conditioning.

PLOWBOY: Do you ever use the water in the drums for anything else?

HOLLY: No. All our drinking, cooking, bathing and other household water comes from the well. We pump it out of the ground with a windmill and store it in a 5,000-gallon tank. As long as the wind blows, we can use as much water as we want. When the wind blows so much that the tank overflows, we just shut the windmill off.

PLOWBOY: And when the wind doesn't blow?

HOLLY: Well we've never run out yet. Our storage tank is adequate for two families and it should easily serve three. For four, we might have to build a larger tank. We have two families using our water now and we're planning to build two more homes . . . so we'll soon know if our present setup will serve four households.

PLOWBOY: You're starting your own utility service!

HOLLY: It looks like it, doesn't it.

PLOWBOY: How do you get the water from the storage tank to the houses?

HOLLY: It feeds by gravity. There are no pumps.

PLOWBOY: As I understand it, you don't have any water heater in your home either.

HOLLY: No. We use the sun to heat the water we want to heat. There's one solar heater up there by the windmill . . . that's the new one. The other, which is outside one of the bedrooms, has been working since last fall. Yesterday morning, before he took a shower, Steve measured the water's temperature and it was 150°. So it's very hot. We have no problem heating water.

PLOWBOY: Wow. You seem very self-sufficient. You heat your house with the sun, you warm your water the same way, you pump that water out of the ground with a windmill and you let it run into your house by gravity. What about electricity? Do you generate that too?

HOLLY: No, we're hooked up to the city's system . . . but we don't use very much of what they have to sell. We cook with propane, so the only electricity we need is what we use for the refrigerator, washing machine and lights. There are four of us—generally we say we're a family of five since there's always somebody extra living here—but our consumption of electricity averages only about three kilowatts per day in the summer and five in the winter. That's not very much.

PLOWBOY: I'm from back east, as you know, and your New Mexico weather seems very windy and extremely dry to me. Do you have any problems with dust or sand out here?

HOLLY: Yes, a lot.

PLOWBOY: Is there a solution for that?

HOLLY: Just a great deal of proper planting . . . and the construction of something like the retaining wall we put in behind our zome. The sand here tends to erode and we put the wall in to keep the hill from washing away. The rise, in turn, protects our house from the strong west wind.

PLOWBOY: Does the zome need more protection than an ordinary home?

HOLLY: Oh no. Our last house—a conventional one—shook when the wind blew. This one doesn't. It doesn't have nearly as many air leaks either. The zome *is* noisy though. It creaks in the morning when the sun comes up and warms the aluminum skins and makes them expand. It creaks again every time a cloud passes in front of the sun and makes the skins contract.

The zome is always settling and popping . . . but it never feels unsteady. It never makes you feel insecure.

PLOWBOY: No, as a matter of fact, those creaks are really nice once you know what they are. The house feels very sound.

HOLLY: It is. I especially like to walk on its roof.

PLOWBOY: Can you?

HOLLY: Yes, it's very strong. You can follow the geometry, like little highways.

PLOWBOY: How much weight will the structure hold?

HOLLY: All I know is that it will support more than a conventional building. Steve load-tested the first little zome we built —I think it was 300 or 400 square feet—and after we had stacked four tons on its roof we just gave up.

PLOWBOY: I've noticed that you have a couple of windows in your zome that don't open. Is there a reason for this?

HOLLY: Right. It's that old dust problem again. Instead of having cross ventilation in every room, we like to open one or two big windows and a ventilator on top of the house.

PLOWBOY: That little hatch in the ceiling . . . is that one of the ventilators?

HOLLY: Yes. There are several in the zome. We open them every night in the summer to cool the house and we close them again in the morning.

PLOWBOY: And these skylight-type windows I see?

HOLLY: Those are the Skylids we sell. They open and close themselves automatically.

PLOWBOY: What do your children think of all this?

HOLLY: They really care and they participate in making the house work. The children roll the big doors up and down so that we don't lose heat. They know we can't turn up the thermostat in the winter and—since they don't want to be cold—they make sure they close all the windows and doors during cold weather. When I forget to close the summer venti-

lators in the morning, they do it. I think the house is good for
them . . . and they for it.

PLOWBOY: Have you noticed any particular psychological
effects that the zome has exerted on you?

HOLLY: We had lived in a bus and a barn for seven months
before moving into this home and so just being in the zome
seemed wonderful and luxurious from the very start.

The house is fun to live in. Each time we go away and stay
in someone else's home I think, "Wow, that's really nice,"
when we come back. The high ceilings make you feel good.
The shapes work. I like the fact that there are no doors. You
can move through the place without opening or closing anything and that's nice. You can move freely, yet each room has
privacy from all the others. The geometry allows things like
that to happen.

I really like it when the big doors are down in the winter
and we're heating the zome, because light comes in around all
the drums and the skylights are open and the place feels so
light and airy. And in the summer, when it's hot and bright
outside, we close the big doors and the skylights . . . and the
house seems so shady and cool. It's just a fun place to live.

PLOWBOY: What _don't_ you like about the house?

HOLLY: Well . . . there are still some leaks in the roof, but
they're not a major thing.

PLOWBOY: Do you plan to settle in here permanently, or will
you build another home and move into it?

HOLLY: I think it would be easier for Steve to move on than
for me. When we finally got into this house I was exhausted.
Right now I can't wait for the trees to get big and the garden
to start producing. For Steve, though, it's all just part of a
continuing experiment . . . and as soon as he finishes something, he's ready to move on. Yes, as long as we're busy building Zomeworks, I think we'd do it all over again. We
both hope to keep getting jobs so we can continue our
experiments. ◓

Zomeworks manufactures, sells and installs a number of solar
energy devices in addition to Steve Baer's zomes. You'll find the
company listed in the back of this book (see Solar, Hardware).

MIKE OEHLER:
THE HOMESTEAD SOLAR SHOWER

Almost everyone enjoys a hot shower ... nothing feels quite so good. The jets of warm water invigorate the skin and make it tingle, and the constant flow rippling down over the body is a massage. In particular, few things raise the morale of an outdoorsman—who's just come in out of the field or woods coated with a couple of days' grime—as much as soaping down under a steaming spray and stepping into clean, sunshine-dried, fresh-air-fluffed clothes.

To me, hot showers are one of the true achievements of civilization, ranking right up there with window glass, the wheel and the stove. So, five years ago when I bought my homeless homestead, the comfort of one of those luxurious baths was what I missed most. I gave the problem a lot of thought that first season, especially as I came up gasping after that daily plunge into a nearby mountain stream. Under those conditions soap didn't even lather ... it just coated my skin like the grease it came from. "There must be a better way to bathe than this," I thought.

The solution was simpler for me than for some homesteaders because I did have access to water under pressure: part of my community's supply that comes in straight from Caribou Creek in the Selkirk Mountains a mile or two to the west. The question was how to get the liquid hot and pouring down on top of my head in a controllable amount. A butane

heater was out, because of the initial cost and continued expense of operation. An electric heater was impossible for the same reasons ... and also because I had no electricity and didn't want any. Some sort of wood-burning device seemed more reasonable, but it would have taken days of pipe fitting and welding to get a system together. That was more work than I wanted ... as was chopping wood to feed the contrivance.

Then I remembered the story of the girl and the black bathtub, and—since I'd noticed that my garden hose always heated up when it lay in the sun—I coiled up a couple of lengths one day and threw some clear polyethylene over the pile. Presto, a solar water heater! All that remained was to spend an hour pounding together a shower stall out of some old barn wood and a tarp (a necessary step because my water line is located on a portion of my 40 acres that's visible to neighbors).

Since the nozzle came free with the hose and the polyethylene was scrap, the whole contraption cost not a penny ... and it works. (To adjust the temperature I step closer to or farther back from the spray.) Though there's only a hundred feet of coil under the poly, my device gives me warm water at least until October. This year I'll probably invest in another hundred-foot length and a second—maybe even a third—plastic cover and see if I can't get hot showers right up till the snow flies. I still use the hose in the garden, too, when I don't need it for a heater.

What's the story of the girl and the black bathtub? Well, seems there was this clever little sweetheart living alone in the woods without the usual amenities, and she missed her daily hot tub bath. (A sure sign of mental aberration, to my thinking, is the female preference for wallowing in dirty water when the option is a pure, sparkling hot shower. Fertile grounds for psychiatric exploration, that.) At any rate, one day this gal got herself a secondhand bathtub, painted it black inside and dragged it out to a sunny clearing. From then on she filled the receptacle with water in the morning and came home each evening to a hot dip.

Which just goes to show that where there's a will—and sunshine—there's a way ... and, I suppose, that mere males have no monopoly on converting solar energy into satisfyingly warm bath water. ●

KENNETH WHETZEL'S
SOLAR
HEATER

Ever wonder whether you could put the sun's energy to work for you where you live? Well, a former neighbor of MOTHER's asked himself that question . . . and to find the answer, he built a solar water heater that worked way up in northern Ohio.

Though Kenneth Whetzel describes his little machine as "experimental", there's nothing tentative about the hot water it produces. Ken likes his shower about 105°, and there wasn't one day in all the time the test system was running that he couldn't have washed comfortably in the device's output (had he been equipped to do so). That's not bad for 60° weather. It should be noted, however, that since Ken didn't intend actually to use his heater's product, the contents of the tank are routed back through the collector . . . an arrangement that makes the model operate more efficiently than a working system in which the warmed liquid is frequently drained off.

The collector that produced these results is a 2' X 4' piece of sheet metal with about 24 feet of half-inch copper tubing soldered to it in a zigzag pattern. This whole heat-absorbing area is contained inside a wooden frame sealed over with clear plastic sheeting. The tubing that carries hot water away from the enclosure is insulated with a layer of half-inch foam rubber and leads to a raised 11-1/2-gallon reservoir protected by a styrofoam jacket one inch thick. (Whetzel built the contraption entirely of scraps scavenged from his construction job, so it's hard to say just how much it would cost you to fabricate a similar unit.)

One feature of Ken's design that really cuts the device's cost, and which should be pointed out, is the fact that it needs no mechanism to force water through the collector and into its storage tank. Why? Because of a basic fact of thermodynamics: Water, like air, expands and becomes lighter per cubic measure as its temperature increases. Rather than use electricity to run a pump, Ken took advantage of this principle and set up his creation so that the warmer—and lighter—H_2O rises through the cooler layers and on up the pipe into the top of the tank, where—as it cools—the liquid sinks down into the collector again for reheating.

A very simple, streamlined experiment, isn't it? And best of all, it works. The first day Ken set up his invention (pointed 10° west of south and tilted 30° downward from the horizontal) the water temperature at 7 a.m. was 60°. By the time the experimenter got home from work at 5 p.m., the contents of the tank had been heated to 128° . . . too hot to put your hand into. And—because of some nearby trees—the sun's rays hadn't even hit the collector until about 10 in the morning.

Overnight, Ken's hypothetical bath cooled only to 96°, and when the second day turned out warmer and sunnier than the first (with a high near 70°), Whetzel knew he could look forward to some really impressive readings. Sure enough, by evening his system's water temperature had climbed to 138° . . .

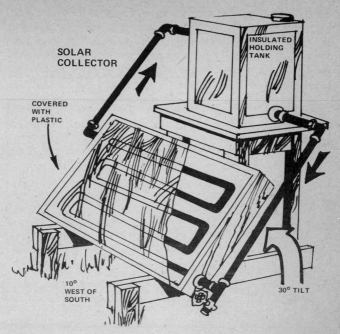

SOLAR
COLLECTOR

INSULATED
HOLDING
TANK

COVERED
WITH
PLASTIC

10°
WEST OF
SOUTH

30° TILT

nearly twice as hot as the surrounding air! Thereafter the tank's 5 p.m. temperature ranged from a low of 108° (a cloudy day) to a high of 148° . . . and on top of that record, the inventor thinks he might be able to pick up 30% in efficiency by the use of reflectors.

Ken was convinced. The last we heard—when he and his wife left for their five-acre homestead in Florida—he intended to employ the results of his experiment to set up two practical solar heating systems: one to warm the house in winter and another for domestic hot water. He figured that three 2' X 8' collectors mounted on the garage roof would supply at least 72 gallons of bath or wash water (1-1/2 gallons to the square foot) per day . . . and probably a lot more, considering Florida's fabled weather.

Our ingenious neighbor also thought his winter heating system might be used to cool the house in summer by circulating cold water from a well, but when we last talked to him he hadn't worked out all the details of that modification. Let us know when you do, Ken! ●

MATERIALS

Cardboard (as required)
Poster board (two sheets)
Aluminum foil (one roll)
Plywood (one piece, 18 by 24 inches)
3/4-inch aluminum tubing (approximately 64 inches)
3/4-inch mounting flange (one)
Grill (one)
Curtain rod (one)
Broomstick (four feet)
Clothesline (one foot)
Glue (as required)
Masking tape (as required)
3/16-by-1-inch bolt with wing nut (one set)

A stove made of paper sounds about as practical as a
pitcher carved from ice, but this reflector cooker—constructed
almost entirely of cardboard—will broil steaks, grill hot dogs,
fry bacon and eggs and make hotcakes and coffee. It will also
heat water for doing the dishes. All that's necessary to make it
work is clear weather, because this stove cooks with sunshine!

Stop to think about it for a minute and you'll remember
that every time we cook—be it with gas, electricity or charcoal
—we indirectly use the sun's energy, which has been stored up
and reconverted to heat. Basically, then, our solar stove's fuel
is nothing really new. Even the use of direct sun heat for
cooking goes back many years. Sun-dried foods have long been
eaten, and crude solar stoves were built a century ago. Besides,
who hasn't heard of cooking an egg on the sidewalk on a really
hot day?

In recent years, however, many advances have been made in
the design of solar cookers. Today there are commercial
models on the market that are fine for campers or for patio
use. One umbrella-like design folds up for easy carrying and
storage and also provides an answer for the skeptic who wants

HOW TO BUILD—AND USE!—A
REFLECTOR COOKER

to know what you do when it rains! Such a cooker is just the thing for trips. If you're dubious about how well the sun can cook a meal, or if you don't have the cash to buy a ready-made stove, get busy and build the one described here. At most, it will cost five dollars. If you use discarded cartons and other salvage material, the outlay will be only a fraction of that.

The reflector framework is cut from fiberboard, approximately 3/16 inch thick, the kind large cartons are made from. Some poster board and aluminum foil will complete the cooker itself. A grill (for hot dogs, hamburgers or pans) is made from plywood, some tubing and an inexpensive hand grill that costs about 50 cents.

Study the plans first to get the overall picture, and to see how much material will be needed. If you want to buy new fiberboard, two sheets 4 by 8 feet will be plenty. These cost about 80 cents each at a box factory or supply house. The other items will be easy to find. Get everything you'll need together and then begin construction. An eager beaver can do the job in a day or so and begin sampling outdoor cooking à la sun right away.

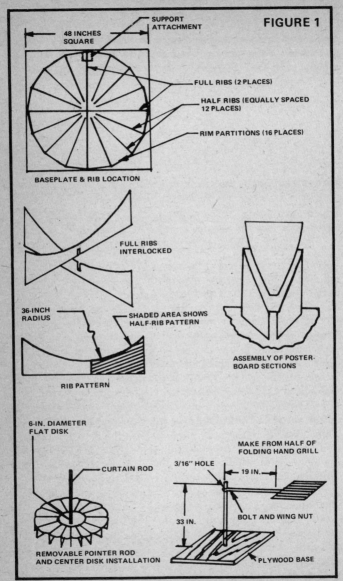

FIGURE 1. General plans for building the reflector cooker.

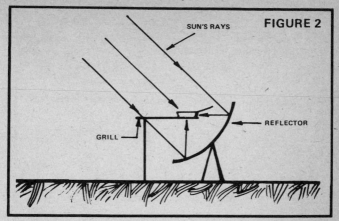

This illustration shows the operating principle of the reflector cooker.

First, cut a base piece 4 feet square from the 3/16-inch cardboard. We'll mark the layout of the reflector ribs right on this base. With a pencil and a piece of string, draw a 48-inch-diameter circle. This is the size our finished cooker will be. Next draw two lines through the center of the base, perpendicular to each other as shown on the plans. These mark the location of the main ribs, which we will make next.

A word about the principle of our reflector cooker will be helpful before we proceed any farther. The sun stove simply focuses all the sun's rays that strike its surface onto the bottom of the grill. Even on a clear winter day the 12 square feet of area in our cooker collects a lot of "warmth", which when shrunk into the 1-foot area at the grill becomes concentrated "heat" (see Fig. 1).

The giant solar furnaces used by some research labs (such as the Mont Louis installation high in the Pyrenees mountains of southern France) use curved reflectors too. They generate thousands of degrees of heat at their focal points, using the same principle. To do this they must be very accurately made and of parabolic shape. This specially shaped curve reflects all the rays onto one tiny spot and gives the furnace a concentration ratio of many thousands to one. Obviously we don't want such high temperatures, for they would melt our pans!

Our reflector will use a radius of 36 inches instead of a true parabolic curve. This results in a larger spot at the focal point.

FIGURE 3

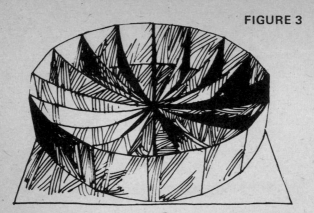

The above sketch shows the assembled framework of the reflector.

Besides this, we will use a number of wedge-shaped sections instead of one bowl-shaped reflector. Thus our focal spot will be roughly the size of the cooking pan, which is ideal for our purposes.

Now that we know the why of what we're doing, let's draw two main ribs as shown on the plans (Fig. 1). Cut these carefully—using a sharp linoleum knife, pocketknife or modeler's razor knife—and be sure to plan ahead so as not to waste material. Each of the main ribs has a notch at the center. Notice that one is on the top and one on the bottom so that they'll interlock.

Using a full rib as a pattern, mark out 12 half ribs as shown on the plans. Before cutting these, cement the full ribs to the base plate on the lines previously drawn. Model airplane glue or a good household cement will work well. While the parts are drying, cut out the remaining ribs.

Three half ribs fit between each quarter section of the circle. Glue these in place, lining up the end of each one with the circle we drew on the base plate. While they're drying, cut the rectangular filler pieces of cardboard. As the plans show, these fit between the outer tips of the ribs to complete the framework (see Figs. 1 and 3).

When the framework is thoroughly dry, we're ready to put on the wedge-shaped pieces of poster board. Since these form the curve that will reflect the sun's rays, we must use poster board that is thin enough to bend easily, yet has sufficient

FIGURE 4

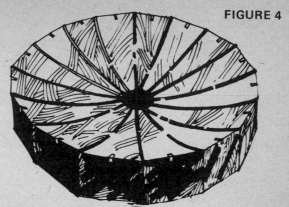

The reflector, in this drawing, is ready for its foil covering.

body to hold the proper shape. Lighter cardboard would have a tendency to ripple and wave.

By means of cut-and-try methods, trim one piece of poster board so that it covers the space between two ribs, with about 1/8-inch overlap all around. Do not cement this in place yet; it will be our pattern for 15 more pieces. Cut the additional sections carefully, making sure they will cover any of the spaces between ribs. (In spite of care, there may be slight inaccuracies in the framework.) It's better to have the poster-board pieces a bit too large than too small.

With all the pieces cut we can now begin to cement them in place. Since butting the joints smoothly against each other would be difficult, we will glue eight sections into alternate spaces first. Spread glue along the tops of two ribs and the intervening filler piece, then lay the poster-board wedge in place and carefully press down so that it touches the ribs at all points. The glue will dry well enough in a minute or two so that you can go on to the next piece. Don't forget to leave every other section open.

Now we can cover the remaining spaces with our second eight wedges of poster board. These will of course lap over the edges of the pieces already glued in place, thus making a strong joint. If you run into difficulty at the center where all the points come together, simply trim them off an inch or two. The hole left can later be covered with a separate piece of poster board.

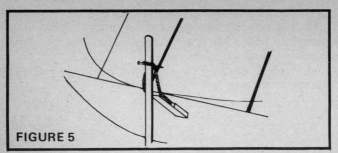

FIGURE 5

Detail of cardboard-clothesline-nail adjustable support bracket.

For added strength, seal all the joints with masking tape as shown in Fig. 4. While this isn't absolutely necessary, it will make a sturdier cooker. The reflector is now ready for application of the aluminum foil that will give it the mirror-like finish we need to collect heat for cooking.

Cut out 16 pieces of smooth-surfaced aluminum foil . . . the kind used in the kitchen for wrapping food. These should be slightly larger than the poster-board wedges to assure complete coverage of the reflector surface. Use rubber cement to stick the foil to the poster board, and be sure to place the shiny side up. Work carefully and try to keep the foil smooth, but don't worry if the finished job isn't perfect. The cooker shown in the illustrations has a few ripples but works well anyway.

We will now install a marker for the focal point of the reflector so that we'll know where to place the grill for the fastest cooking. This marker is simply a small, inexpensive curtain rod of the type used on kitchen doors. It consists of two tubes, one fitted inside the other. Cut a short length of the larger cylinder and insert it into a hole punched in the center of the reflector. Better still, use a drill the same size as the outside section of the curtain rod (or slightly smaller) to give a snug fit. Now cement the tube in place.

The smaller tube will fit into this "holder" and can be removed for easier handling when not needed. As we mentioned before, the proper place to mount our grill is one focal length from the reflector. With a spherical reflector that distance is half the radius or, in this case, 18 inches. As a double check, aim the reflector at the sun and adjust the tilt until there is no shadow visible from the pointer rod. Then hold a piece of wrapping paper with a small hole punched in it right at the tip of the pointer. Move the sheet toward the reflector and then away until the smallest spot of light is observed on the paper. This is the actual focal point, and our pointer rod should be trimmed to this length.

Cut out two squares and one rectangle of cardboard as shown in the detail of the adjustable support (Fig. 5) and cement them to the back of the cardboard base. The squares go first, and then the rectangle. After these are well dried, run a short length of clothesline through the slot and tie the ends in a square knot. Drill holes through a 48-inch length of 1-inch dowel (broomstick or tubing), spacing the holes about an inch apart halfway down the dowel. Insert a nail to engage the loop of clothesline. We can now set up our reflector so that it will stand alone.

To make the grill, first cut an 18-by-24-inch plywood base. Any thickness from 1/2 to 1 inch will do. Mark the center of this base and install a mounting flange for the 3/4-inch aluminum-tubing vertical support (which is 40 inches long).

The adjustable arm is also aluminum tubing, 24 inches long. Flatten one end and bend it around a piece of pipe or a broomstick to make the collar, which fits over the vertical support. Drill a 3/16-inch hole as shown and insert a bolt capped by a wing nut. The other end of the adjustable arm may now be flattened. Be careful to keep the flat area at right angles to the collar so that the grill will be horizontal when installed. Slide the grill in place and the solar cooker is complete.

Now that the work is done, the fun starts. Positioning the reflector is simple if you follow these directions. Stand behind the collector and face it right at the sun. Then tilt the reflector back until the shadow of the pointer rod vanishes as it did when we checked for focal length. This means that the collector is aimed perfectly and that all the sun's rays will be bounced right where we want them.

Holding the reflector in this position, slip the dowel or broomstick through the rope loop and put the nail through the hole just below the loop. With the collector standing on its own feet you can now put the grill in place. Loosen the wing nut on the adjustable arm and move it up or down until the grill rests just above the tip of the pointer rod. As a double check, pass your hand quickly just above the grill. It should be hot, ready for you to start cooking.

FIGURE 6

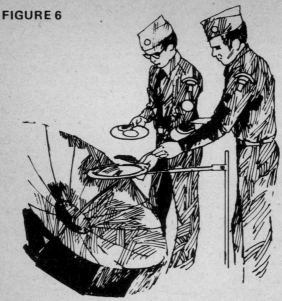

And here's the cardboard reflector cooker completed and in use.

The grill surface itself is fine for cooking hot dogs, burgers or steak (Fig. 6). Grease will drip onto the reflector but will not harm it. For bacon and eggs, hotcakes and the like, place a skillet on the griddle. And, if you like your steaks seared quickly to keep in the juice, use the skillet for them too. By putting it on the grill a few minutes early you can store up extra heat that will cook the steak more rapidly.

Water for coffee, tea or dishwashing can be heated in a kettle or pot. To get the maximum efficiency from your solar cooker, use blackened utensils; however, just about any kind of utensil works satisfactorily. For variety try using a pressure cooker.

Because the sun moves across the sky, the position of the reflector must be changed as time passes. In the early morning or late afternoon it will be nearly vertical, while at noon you will have to place it practically flat on the ground. That's why we drilled so many holes in the support rod. If you plan to boil beans or make stew, occasional adjustment of the reflector will be required to keep the hot spot where it will do the most good. The shadow from our pointer rod is the thing to watch. For bacon and eggs, hot dogs or steak, one setting will usually do the trick.

After cooking your meal and washing the dishes, remove the grill from the aluminum tube and clean it too. Then wipe off the reflector's surface with a paper towel or damp cloth . . . and that's all there is to the job of solar cooking.

Of course, solar stoves won't take the place of other kinds of cooking all the time. When the sun goes down you had better be through cooking . . . and on a rainy day the reflector is not much use except maybe to crawl under to keep dry! But properly used in clear weather this reflector stove will amaze the most skeptical observer. Here are a few of the advantages of solar cooking:

As you discovered when you held your hand close to the focal point, there is no warming-up period with a solar stove . . . it gets hot right away! By the time the fellow with the charcoal brazier works up a good bed of coals you'll be doing the dishes. Besides, he paid for his fuel while yours was free for the taking. And solar energy is available any place the sun shines . . . mountains, desert, beach or your own backyard.

At first the reflection from your cooker might be bothersome, and a pair of sunglasses will be handy. After practicing a while, however, you'll find out where to stand so there isn't any glare . . . and by then you'll have noticed how nice it is not to have your eyes full of smoke. Solar cooking is cool cooking too, because the heat goes into the food on the grill and doesn't roast the chef as well.

You won't need matches to get your cooker going, either, and there's no danger of setting anything on fire with the unit. Lastly, there are no ashes or soot to contend with. And if someone complains about the lack of that charcoal or hickory taste, I suppose you can always provide him with a bottle of liquid smoke!

Seriously, you should have a lot of fun cooking with sunshine. It's safe, it's clean and it's free. Chances are you'll like it enough to want a portable cooker for your next camping trip. That way you won't be tied down to a fireplace and the bother that goes with it. So save up for one of the commercially manufactured folding cookers, or you might even put your ingenuity to work and make a collapsible version of the cardboard unit you've just built. ●

MATERIALS

28-gauge galvanized iron (16 square feet)
No. 6, 3/8-inch sheet metal screws (approximately 24)
2-inch fiberglass insulation (12 square feet)
Double-strength window glass (22 by 24 inches)
Drawer pulls (three)
Flat black paint (one spray can)
2-inch roofing nails (six)
Sealer strip (eight feet)
Aluminum sheet .025 by 22 by 24 inches (four pieces)
Small turn-buttons with installation hardware (four)

The "greenhouse" effect is well known to those who
grow plants in such structures and also to those of us who
have left the windows of an automobile rolled up on a warm,
sunshiny day. The rays of the sun go through the glass well
enough, but the reflections of longer wavelength are unable
to bounce back out of the car. The result is aptly described as
resembling an oven. And that is just what we're going to build
. . . a solar oven that will do a real job of cooking on a clear
day, even in winter.

One aim of solar scientists is to provide a means of cooking
for those countries in which fuel is scarce or expensive. Dr.
Maria Telkes—a well-known experimenter in the field—has
designed such an oven, which she feels might be mass-
produced at a reasonable price. Our design is copied from the
Telkes unit, which has been demonstrated in foreign lands.

Basically the solar oven consists of a box for the food and a
glass cover to admit and trap heat inside the container. The
box shown is made from galvanized iron but could as well have
been aluminum for lighter weight. The reflector panels are of
aluminum.

HOW TO BUILD—AND USE!—A
SOLAR OVEN

Besides the sheet metal parts, we need a piece of double-strength window glass, a sealing strip for the pane and three handles. We will insulate the box with spun glass material two inches thick for greater heat retention.

It will be a good idea to have all materials on hand before beginning the project. One exception could be the sheet metal for the box, in case you decide to let your local sheet metal shop do the cutting and bending for you. This is a good idea unless you're familiar with metalwork, and will result in a more professional job at little additional cost.

If you want to do all the work yourself, and feel that you can handle the job, this is the way to begin: The bottom of the oven is a rectangle of metal, with the corners notched out to allow bending up flanges all around the sides. These are 3/4-inch flanges and they're bent up 90 degrees . . . except for the front edge, which is a closed (acute) 45-degree angle, one inch long, as shown in the drawing.

The right and left side panels may be cut from one rectangle of metal to save material. Lay them out carefully to prevent waste. Again, 3/4-inch, 90-degree flanges are bent onto

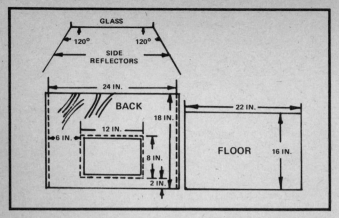

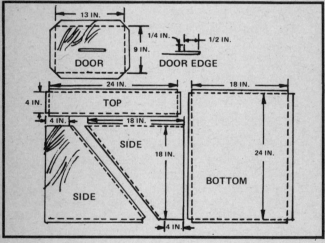

the front and top edges of each panel. The back and bottom edges are left flat. Be sure to make the two sets of bends opposite each other so that you'll have a right-hand panel and a left-hand panel, and not two of a kind!

The oven back has 3/4-inch flanges on each side and an opening cut in it for the door. Notch the corners of the opening at 45-degree angles and bend the 1/2-inch stiffener flanges inward. This will strengthen the door opening and also give the back a finished appearance.

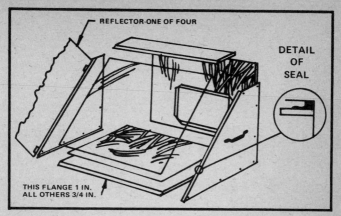

REFLECTOR-ONE OF FOUR

DETAIL
OF
SEAL

THIS FLANGE 1 IN.
ALL OTHERS 3/4 IN.

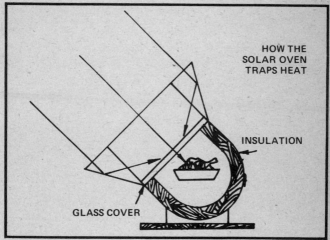

HOW THE
SOLAR OVEN
TRAPS HEAT

INSULATION

GLASS COVER

Now make the top of the box. This is a channel with one 90-degree flange (to fit the back) and one open—or obtuse—45-degree flange (to match the slope of the glass). Next comes two 3/4-by-one-inch retaining angles, each 18 inches long (to hold the pane of glass). The box is now complete except for a door.

The door is the only difficult part to make and care must be taken to bend it correctly. The double, or "hemmed", edge strengthens the panel, and the flange which is left standing will fit into the opening in the back of the box. A snug fit here will make for a neat, effective door that seals properly and helps keep the heat inside where we want it.

A false bottom is needed to prevent the collapse of the insulation in the floor of the oven. This bottom is a rectangle of metal cut to the size shown in the drawing. Make sure it is not so large that it contacts the front, sides or back of the box. This would cause heat loss by conduction to those parts.

It might be well to mention here that an alternate method of construction can be used that employs a little ingenuity and the "do it yourself" aluminum sheets and angles available at the hardware store. This approach uses flat sheets, with angles attached to them, instead of flanges bent from the sheets themselves. Of course, the 45-degree angles would have to be eliminated, and a slightly different sealing technique used for the glass, but some builders may prefer giving the idea a try.

Now, with the metal parts formed either in the sheet metal shop or at your own workbench, you're ready to begin assembly of the oven. The simplest way to put the unit together is with 3/8-inch, No. 6 sheet metal screws. They're available at the sheet metal shop, or your hardware store. If you're using aluminum, substitute hardened aluminum screws, since different metals coming in contact with each other may cause a corrosive action.

Mark pencil guidelines 3/8 inch from the bottom edge of the side panels, spaced as shown on the drawing. Center-punch the holes and drill with a No. 40 drill. A hand drill is fine; an electric drill is even better for this purpose.

Now, place the bottom of the oven on a flat surface, and hold the properly positioned side panel against it. Drill through the holes in the side panel and on into the flange of the bottom. It's a good idea to put in a screw as each hole is drilled to insure perfect alignment and prevent shifting of the parts. Notice that the bottom flange overlaps the side but no holes are drilled at this point.

With both side panels attached to the bottom, the back of the box may now be put in place and holes drilled to hold it there. Continue to keep the parts carefully lined up and to insert screws as you progress. The oven is taking shape now, and lacks only its top. Before we put it on, however, we will install the glass in the front of the box. Needless to say, care must be taken during this operation so that the pane will not

be broken. Don't cut your fingers on the edges!

Clean the glass carefully with water. Then glue the sealing strip around its edge with cement (Goodyear *Pliobond* works well), following the directions with the adhesive to insure a strong joint. If you were able to find a sealer that fits over the edge of the glass the job will be easy. If you're using the bulb type, additional care will result in a neat assembly.

When the sealing strip is attached and properly "set" the glass may be put in place in the oven. Slide it down through the top, which we have left open for this purpose. For this operation lay the oven on its front face, being sure to have a perfectly flat surface to work on.

We will now install the 18-inch angles that hold the glass in place. Carefully drill holes in the sides of the box as shown on the drawing, locating them so that they will match the angles when the pieces of metal are put in position. Slip the angles through the opening in the top and set them on the glass with the 1-inch leg flat against the side of the box.

Working from the top, or reaching through the opening in the back of the box, press one angle very lightly against the glass. Do not force the glass so that it flattens the sealing strip, because—in addition to its sealing function—this strip acts as a cushion to prevent breakage of the glass. While holding the angle, mark through the holes in the side to indicate the proper location for the holes in the angle. Remove the angle, drill it, then replace the bracket and anchor it with sheet metal screws. Repeat this process on the other side.

With the glass installed, the oven's top may be put on and holes (for screws) drilled through it and into the back and sides of the cooking unit. Notice that the top fits down over the back and side panels.

The oven is now complete except for the carrying handles on each side and a similar handle on the door. These are attached with screws.

Fit the door into the opening and mark the holes for the turn-buttons that hold the door tight. Drill 3/16-inch holes in the back panel, and install the turn-buttons with nuts, bolts and washers. The washers hold the buttons away from the metal so they will clear the hemmed edge of the door.

The spun glass insulation is now cut to proper shape with a sharp knife or linoleum cutter. Use a straightedge for accurate trimming. Plan carefully so as not to waste material. The bottom piece can be beveled 45 degrees at the front if care is taken. Paint the inside surfaces of the insulation with flat black enamel, using—if you like—a pressure can for convenience.

After the paint is dry, the insulation is glued into the box with Pliobond or its equivalent. To do this, remove and set aside the back of the box. Then, positioning the oven with the glass down, cement the top insulation in place first and allow the adhesive to dry. Next, tip the box right side up and cement the bottom insulation in place. Press five 2-inch roofing nails point-down into the insulation and lay the false bottom over them. This bottom piece is painted flat black too. The side insulation can now be cemented into place and the box is complete except for the back.

Cement insulation to the back panel, cut the small rectangle from the opening and place it on the inside of the door. The back may now be carefully put back and the screws inserted that hold it in place. Lay an oven thermometer inside, fasten the door in place, and you're ready for the reflector panels, which are hinged to the box as shown in the drawing.

In tests the box itself will reach an inner temperature of only about 250 degrees. This is because heat loss to the surrounding air prevents the temperature inside from climbing higher. If we could increase the amount of heat going into the box, however, the oven would get hotter. For this reason we add the aluminum reflector plates shown in the drawing. Use Alclad if it's available.

Rivet two hinges to each reflector and be sure to mount two reflectors on the ends and two on the sides. If the Alclad sheets have red lettering on one side, use the opposite surface for your reflectors. Attach the hinges to the box with sheet metal screws. Install the bottom reflector first, then the sides, and finally the top. Besides their primary purpose, the reflectors also protect the glass.

Open the side panels 30 degrees to the received rays of the sun to reflect their heat into the box. This angle will always suffice for the side reflectors if you face the oven directly toward the sun. The 45-degree tilt of the glass is a compromise angle that gives all-around performance. However, a little thought will tell you that for maximum performance the angle of the top and bottom reflectors will vary with the position of the sun in the sky.

The discussion sounds complicated, but in practice adjusting the oven is very simple. Set it out in the open, preferably on a wooden table, and face it toward the sun. Open all the reflectors and swing the top one up and down while you watch the inside of the oven. You'll be able to tell when you have it at the proper angle by the reflection of the sun's rays on the dull black insulation. Bend the end of a piece of galvanized wire to act as a stop, insert this wire into a hole in the top reflector, and wrap the free end around the loosened screw as shown in the drawing.

Swing the side reflectors into position, while you check the angle they make with the glass by means of a cardboard template. Using two wires, attach the movable side panels to the top reflector. Now swing the bottom reflector up while you, again, watch the inside of the oven. When it's properly positioned, fix two wires in place from the bottom reflector to the side reflectors, and your solar baker is ready.

The test oven shown in the illustrations reached a temperature of 350 degrees in 15 minutes. This was in Arizona in mid-January, with the air temperature in the low 60's. The first time it was used, the unit baked a loaf of bread in just over an hour ... and then cooked a three-pound roast in three and a half hours! A whole meal can be prepared in the solar oven. The menu is limited only by your imagination. ●

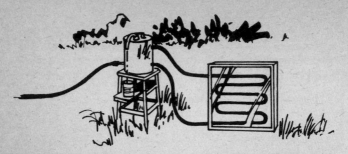

HOW TO BUILD—AND USE!—A
SOLAR WATER HEATER

To risk a pun, the sun really shines when it comes to heating . . . either air or water. Conversion of solar rays into heat can be done with an efficiency as high as 50 percent, as compared with the 11 percent efficiency of the solar battery. There are thousands of solar water heaters now in operation, and we may expect widespread use of the sun as space heater and water heater in the future.

The water heater described in this chapter is not intended for domestic use, but primarily to demonstrate the principle of heat transfer and its use in this application. However, the five-gallon tank would make a good supply of the heated liquid for camping trips or for a cabin that has no provision for hot water. If desired, an enlarged version of the heater could be installed on a roof, connected to a water supply and used as a permanent source of hot water.

We'll begin our heater with the collector box itself. Make its sides from 1-by-4 material. Redwood, while desirable, is not absolutely necessary since there will be no dripping or condensing of water which might rot the wood.

At the lumberyard where you buy the 8-foot-long board (1 by 4 inches), have a 1/8-inch-wide groove cut in the plank to a

MATERIALS

1-by-4-inch redwood board (eight linear feet)
1/2-inch plywood (one piece 24 by 24 inches)
Single-weight window glass (one piece, cut to measure)
3/8-inch O.D. copper tubing (approximately 16 feet)
Sheet copper (22 by 22 inches)
1/2-inch copper tubing (three inches)
1/2-inch valve (one)
3/4-inch female hose fitting (one)
5-gallon can (one)
3/8-inch I.D. plastic tubing (10 feet)
1/4-by-1½-inch wood screws (approximately 30)
Flat black paint (one pint)

depth of 3/8 inch. Locate the cut 1/2 inch from one edge. This is the slot for the glass window.

The next step is to cut the board into four pieces, two 24 inches long and two approximately 22-1/2 inches long . . . being sure to keep the ends square both ways. The glass, of course, should fit snugly.

Next cut out a square of plywood 24 inches on a side and place the 1-by-4 pieces on it to make sure they fit. Assemble the sidepieces to the back with wood screws.

Take the box apart at this point and clean chips and shavings from the holes. Drill two 1/2-inch holes in one of the sidepieces as shown in Fig. 1 (one inch "up" from the back). These holes accommodate the copper tube coil which will carry water from the tank to the collector and back again. Now cement aluminum foil to the inside surface of the plywood base. This reflective material serves to bounce back radiated heat so that it will not be wasted.

Next, five small spacer blocks (1-inch cubes) are nailed into place as shown on the drawing. These blocks are the same thickness as the distance from the edge of the 1-by-4 piece to the 1/2-inch holes, and thus serve to hold the coil the proper distance from the plywood base. Small finishing nails will be

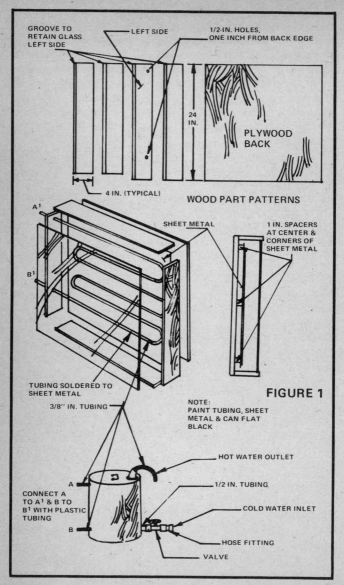

GROOVE TO RETAIN GLASS LEFT SIDE

LEFT SIDE

1/2-IN. HOLES, ONE INCH FROM BACK EDGE

24 IN.

PLYWOOD BACK

4 IN. (TYPICAL)

WOOD PART PATTERNS

A¹

B¹

SHEET METAL

1 IN. SPACERS AT CENTER & CORNERS OF SHEET METAL

TUBING SOLDERED TO SHEET METAL

3/8'' IN. TUBING

NOTE: PAINT TUBING, SHEET METAL & CAN FLAT BLACK

FIGURE 1

HOT WATER OUTLET

1/2 IN. TUBING

COLD WATER INLET

CONNECT A TO A¹ & B TO B¹ WITH PLASTIC TUBING

A

B

HOSE FITTING

VALVE

FIGURE 1: General plans for fabrication of solar water heater.

fine for attaching the spacers, but it's best to drill a hole through each block first to prevent splitting the wood.

With the box itself completed, we can begin work on the copper coil and the collector plate. These are important parts of the heater, since they transfer the intercepted heat from the sun to the water inside the tubing of the coil. Copper is used because it's a very good conductor and will quickly carry heat to the water. Copper is quite expensive, however, and you may want to substitute galvanized iron for the plate to hold down cost somewhat.

If you use a copper sheet, have it cut to exact size. It's sold by weight, and there's no need to pay for scrap. Notice that the size specified allows 1/4-inch clearance all around the inside of the box. Before working with the copper sheet, trim a small piece from each corner at a 45-degree angle to prevent the possibility of being scratched or cut by the sharp edges.

We will bend the heating coil from 3/8-inch copper tubing, the flexible kind that comes in a roll. The length called for in the list of materials allows for trimming. First of all, straighten out the tubing and make it as flat and true as you can. It's quite soft, and a little time spent should result in a smooth job. Now lay the tube across the flat sheet of copper, with a foot or so extending beyond the edge. Mark the start of the first bend in the tubing with a pencil and then carefully form it with your fingers into the U-shape shown. Work slowly and evenly so that you will not flatten the tube excessively.

After the first bend is made, replace the tubing on the sheet and make sure the bend is in the proper position and that sufficient tubing extends past the edge of the sheet. Mark the second bend and proceed as before. Continue to form the coil in this manner until the sheet is covered in a series of S-turns as shown.

Trim the long end of the tubing, check the shape of the coil once more and then lay it on a flat surface to see that it is level. Spend as much time as required to make the tubing lie perfectly flat, using your fingers and tapping it lightly with a rubber or wooden mallet for the finishing touches. The tubing must touch the sheet along its full length for the best heat transfer.

When you're completely satisfied with the job, the copper coil may be soldered to the sheet. Clean the tube and the sheet with emery cloth so that the solder will stick properly. Lay the

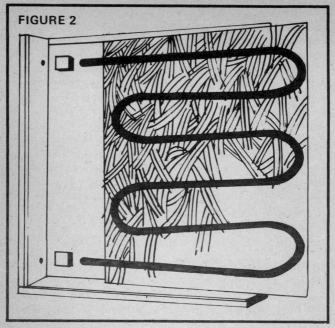

FIGURE 2

This drawing shows the partially assembled solar water heater.

sheet on a wooden surface (the inverted collector box itself will do nicely) and place the coil in position. Remember that the ends of the tubing must fit through the holes drilled in the 1-by-4. Now lay a board over the coil, and weight it to keep the tubing in place. You're ready for the soldering operation.

A small torch is handiest for this purpose, but a soldering iron will do the job too. If you aren't equipped for such work, have it done at a sheet metal shop. Solder as shown in Fig. 1 (about every six inches). Be sure to hold the tubing flat on the sheet. Heat will cause the copper to warp slightly, but it will return to its flat position upon cooling.

With the job complete, clean any excess soldering paste from the copper and paint the entire assembly with flat black paint. Apply a second coat of paint for good measure and set the copper plate and tubing aside until they're completely dry.

The coil assembly may now be slipped into the box, with the ends of the tubing carefully inserted through the 1/2-inch holes (see Fig. 2). Tack the copper sheet to the spacer blocks when you're sure it fits properly and will not have to be removed.

Unscrew the top 1-by-4 piece of wood. Slide a heavy piece of cardboard into the grooves. Trim to fit and have your supplier cut a pane of glass to this measure. Fit the glass into the slots and replace the top piece. The collector is now complete and we can begin work on the water tank.

A round, five-gallon can with a narrow, screw-top spout is used for the storage of heated water. The one here was a discarded oil container obtained from a local distributor. Other types of containers are suitable and may be substituted if the round type shown is not available. For example, a square, lightweight can will fill the bill. This type is usually on sale at hardware and surplus stores.

Clean the can of any residue of oil or other liquid. This is done for two reasons. First, we don't want the water contaminated and, second, heat from soldering operations might set fire to the liquid. So do the cleaning carefully, and flush the container with water several times before you do any work on it.

Two short lengths of 3/8-inch copper tubing are soldered to the can. Location and correct dimensions are shown in Fig. 1. First drill a 1/4-inch hole each place a tube is to be installed. Next drive a center punch or other tapered piece of material into the opening. This enlarges the hole and also forces the metal inward. Check frequently during this flaring process to insure a snug fit of tubing. The depression formed in this way will hold more solder and make a stronger joint.

If a painted can is used it will be necessary to scrape the areas where soldering is to be done. When the metal is clean and bright, insert the tubing (which has been cleaned too). Using a torch or soldering iron, let solder flow into the depression and around the tube. This operation is easier if the can is positioned with the tube pointing straight up.

The hot-water outlet is also a length of 3/8-inch tubing, soldered to the screwed-on cap of the can. Use the "flaring" method again so that a strong joint will result. Notice that the tube is bent into a U-shape.

We are now ready to do the plumbing for the cold-water supply line. Instead of a 3/8-inch tube, use 1/2-inch tubing for this connection. Attach a simple shut-off valve to the tube,

FIGURE 3

The author draws a cup of hot water from his solar water heater.

using compression-type fittings that come with the valve. Your dealer will explain how these fittings are installed. Another short length of 1/2-inch tubing extends from the valve. The free end of this tubing is soldered inside a brass garden-hose fitting of the type used with a plastic hose.

With the soldered joint made and the compression fittings tightened securely, you can connect the tank to the end of the garden hose and check for leaks. Turn on the water at the faucet, open the valve at the tank and cork the tubes that will lead to the collector. When the tank is full, water will overflow from the hot-water supply outlet. Mark any leaks, drain the tank and repair as necessary. The reservoir is now ready to be attached to the collector coil.

Our heater would be of little use if only the water in the coil itself became hot . . . this would barely be enough to wash one's hands! Fortunately there's a phenomenon called thermosyphoning which we shall make use of to heat the whole tank of our hot-water system.

If we made a very large collector, the coils would hold ample hot water. Another method would be to install a pump to circulate water between coils and tank. This would cost more money and also make our heater more complicated. Thermosyphoning is the ability of water to circulate of its own accord when heated . . . given certain conditions. For our purposes, the most important of these conditions is that the supply tank be located *above* the coil.

Fig. 3 shows the tank mounted on a wooden stand, with the bottom of the tank about on a level with the top of the collector. As the coil heats water inside it, this water rises and is replaced by cooler water drawn from the bottom of the reservoir.

Set up the collector facing the sun (using a hinged prop on the back of the box) and place the tank on its stand to one side. Install the plastic hose between the two bottom tubes, using hose clamps for a watertight connection. Clamp one end of the second plastic hose to the upper tube of the collector, but leave the other end free.

Fill the tank. When water flows from the open plastic hose, hold it with your finger until water also flows from the top circulation tube of the tank. Then quickly slide the hose onto the tube and clamp it. This prevents air bubbles from being trapped in the lines. When the hot-water outlet overflows, close the tank valve.

Operation of the heater is simple. You will notice that the upper hose quickly gets hot, while the lower one stays relatively cool. Water is circulating now, and eventually all of it will be warmed by the coils. To draw hot water, open the valve at the bottom of the storage tank. Cold water comes in and forces hot water out the top. ●

METHANE
TURN WASTE INTO ENERGY

The transformation of sewage into increasingly precious fertilizer and fuel may seem complicated, magical and mysterious. Instead, it's actually one of nature's simplest, most basic and straightforward processes . . . as the following pages will show.

Directly overleaf, in an article compiled from one of the best books on the subject, you'll find a concise explanation of anaerobic digestion and how to make it work for you. That piece is followed and expanded upon by an interview with Ram Bux Singh . . . who has probably directed the construction of more family-, homestead- and village-sized methane generators than anyone else in the world.

After Ram Bux Singh, you'll meet L. John Fry . . . quite possibly the only other man on earth who knows as much as Singh about small anaerobic digesters.

Then the fun begins! Robert C. McMahon shows you how to put together a tabletop composter that really produces ignitable methane. The next step up is Roy Dycus' 55-gallon drum digester (small enough to construct quickly but large enough to fuel a gas burner).

The light discussion of Al Eliason and Joe Pelliccio's Parsonage Hill Methane Plant that follows should give you some ideas about recycling readily available items (such as 275-gallon fuel oil tanks) into composting units of practical size.

And finally, the section is rounded off with a short history of methane experiments here at THE MOTHER EARTH NEWS and a discussion of the areas of do-it-yourself gas production we intend to explore in the near future.

Yep! It really *is* easy to make your own methane. Just like natural gas, however, the fuel *can* asphyxiate you or explode if mishandled. Read this entire section *before* you begin your first experiment with the gas and always observe *all* the precautions you find mentioned herein. ●

METHANE
EXPERIMENTS
IN INDIA:
GOBAR GAS

It's been a wild, exciting ride . . . but our blindly wasteful squandering of the planet's fossil fuels will soon be a thing of the past. In the United States alone (the worst example, perhaps, but not really unusual among "modern" nations), every man, woman and child consumes an average of three gallons of oil each day. That's well over two hundred billion gallons a year.

If we continue burning off petroleum at only this rate—which isn't very likely since population is climbing and the big oil companies remain chained to "sell-more-tomorrow" economics—experts predict the world will run out of refineable oil within (are you ready for this?) 30 years.

So where does that leave us? Well, number one, we obviously must get serious about population control and per-capita consumption of power and, number two, if we don't want to see brownouts and rationing of the power we do use . . . we'd better start looking around for ecologically sound alternative sources of energy.

And there are alternatives. One potent reservoir that's hardly been tapped is methane gas.

Hundreds of millions of cubic feet of methane—sometimes called "swamp" or bio-gas—are generated every year by the decomposition of organic material. It's a near-twin of the natural gas that big utility companies pump out of the ground and which so many of us use for heating our homes and for cooking. Instead of being harnessed like natural gas, however, methane has traditionally been considered as merely a dangerous nuisance that should be gotten rid of as fast as possible. Only recently have a few thoughtful men begun to regard methane as a potentially revolutionary source of controllable energy.

One such man is Ram Bux Singh, director of the Gobar Gas Research Station at Ajitmal in northern India. Although some basic research into methane gas production was done in Germany and England during World War II's fuel shortages, the most active exploration of the gas' potential is being done today in India.

And with good reason. Population pressure has practically eliminated India's forests, causing desperate fuel shortages in most rural areas. As a result, up to three-quarters of the country's annual billion tons of manure (India has two cows for every person) is burned for cooking or heating. This creates enormous medical problems—the drying dung is a dangerous breeding place for flies and the acrid smoke is responsible for widespread eye disease—and deprives the country's soil of vital organic nutrients contained in the manure.

The Gobar (Hindi for "cow dung") Gas Research Station—established in 1960 as the latest of a long series of Indian experimental projects dating back to the 1930's—has concentrated its efforts, as the name suggests, on generating methane gas from cow manure. At the station, Ram Bux Singh and his co-workers have designed and put into operation bio-gas plants ranging in output from 100 to 9,000 cubic feet of methane a day. They've installed heating coils, mechanical agitators and filters in some of the generators and experimented with different mixes of manure and vegetable wastes. Results of the project have been meticulously documented and recorded.

This comprehensive eleven-year-long research program has yielded designs for five standardized, basic gobar plants that operate efficiently under widely varying conditions with only minor modifications (see construction details of 100-cubic-foot digester that accompany this article)...and a treasure trove of specific, field-tested principles for methane gas production.

Ram Bux Singh has compiled much of this information into a booklet, Bio-Gas Plant, that he has sold by mail from India. Airmail service from that country to the United States is so expensive, however, that Singh has asked MOTHER to reprint his book for distribution in the U.S. and Canada. The following information has been adapted, by permission, from the book:

GLOSSARY OF METHANE TERMS

AEROBE: A micro-organism that can live and grow only where free oxygen is present.

AEROBIC: Able to live or grow only where free oxygen is present.

ANAEROBE: A micro-organism that can live and grow where there is no free oxygen. Anaerobes get oxygen from the decomposition of oxygen-containing compounds.

ANAEROBIC: Able to live or grow in the absence of free oxygen.

BIO-GAS: A term apparently coined by Ram Bux Singh in the early 1950's to denote the mixture of methane (54—70%), carbon dioxide (27—45%), hydrogen (1—10%), nitrogen (.5—3%), carbon monoxide (.1%), oxygen (.1%) and hydrogen sulfide (trace) formed in an anaerobic digestion tank.

HYDROGEN SULFIDE: H_2S. A poisonous, inflammable gas with the nauseating smell of rotten eggs.

METHANE: CH_4. A colorless, odorless, inflammable gas which may be formed by the decomposition of vegetable matter. Methane is the main constituent of natural gas and is used as a fuel and for illumination.

NATURAL GAS: A mixture of gaseous hydrocarbons, mostly methane, that forms naturally from fossil deposits in certain places in the earth. It is used as a fuel.

FERMENTATION

There are two kinds of organic decomposition: aerobic (requiring oxygen) and anaerobic (in the absence of oxygen). Any kind of organic material—animal or vegetable—may be

FACTS ABOUT GOBAR GAS

- Cow dung gas is 55—65% methane, 30—35% carbon dioxide, with some hydrogen, nitrogen and other traces. Its heat value is about 600 Btu per cubic foot.

- A sample analyzed by the Gas Council Laboratory at Watson House in England contained 68% methane, 31% carbon dioxide and 1% nitrogen. It tested at 678 Btu.

- This compares with natural gas's 80% methane, which yields a Btu value of about 1,000.

- Gobar gas may be improved by filtering it through limewater (to remove carbon dioxide), iron filings (to absorb corrosive hydrogen sulfide) and calcium chloride (to extract water vapor).

- Cow dung slurry after digestion is composed of 1.8—2.4% total nitrogen (N), 1.0—1.2% phosphate (P_2O_5), 0.6—0.8% potash (K_2O) and from 50 to 75% organic humus.

- About one cubic foot of gas may be generated from one pound of cow manure at 75° F. This is enough gas to cook a day's meals for 4—6 people.

- About 225 cubic feet of gas equals one gallon of gasoline. The manure produced by one cow in one year can be converted to methane which is the equivalent of over 50 gallons of gasoline.

- Gas engines require 18 cubic feet of methane per horsepower per hour.

broken down by either process, but the end products will be quite different. Aerobic fermentation produces carbon dioxide, ammonia, small amounts of other gases, considerable heat and a residue which can be used as fertilizer. Anaerobic decomposition—on the other hand—creates combustible methane, carbon dioxide, hydrogen, traces of other gases, only a little heat and a slurry which is *superior in nitrogen content* to the residue yielded by aerobic fermentation.

Anaerobic decomposition takes place in two stages as certain micro-organisms feed on organic materials. First, acid-producing bacteria break the complex organic molecules down into simpler sugars, alcohol, glycerol and peptides. Then—and only when these substances have accumulated in sufficient quantities—a second group of bacteria converts some of the simpler molecules into methane. The methane-releasing micro-organisms are especially sensitive to environmental conditions.

TEMPERATURE

Anaerobic digestion of waste material will occur at temperatures ranging from 32° to 156° F. The action of the bacteria responsible for the fermentation decreases rapidly below 60° F, however, and gas production is most rapid at 85–105° and 120–140° F. Different bacteria thrive in the two ranges and those active within the higher limits are much more susceptible to environmental changes. Thus, a temperature of 90° to 95° F is the most nearly ideal for stable methane gas generation.

ACIDITY

The proper pH range for anaerobic fermentation is between 6.8 and 8.0 and an acidity either higher or lower than this will hamper fermentation. The introduction of too much raw material can cause excess acidity (a too-low pH reading) and the gas-producing bacteria will not be able to digest the acids quickly enough. Decomposition will stop until balance is restored by the growth of more bacteria. If the pH grows too high (not enough acid), fermentation will slow until the digestive process forms enough acidic carbon dioxide to restore balance.

CARBON-NITROGEN RATIO

Although bacteria responsible for the anaerobic process require both elements in order to live, they consume carbon about 30 to 35 times faster than they use nitrogen. Other conditions being favorable, then, anaerobic digestion will proceed most rapidly when raw material fed into a gobar plant

This Indian bio-gas plant produces 500 cubic feet of fuel a day.

contains a carbon-nitrogen ratio of 30:1. If the ratio is higher, the nitrogen will be exhausted while there is still a supply of carbon left. This causes some bacteria to die, releasing the nitrogen in their cells and—eventually—restoring equilibrium. Digestion proceeds slowly as this occurs. On the other hand, if there is too much nitrogen, fermentation (which will stop when the carbon is exhausted) will be incomplete and the "leftover" nitrogen will not be digested. This lowers the fertilizing value of the slurry. Only the proper ratio of carbon to nitrogen will insure conversion of all available carbon to methane and carbon dioxide with minimum loss of available nitrogen.

PERCENTAGE OF SOLIDS

The anaerobic decay of organic matter proceeds best if the raw material consists of about 7 to 9 percent solids. Fresh cow manure can be brought down to approximately this consistency by diluting it with an equal amount of water.

BASIC DESIGN

Central to the operation and common to all gobar plant designs is an enclosed tank called a digester. This is an airtight tank which may be filled with raw organic waste and from which the final slurry and generated gas may be drawn. Differences in the design of these tanks are based primarily on the material to be fed to the generator, the cycle of fermentation desired and the temperatures under which the plant will operate.

Tanks designed for the digestion of liquid or suspended-solid waste (such as cow manure) are usually filled and emptied with pipes and pumps. Circulation through the digester may also be achieved without pumps by allowing old slurry to overflow the tank as fresh material is fed in by gravity. An advantage of the gravity system is its ability to handle bits of chopped vegetable matter which would clog pumps. This is quite desirable, since the vegetable waste provides more carbon than the nitrogen-rich animal manure.

CONTINUOUS FEEDING (LIQUIDS)

Complete anaerobic digestion of animal wastes, such as cow manure, takes about fifty days at moderately warm temperatures. Such matter—if allowed to remain undisturbed for the full period—will produce more than a third of its total gas the first week, another quarter the second week and the remainder during the final six weeks.

A more consistent and rapid rate of gas production may be maintained by continuously feeding small amounts of waste into the digester daily. The method has the additional advantage of preserving a higher percentage of the nitrogen in the slurry for effective fertilizer use.

If this continuous feeding system is used, care must be taken to ensure that the plant is large enough to accommodate all the waste material that will be fed through in one fermenta-

A bio-gas plant in India that produces 250 cubic feet of fuel a day.

tion cycle. A two-stage digester—in which the first tank produces the bulk of the methane (up to 80%) while the second finishes the digestion at a more leisurely rate—is often the answer.

BATCH FEEDING (SOLIDS)

Bio-gas plants may be designed to digest vegetable wastes alone but, since plant matter will not flow easily through pipes, it's best to operate such a digester on a single-batch basis. With this method the tank is opened completely, old slurry removed and fresh material added. The tank is then resealed.

Depending on the fermenting material and temperature, gas production from a batch feeding will begin after two to four weeks, gradually increase to a maximum output and then fall off after about three or four months. It's best, therefore, to use two or more batch digesters in combination so that at least one will always be producing gas.

Because the carbon-nitrogen ratio of some vegetable matter is much higher than that of animal wastes, some nitrogen (preferably of organic origin) usually must be added to the cellulose digested this way. On the other hand, vegetable waste produces—pound for pound—about seven times more gas than animal waste, so proportionally less must be digested to maintain equal gas production.

AGITATION

Some means of mixing the slurry in a digester is always desirable, though not absolutely essential. If left alone, the slurry tends to settle out in layers and its surface may be covered with a hard scum which hinders the release of gas.

This is a greater problem with vegetable matter than with manure, since the animal waste has a somewhat greater tendency to remain suspended in water and, thus, in intimate contact with the gas-releasing bacteria. Continuous feeding also helps, since fresh material entering the tank always induces some movement in the slurry.

TEMPERATURE CONTROL

Although it's relatively easy to hold the temperature of a digester at ideal operating levels by shading a gobar plant located in a hot region, maintaining the same ideal temperature in a cold climate is somewhat more difficult.

The first and most obvious provision, of course, is insulating the tank with a two- or three-foot-thick layer of straw or similar material that is, in turn, protected with a waterproof seal. If this proves insufficient, the addition of heating coils must be considered.

When hot water is regulated by a thermostat and circulated through coils built into a digester, the fermenting process may be kept at an efficient gas producing temperature quite easily. In fact, circulation only for a couple of hours in the morning and again in the evening should be sufficient in most climates. It is especially interesting to note that using a portion of the gas generated to heat the water is entirely feasible . . . *the resulting enormously increased rate of gas production more than compensates for the gas thus burned.*

GAS COLLECTION

Gas is collected inside an anaerobic digester tank in an inverted drum. The walls of this upside-down drum extend down into the slurry, forming a "cap" which both seals in the gas and is free to rise and fall as more or less gas is generated.

The drum's weight provides the pressure which forces the gas to its point of use through a small valve in the top of the cap. Drums on larger plants must be counter-weighted to keep them from exerting too much pressure on the slurry. Care must also be taken to insure that such a cap is not counter-weighted to less than atmospheric pressure, since this would allow air to travel backwards through the exhaust line into the digester with two results: destruction of the anaerobic conditions inside the tank and possible destruction of you by an explosion of the methane-oxygen mixture.

The radius of an inverted drum should never be less than three inches smaller than the radius of the tank in which it floats, so that minimal slurry is exposed to the air and maximum gas is captured.

ABOVE- VERSUS BELOW-GROUND DIGESTERS

Gobar tanks built above ground must be made of steel to withstand the pressure of the slurry and it's simpler and less expensive to construct underground methane plants. It's also easier to gravity-feed a tank built at least partially beneath the earth's surface. On the other hand, above-surface models are easier to maintain and, if painted black, may be partially heated by solar radiation.

_____

These brief excerpts from Ram Bux Singh's books should make it obvious that methane gas production from manure and vegetable waste is no armchair visionary's dream. It's being done right now and over 2,500 gobar plants are currently operating in India alone.

Here, in the U.S., our more than four hundred million cattle, pigs and chickens produce over two billion tons of manure a year . . . enough to spread four feet deep over an area of five hundred square miles! This valuable natural resource can be used to generate both *combustible gas—thus relieving part of our reliance on fossil fuels—*and *a fertilizer richer in nitrogen than raw manure.*

Instead of contributing mightily to our water pollution crisis as feedlot runoff, this bountiful end product of animal life could be turned to our advantage . . . as an economical and ecologically sound power source! ●

AN INTERVIEW WITH INDIA'S GOBAR GAS EXPERT, RAM BUX SINGH

It is now quite apparent that the days of unlimited and constantly increasing consumption of fossil fuels are "all over but the shoutin' ".

We maul and tear whole states with monster shovels, feed the coal we uncover to voracious power plants that belch out sun-darkening clouds of pollution, distribute the electricity that results through thousands of miles of ugly pylons and cables . . . and still watch our cancerous cities suffer an increasing number of "brownouts" and complete power failures each year.

Even the major oil companies (which have a vested interest in making us believe that the wild ride can go on and on) now ration their dwindling stocks of natural gas and predict that the world's reserves of petroleum will be exhausted in 30 to 50 years.

Clearly, something must be done . . . and most concerned environmentalists find it difficult to believe that the "something" is the development of nuclear power. At least not as long as the AEC stupidly continues to promote the fission

process with its built-in dangers of runaway reactors, thermal
and radioactive pollution. And fusion? Well, yes . . . maybe.
But that approach to the controlled and sustained harnessing
of nuclear energy is still only a dream.

Damn it, what we (and the planet) really need—first and
foremost—is less instead of more: less human population and
less per-capita consumption of power and the things we manu-

facture with it. Secondly—and just as important—we must instigate an immediate crash program of research into ways of utilizing solar, wind, water, wave and other natural sources of the energy we do use. And that research must be relentlessly directed away from the development of centralized, capital-heavy, tightly controlled, "dirty" energy systems . . . and toward the nurturing of decentralized, inexpensive, controlled-by-individuals-at-point-of-use, "clean" power sources.

It's a tall order but, luckily, some good men have accepted the challenge. A few have even successfully demonstrated alternative sources of energy that both satisfy all the stringent requirements laid down in the paragraph above . . . and work. One of those men is Ram Bux Singh.

For almost 18 years, Ram Bux Singh has directed experiments at the Gobar ("gobar" is Hindi for "cow dung") Gas Research Station at Ajitmal in northern India. His primary responsibility there has been the development of low-cost and simplified digesters designed to convert plant and animal waste into composted fertilizer and methane for fuel.

In the course of his work, Singh has personally overseen the construction of at least 200 "bio-gas" digesters and has become possibly the planet's foremost authority on the construction of village- and farm-sized waste processing units.

Ram Bux Singh's fame spread to this country only recently when a few dedicated ecology enthusiasts began combing the world's literature for information about natural and non-polluting power sources. Eventually they discovered Singh's work with village- and farm-generated methane—which is as natural and non-polluting as a compost pile—and called it to the attention of such U.S. publications as The Whole Earth Catalog and THE MOTHER EARTH NEWS. As a result of articles appearing in those periodicals, Mr. Singh now receives as many as 10 letters a day from the United States . . . all asking for more information about his experiments.

Thanks, in part, to his correspondence with individuals, government officials and universities in this country, Ram Bux Singh has developed a keen interest in helping to design, construct and promote the use of bio-gas plants here in the United States. "Two billion tons of manure is wasted annually in the U.S.," he says, "and that is actual food and actual power that you could save with the inexpensive composters we have developed in India."

When MOTHER learned that Mr. Singh was visiting this country last summer, she immediately invited him to her Madison, Ohio location to direct some of her people in the construction of a homestead-sized bio-gas plant. MOTHER's staff found Ram Bux Singh to be an intelligent, alert, highly personable and extremely capable gentleman and they enjoyed his visit immensely. Mr. Singh speaks four languages—Hindi, English, Urdu and Persian—and (lucky for MOTHER) the following interview was conducted in English shortly after THE MOTHER EARTH NEWS' prototype methane generator was completed.

PLOWBOY: Ram Bux Singh, thanks largely to *The Whole Earth Catalog* and THE MOTHER EARTH NEWS, your efforts to convert manure and other natural wastes into methane have become fairly well known here in the United States. Did you originate the idea of producing non-polluting fuel from such sources?

RAM BUX SINGH: Oh no. The idea of taking out the gas from farm waste, vegetable waste—even human excreta—is very old and was demonstrated at an exhibition in London in 1871. In 1905 a very large plant designed to produce both gas and good fertilizer from waste was installed in Bombay, India. Then, during World War II, due to the shortage of conventional fuels, the Germans built many bio-gas plants for both the fertilizer and the methane that the digesters would make. They compressed the gas and used it for driving tractors and farm machinery. The idea is not a new one.

Today—in Algeria, in South Africa, in Korea, in France, in Hungary and in many other countries—thousands of bio-gas plants are in use. The idea does not belong to me or to the government of India.

PLOWBOY: But you have been experimenting with methane conversion for some time and your work in the field is considered quite important by scientists and technicians all over the world. Obviously you've contributed something of value to the search for ways to recycle waste into non-polluting fuel.

RAM BUX SINGH: Yes, I have worked on this problem for some time. In 1955, the government of India appointed me to simplify the construction of bio-gas plants. There was no question that such units would produce methane but, up to that time, most gas generators were very large and costly. Even the small plants built in Germany during the war were quite expensive. So what we have done at the Gobar Gas Research Station in India is to simplify the construction of bio-gas generators. We have designed efficient plants that are small enough for a single village or one farmer to build and we have found ways to construct these gas generators for very little money. We have made the bio-gas plant economical for small farms.

Let me give you an example of what we have done. When I recently visited a sewage plant at Charleston, West Virginia, the engineer there told me that seventy million dollars had been spent on the facility. If we were to try to scale down to village or farm size the technology used in that plant, the smaller waste disposal unit might still cost half a million dollars. Now, no village in India and no farmer—even in the United States—is going to spend a half million dollars to process waste. But we have designed bio-gas plants which both purify waste and produce non-polluting fuel . . . and some of these units can be built for as little as $100! With our designs and a relatively minor investment, then, a farmer or small group of people can now construct a self-contained system that will recycle plant and animal waste into high-quality fertilizer and non-polluting fuel. The fuel can then be used to cook with, to heat the farmhouse and to power machinery. A bio-gas plant can make a farm more self-contained and independent.

PLOWBOY: In other words, while the radicals *talk* about it, you're *really* bringing power to the people!

RAM BUX SINGH: Yes.

PLOWBOY: It's this idea of homemade power, you know, that has excited so many people in this country. The idea of running a car or heating a house with non-polluting fuel that is generated from waste right in one's own backyard is tremendously attractive to individuals fed up with oil spills, strip mining and smog. Yet I notice that you emphasize the fertilizer produced by a bio-gas plant just as much as you emphasize the methane which comes from such a unit.

RAM BUX SINGH: Oh yes. The fertilizer is very important, especially in a country like India where the farmers do not have so much money with which to buy chemical plant foods. You are rich enough here to purchase the commercial fertilizers and you do not think so much of conserving the natural nutrients for your crops. But I believe you will. As your population increases and you farm more intensively and the movement to cooperate with nature gains strength in the United States, I believe you will think more and more about conserving your natural plant foods. You will begin to think more and more of the bio-gas plant as a source of both power *and* high-quality fertilizer.

PLOWBOY: What do you mean by "high-quality"?

RAM BUX SINGH: We have calculated through many university lab tests in India that the fertilizer which comes from a bio-gas plant contains three times more nitrogen than the best compost made through open-air digestion. If you compost chicken manure, for example, the finished compost will have in it only 1.58 to 2% nitrogen. The same manure digested in a bio-gas plant will analyze 6% nitrogen.

PLOWBOY: Where does this extra nitrogen come from?

RAM BUX SINGH: It is already in the manure. The nitrogen is preserved when waste is digested in an enclosed bio-gas plant, whereas the same nitrogen evaporates away as ammonia during open-air composting. The bio-gas plant does not make extra nitrogen, it does not create nitrogen . . . it merely preserves the nitrogen that is already there.

PLOWBOY: OK. I can see how the nitrogen is caught and contained when plant and animal waste is digested inside a closed bio-gas plant, but what about other elements? Is anything lost or eaten up by the bacteria in the tank? Do they take anything out of the organic material so that, over a period of years, you'll be putting back less and less on the fields you fertilize with waste processed in a bio-gas plant?

RAM BUX SINGH: No, nothing is used up. This is the perfect fertilizer-making machine and it has been tested all over the world. There is no better way to digest or compost manure and other organic material than in a bio-gas plant. I think you can compare the bacteria in a digester tank to fishworms. Fishworms help the soil by eating organic matter, passing it through their bodies and expelling it as very rich fertilizer. They live by breaking waste material down into food for plants. It is the same with the bacteria in a methane digester.

PLOWBOY: Yes, that's a good example.

RAM BUX SINGH: You may also think of it another way. Seven cubic feet of methane gas can be generated from one pound of dry leaves but only one cubic foot of gas will come from one pound of cow dung. The cow dung, on the other hand, is just that much richer a fertilizer than the leaves. You can say, then, that the cow has digested the leaves and partly turned them into plant food. When the cow manure is then composted in a bio-gas plant, the bacteria there merely further process—or refine—the former dry leaves into a still richer plant food. It is all very natural.

PLOWBOY: We've heard much about your experiments with cow manure at the Gobar Gas Research Station in India. Have you successfully processed other kinds of waste?

RAM BUX SINGH: Yes, we have experimented with many types of digesters in India and our most successful work has been with chicken manure. Chicken droppings are easily digested, produce large quantities of methane and—when processed—make a fertilizer with a very high nitrogen content.

PLOWBOY: What about human waste?

RAM BUX SINGH: Human excreta is very rich and should produce much gas and very good fertilizer. The two or three plants we have set up for processing this waste have not been successful, however, because of the modern flush toilet. There is just too much water with the excreta . . . too much liquid for the digesters to handle. If we could separate the water from the human waste, though, I think we would find our own excreta to be the very best of all for recycling into fuel and fertilizer.

PLOWBOY: Over and above our excreta—our personal waste—have you experimented with human waste in general? Have you built a plant to handle all the garbage and wastepaper and other sewage that people generate every day?

RAM BUX SINGH: Yes, we have built plants of that type . . .

sewage plants with the primary purpose of—*not* to make the gas and *not* to make the fertilizer—but to keep the city environmentally fit. We have done this in many cities in India. The biggest of these installations is in Delhi. There, four 400-horsepower engines are running on the methane from the plant and those engines drive generators which produce electricity. The fertilizer from the sewage plant is given to the farmers in the area.

There is one difficulty also with these installations however, and that is the high percentage of paper and related materials that people discard. This waste is not rich enough in nitrogen and it does not produce a great deal of methane nor does it make the best fertilizer. Too, just like the excreta, this material is usually accompanied by far too much water and it is difficult to digest.

PLOWBOY: You say that the ordinary sewage from a city is not rich enough in nitrogen for best digestion in a bio-gas plant. Isn't there anything you can do about that?

RAM BUX SINGH: Yes, of course. You can seed the mixture—before it goes into the plant—with nitrogen. Let me explain:

The anaerobic bacteria that do all the work in a bio-gas plant consume carbon about 30 times faster than they use nitrogen. They work most efficiently, then, when the waste fed to them has that balance. When the carbon is 30 parts and the nitrogen is one part, the material put into a bio-gas plant will digest very rapidly and will produce much gas and good fertilizer. Results will not be as good when the carbon-nitrogen proportions are anything else.

For instance, sawdust has no nitrogen at all. Simply carbon is there. If you put nothing but sawdust into a bio-gas plant, it will not digest even in 200 days. But if you add enough nitrogen—either naturally, in the form of manure, or chemically—to make a 30-to-1 working ratio, the bacteria will rapidly process the mixture into methane and fertilizer.

PLOWBOY: So, for best results, you must analyze the material you put into a bio-gas plant?

RAM BUX SINGH: Exactly. You cannot guess. Many people have written to me that they have installed a plant of a certain size and filled it with so many leaves and so much of this and that . . . and the unit does not produce gas. It does not digest the material. I write back and tell them that they have not calculated the ratio of carbon to nitrogen in the material. When you load a digester with grass, leaves and other high-carbon waste, you must also mix in enough nitrogen to make the material ferment.

In the beginning, if you do not know how much carbon or nitrogen is in the different materials you have to process, you can send samples to the nearest university lab or county agent and have the grass and straw and other matter analyzed. After that, you'll soon learn to judge the percentages.

PLOWBOY: And from then on, it's just a simple chemical reaction.

RAM BUX SINGH: A very, very simple reaction. When a bio-gas digester is properly built, loaded with the correct mixture of carbon and nitrogen and held at the appropriate temperature, there is no difficulty at all. There is no way you can make it *not* work.

PLOWBOY: What is that "appropriate temperature" you've just mentioned?

RAM BUX SINGH: When a digester loaded with the proper carbon-nitrogen mixture is maintained at 90 to 95° Fahrenheit, in 40 days the material will produce 95% of the gas it is capable of producing.

PLOWBOY: And if you maintain the digester and its contents at, say, 110° F.

RAM BUX SINGH: Yes, you can use 110° . . . even up to 118° F. Above 110, however, much gas will come but the production is not easy to maintain . . . and above 118°, the bacteria will die.

PLOWBOY: Let's say you do use 110° F. What will the digestion time be then?

RAM BUX SINGH: It would come down to about 28 days at that temperature.

PLOWBOY: And how far can we go in the direction of minimum operating temperature?

RAM BUX SINGH: First-class digestion takes place between 90 and 100° F. Between 75 and 90°, a bio-gas plant works . . . but not nearly so well. At 60 to 75°, there is digestion but only very slow production of methane . . . and below 50 or 60°, the whole process is arrested.

PLOWBOY: OK, now. You've just said that a bio-gas plant loaded with a 30-to-1 mixture of carbon and nitrogen will, when held at a temperature of 90 to 95° F, produce 95% of the gas that the waste is capable of generating . . . and will do it in 40 days.

RAM BUX SINGH: Yes.

PLOWBOY: Which brings up the point that—once a definite length of time is established for the digestion of material in a bio-gas plant—the unit can then be operated in either of two ways.

RAM BUX SINGH: Yes. We have designed some bio-gas plants for what we call "batch feeding" and some for "continuous feeding". We can even switch some of our units back and forth from one method of operation to the other.

For the batch cycle, a bio-gas tank is opened and filled with the waste material to be processed. The digester is then sealed and the methane gas collected as the matter inside decomposes. After 40 days, the tank is again opened and the composted fertilizer is taken out. The digester is then filled again and resealed for another cycle. Actually, the tank does not have to be opened if it is designed properly. Instead, with the proper inlet and outlet pipes and a pump, the waste—in slurry form—can be pumped in and out.

With the continuous feeding method, a bio-gas plant is filled once. Then, as the bacteria inside begin to change the waste into methane and fertilizer, new and undigested matter in the amount of one-fortieth of the volume of the tank is added each day. If the digester is properly designed, the digested one-fortieth of the material in the tank will be forced out as the fresh waste is piped in. In this way, new material is constantly added to the mass in the bio-gas plant and spent matter is constantly expelled. The unit, then, steadily consumes waste and just as steadily produces methane and fertilizer.

PLOWBOY: But how do you make such a digester operate so efficiently? How do you make sure that only digested material is forced out as you pump in the fresh matter to be processed?

RAM BUX SINGH: It is very simple. Unprocessed waste is heavy. As the bacteria digest it, the matter becomes lighter and lighter. Merely by positioning the inlet pipe in the bottom of the tank and by placing the outlet at the top of the mass, we use this natural principle to our advantage. The tank can hold only so much and—as we force a small amount of new material into the bottom of the digester every day—a corresponding amount of processed matter is forced to overflow through the outlet.

PLOWBOY: Very clever and very interesting!

RAM BUX SINGH: Yes, and we have taken that idea one step further in our more complex bio-gas digesters. Because we have found, you see, that a really big plant works more efficiently on a 60-day cycle and we have also learned that the material in such a tank gets lighter during its first 30 days of digestion and again heavier during the last 30 days. So we build those big bio-gas plants with both inlet and outlet near the bottom and separated by a wall that goes all the way across the tank.

We operate such a plant by filling the first half once and then, when digestion begins, we pump in fresh material . . . one-sixtieth of the digesting mass' volume. As we force this fresh matter in at the bottom of the first half of the tank, the partly digested material on top flows over the wall into the second section of the plant. There, the waste slowly sinks as its processing is completed until, finally, the completely digested material is forced out the outlet pipe in the bottom of that second half of the tank.

With such a system, approximately 80% of the methane produced comes from the first half of the digester and 20% comes from the second section.

PLOWBOY: Yes, and I see here in some of your drawings of those bigger bio-gas plants that you call for rather complicated and expensive-looking heating coils and agitators out in the middle of the tanks.

RAM BUX SINGH: Such mechanisms are necessary in the larger plants. The manure and waste being processed must be warmed and stirred uniformly so that it will all digest at the proper rate.

PLOWBOY: But the small bio-gas plant you've designed for THE MOTHER EARTH NEWS doesn't have any heating coils or agitators in it.

RAM BUX SINGH: No. They are not necessary in such a little digester. When the jacket around the holding tank is filled with hot water, the material in the main tank will be warmed quite well all the way through. In the same way, this digester is small enough that merely pumping the waste matter in and out of the main chamber will sufficiently agitate the fermenting mass.

PLOWBOY: At that, I understand that MOTHER's bio-gas plant is somewhat more complicated than most of the homestead-sized digesters you install in India.

RAM BUX SINGH: Yes. In India, where it is warmer, there is no need to put a water jacket around the main tank and there is no need to wrap a bio-gas plant in insulation. This digester, however, has the additional features because it is expressly designed for the colder climate you have here in the northern United States. The additions make it both more complicated and expensive to build than most small bio-gas plants constructed in India.

PLOWBOY: I think you've told some of the people who helped build this plant for MOTHER that it can be operated several ways.

RAM BUX SINGH: It is a batch-feed digester but it can also be operated on a daily-feed, a weekly-feed and on a 15-day-feed cycle. We have designed this bio-gas plant to work in many ways so that you may learn about our ideas and report on them in THE MOTHER EARTH NEWS. There is much interest in methane gas production in the United States but, so far, there have been hardly any bio-gas systems built here. We wanted this one to provide you with as much information as possible.

PLOWBOY: As I understand it, you're setting up THE MOTHER EARTH NEWS digester with a water jacket in which heated water will be circulated to keep the main tank at its optimum temperature of 90–95° F. The design also calls for a heavy-duty mud pump—run by a two-horsepower electric motor—to force the waste material into the bio-gas plant, to circulate the matter as it ferments there and to push the digested material out of the tank.

RAM BUX SINGH: Yes, that is correct.

PLOWBOY: Well, it's going to take some energy to heat that water and run the pump. Will the methane generated in the plant be worth it?

RAM BUX SINGH: Oh, yes. Each month, this plant should make about 6,000 cubic feet of methane. The digesting material needs to be stirred only 20 minutes a day or a total each month of about 10 hours. Since a gasoline engine consumes 18 cubic feet of methane per horsepower per hour, the two-horsepower engine necessary to drive this bio-gas installation's pump will use about 360 cubic feet of the gas each month. If we were to fuel the hot water heater with methane, we would find that the gas it consumes would be much less than this . . . we could even cut that further by warming the water jacket with waste heat from the engine. In all, we should net more than 5,000 cubic feet of methane and much valuable fertilizer from this plant every month. A generator like this one should pay for its initial investment in three years.

PLOWBOY: And just how good will this methane be?

RAM BUX SINGH: In India, when we process cow dung in a bio-gas plant, the methane that results tests about 650 Btu per cubic foot. I think it will be higher in this country because you feed your cattle so much grain. I think it will be also higher here in the United States because your cow manure from the barn is already in a slurry and contains the urine, whereas—in India—the cow dung we use is dry.

PLOWBOY: Well, let's just say that we do as well as you do in India. Let's say we generate methane with a value of only 650 Btu per cubic foot. How does that compare to the natural gas that is piped out of the ground for heating, cooking and industrial use?

RAM BUX SINGH: Natural gas, in this country, is about 1,100 to 1,200 Btu per cubic foot.

PLOWBOY: So the methane from a bio-gas plant is only about half as efficient as the natural gas we buy.

RAM BUX SINGH: Yes, but that is not bad. In England, for example, they take a low-grade coal and process it into coal gas which is then piped into factories and homes as fuel. This coal gas is a very important source of power in England at this time, yet it only has a Btu rating of 450. The methane from a bio-gas plant, then, is one-and-one-half times more efficient than that.

But even this is not the important point. The important thing to remember is that, in England, they are going to the trouble to process the coal into gas with a Btu value of 450 . . . while in this country, you are making really no effort to save and use the 650-Btu gas that is evaporating and going to waste on every farm.

PLOWBOY: Well, we're making the effort now . . . that's why we have you here!

RAM BUX SINGH: Yes.

PLOWBOY: Actually, it goes past even the methane and fertilizer we're wasting on the farms. I believe you're working on plans for a prefabbed bio-gas plant that can be installed in city houses.

RAM BUX SINGH: Yes. Much real and potential energy goes to waste even in the cities of the United States. There is all the garbage—the vegetable trimmings, the spoiled food, the leftovers—that most families have. There is the dung from pets and the human excreta. The grass clippings, the weeds and the leaves. All this can be composted into much usable methane and fertilizer.

There is also other waste that could be used to operate a bio-gas plant. For example, the average temperature of bath water is 150 to 180° F. Even after use, the water has a temperature of 110° and, in the United States, you use about four to six cubic feet of this water per person per day. If you were to run this spent water into the jacket of a digester, it would warm the bio-gas plant to its optimum operating temperature and keep it there at absolutely no cost.

PLOWBOY: But what if everyone takes their bath in the morning or only once every two or three days?

RAM BUX SINGH: It makes no difference. If the bio-gas plant is properly insulated, it will need this hot water only once every 72 hours. The spent bath water alone is enough to heat the plant.

PLOWBOY: That makes a lot of sense. By recycling city wastes the way you suggest, we could go a long way toward making our lives more enjoyable while we preserve the planet's resources and drastically curb the way we pollute.

RAM BUX SINGH: Yes. That's why I would like to work with a factory in this country to develop and mass-produce a series of prefabbed digesters that people could buy and install and put into use quite easily. One of these bio-gas plants should be heavily insulated for your northern states and the other could be designed less expensively for your hotter climates. Both digesters should be available in two or three sizes. With only a little work, a manufacturer could develop a line of bio-gas plants that would sell quite well in this country. If any factory owner wants to manufacture these plants, I will work with him and help him to do it.

PLOWBOY: And in the meantime?

RAM BUX SINGH: In the meantime, I am getting five, six, seven . . . even ten letters a day in India sent to me from the United States. These are letters from people who want to know how to build and operate a bio-gas plant . . . from people who want to buy my books on the subject. I answer the letters and send the books, but it takes much of my time and the mail from India to here is often slow and the books are sometimes lost.

I would like it if soon a book written by me should be published by THE MOTHER EARTH NEWS. Then you can answer those letters and make the book available here and help the people in this country to learn about the bio-gas plants.

PLOWBOY: We'll publish that book, Ram Bux Singh, just as soon as we can. For the present, though, we'll have to be content to test the digester you've helped us build and to continue reporting on your work in our magazine.

RAM BUX SINGH: That is very good. Thank you.

PLOWBOY: And thank you, sir. ●

Mr. Singh has written a small, comprehensive handbook based on his methane experiments. It's titled Bio-Gas Plant *and it's been printed in both India and the U.S. Sources of the book are listed in the bibliography at the back of this book (see* Methane, Publications*).*

There lives in Santa Barbara, California a most interesting man. Because long before most of us even suspected that organic waste could be recycled into both high-quality fertilizer and a very low-pollution fuel, this fellow was experimenting with the idea. And long before many of us were even close to solving scum and pH and other anaerobic digester problems, this inventive cuss had singlehandedly and successfully figured out how to turn a very awkward mountain of pig manure into a most handy plant food and more than enough methane to drive a diesel engine day and night for a solid six years.

This unheralded genius is L. John Fry and his improved design for anaerobic digesters may someday be as famous as James Watt's steam engine. In the meantime we can personally

AN UNHERALDED
METHANE GENIUS:
L. JOHN FRY

vouch for the fact that L. John Fry is a genuine storehouse of information on the subject of recycling plant and animal waste directly into fertilizer and methane gas (a valuable skill indeed in these days of developing food and fuel shortages). He's also an all-round Good Guy who is most eager to transmit his knowledge to others . . . as Cass Wester found out when she recently interviewed Mr. Fry in Santa Barbara.

PLOWBOY: Mr. Fry, how did you begin your involvement with methane production?

FRY: Well, I'm from Great Britain actually, and I was a pilot during the Second World War. After that I went to live in South Africa and was there a total of seventeen years. During that time I built up a farm from scratch.

PLOWBOY: This was your pig farm?

FRY: Yes. It took about five years to make the operation begin to pay. Then, when the enterprise started to become financially stable and I thought all my troubles were over, I found we had quite a problem on our hands . . . and that problem was getting rid of manure. We had two tons—wet weight— a day to dispose of and, at that time, there was no "official system" of using the material.

I tried composting the waste from our hogs and found that it involved an enormous amount of work . . . four days labor a week. Then, as soon as we'd finished composting the manure, we had to put it out on the land . . . spread it and dig it in. The whole thing became a very big do.

Along about that time I heard of experiments being done with methane digestion, but it was with chicken droppings and I didn't know if it would work with pig manure. So I went around to the local sewage works and talked to the engineers there and they said they thought it *might* work, but they weren't at all sure and that I'd have to bring them a specimen and they'd try it out.

PLOWBOY: Did you?

FRY: No, I just went ahead and tried it on my own. I built what we call a sump digester . . . just a 55-gallon drum with a smaller drum turned upside down inside it. It was most effective and from that I made a whole range of calculations for, first of all, a medium-sized methane plant and, finally, a full-scale digester that would process all the manure on the farm.

PLOWBOY: Getting started with a whole new process of any kind is always the hardest part. Did you experience any unusual difficulties during the early stages of your research?

FRY: Curiously enough, one of the most difficult parts of all was determining the exact amount of manure my farm produced each day. It sounds quite easy . . . but when you have a thousand pigs and something like six people cleaning sties, it's very hard to establish just how much manure you have.

We finally did it, in the end, with a tripod and spring scale. We weighed every wheelbarrow load and subtracted the weight of the barrow and averaged the approximately 26 loads of manure a day over a week and found that we had about two tons—or 1,350 pounds dry weight—of fresh waste a day. We had to reduce it to dry weight figures, of course, to determine digester capacity.

Once I had the calculations in hand I went to a local university and studied everything I could find on waste disposal in general and anaerobic digestion in particular. I also visited the local sewage works, where I learned a great deal more than I did at the university.

Eventually I got down to designing . . . planning and drawing up our main plant. I didn't hurry this step too much. Rather, I spent about three months working out each portion in detail. I carefully calculated exactly what I was going to do and how I'd do it. Then I coordinated the whole thing into one master plan.

PLOWBOY: Did you have any mechanical or engineering experience to draw on while you were doing this design work?

FRY: No, but I did have some knowledge of construction because I had built all the sties on the farm and I had devised a number of cost-cutting ideas at that time. As a matter of fact, I'd like to apply some of those schemes to the construction industry right here in California. I think they'd apply and would allow the contractors who use them to fabricate buildings at less-than-current expense.

The original sump digesters that L. John Fry built on his South African pig farm. The upper drums have been forced up by methane gas.

Anyway, I got down and built the whole unit and I must admit that it did take a little courage to spend $10,000 putting up a thing I couldn't be absolutely sure would work.

I remember that one of my closest friends came around to the farm one day and said, "Look, you know, it's a terrible shame to spend all that good money on this project and . . . I mean, do you really think it will produce gas and all that?" And I said, "Oh yes, I'm quite sure it will" . . . but I wasn't *absolutely* certain the digester would work, you know.

L. John Fry and friends pose next to one large and several small sump digesters that he experimented with on his South African farm.

PLOWBOY: You must have been all but convinced, though . . .

FRY: I had a strong suspicion.

PLOWBOY: . . . convinced enough to include a diesel engine to run on the gas that you thought the digester would produce.

FRY: Well the engineroom was sort of an afterthought. It was the final touch to the whole thing. I actually got the digester in operation, I should think, by the end of 1957 . . . and I started putting the engineroom together in 1958.

I bought that diesel powerplant—one of the old-fashioned, very slow-running kind with the big flywheels—in a scrap yard. It was all covered with rust and looked absolutely deplorable. We cleaned it up and got it into the engineroom and with a great deal of very involved mathematics, trued it up with a drive shaft that took the power off to all sorts of different areas on the farm . . . for pumping water and generating electricity and so on.

One pump on the line circulated water between the engine and pipes inside the gas-producing tank so that the water which cooled the powerplant kept the digester warm while the digester provided the fuel that kept the engine running. This, of course, was a perfect cycle and a very efficient one.

PLOWBOY: How large was this engine?

FRY: Thirteen horsepower . . . and it turned a 6-kilowatt electrical generator and did all manner of other work. This was a problem in itself, I should point out, because the engine had to be kept on a fairly heavy load—between 80 and 90 percent capacity—in order for it to run smoothly and evenly. The governor was a pretty complicated thing, believe me. It had an automobile shock absorber built into it so that it couldn't "hunt"—open and close suddenly—and by the time I finished it, it was a supreme mass of gadgetry. But it worked beautifully and the engine ran day and night for six years.

PLOWBOY: The unit ran continuously for six years?

FRY: Yes. Oh, we wore out the water pumps once or twice and had to replace them . . . and the alternator we drove for a couple of years with another diesel gave me constant trouble because of the load it had to carry . . . but the system actually worked very well. None of the breakdowns were connected, in any way, with the fact that we were powering the engines with methane. Except for the spark plugs—and that was the one thing that was rather peculiar—we found that we had to set a very small gap indeed on the spark.

PLOWBOY: But didn't you have any corrosion problems? I've heard that the hydrogen sulfide in homemade methane can really eat up the metal in digester tanks. I've also been told that this H_2S will ruin an engine if it isn't filtered out of the gas before the methane is used as fuel.

FRY: Well, let me answer that by first describing the manner in which we fed methane to the engines. I actually used the vapor in two ways. For the smaller diesel I just led gas into the powerplant's air intake and, by a series of careful measurements, I found I could run the engine fully loaded on a mixture of 87 percent methane and 13 percent diesel fuel. We ran it that way for a couple of years and it used so little diesel fuel that it was unbelievable. We practically never topped up the tank.

Fry pulls over the flywheel on the 13-hp diesel engine which he converted to operate on methane produced from hog manure.

Now, the larger diesel was run on straight methane. When I bought it in that scrap yard it didn't have a fuel pump or injector nozzle and the man there told me I was wasting my money. "By the time you've gotten all that extra gear," he said, "you might as well have bought the thing new." I said, "Well, look. I don't need all that because I'm going to run this diesel with a spark plug." And he said, "You must really be out of your mind. You can't do it." I said, "No. You don't understand. I'm not going to use ordinary fuel. I'm going to operate the engine on methane made from pig manure." And he said, "Well, good luck—very good luck—to you." He obviously didn't believe me.

Anyway, we did run the diesel on straight methane. I had a bit of a battle with it at first and I bought some methanol at one stage and poured it into the air intake, but that proved quite unnecessary. I found that you can start a methane-fueled diesel powerplant—without any sort of choking action—no matter how cold the weather.

What we did was to simply pipe gas out of the digester at an indicated pressure of six inches on a water gauge. This is quite a way under one-half pound to the square inch. We led the methane into a series of gas holders—each of which held about 300 cubic feet—and then straight into the engine through a valve in the powerplant's air intake. That was all.

I had heard about this H_2S problem, of course, and I did try putting the gas through a drum filled with iron filings—which are supposed to absorb the hydrogen sulfide—but that was only a short-term experiment and, frankly, I don't think it made any difference at all. I also attempted to dry the methane by passing it through wood shavings and I couldn't see that that made any difference either.

For six years, then, we ran our big diesel on straight methane just as it came from the digester—with no special compressing and no filtering—and I don't believe that it ever harmed the engine in any way. Nor do I think the methane corroded the digestion tanks or plumbing. In fact, the main units were constructed of just 24-gauge steel—very thin metal —and the only place where I noted any corrosion was the line—the high-water mark—where the slurry and air met inside the tanks . . . and that had nothing to do with the methane.

PLOWBOY: It certainly sounds as if your use of methane was a complete success . . . but what about the production of that fuel? Was it messy or smelly in any way?

FRY: No, not at all. Quite the contrary. We made a basin about eight by twelve feet and two feet deep. It had a tiled edge around its top—rather like a toilet bowl, in fact—so that as manure was tipped in, the waste couldn't slop and splash back out. When the 26 wheelbarrow loads had been put in each day, we added—I suppose—150 to 200 gallons of water. Then we mixed the manure and water into a slurry and used an ordinary garden rake to skim off all the straw and alfalfa and other things that hadn't gone through the pigs.

At that point a man pressed a button on an electric pump and the whole mess just whooshed down through an enormously strong steel grid, through a sand trap and into the methane plant. As the last bit went down the drain, a hose was turned on and everything was washed down and left spotless. There were no smells, no odors and no flies.

The fly eggs that were already in the manure, you see, would go into the plant and that was the end of them. It was really remarkable, actually, how the fly menace cleared up on the farm over a period of a few months. There were *practically* no flies left.

The whole place cleared up, in fact. The stench from the compost was gone, there was no more dust or dirt flying around, reinfestation of roundworms stopped altogether and the pigs were certainly healthier.

PLOWBOY: That sounds too good to be true.

FRY: The farm became quite a showplace and drew literally hundreds of visitors every year. My original idea was to charge a 50¢ admission fee and I'm sorry I didn't keep to that notion because I could have made a *lot* of money.

PLOWBOY: Did your work generate any interest outside South Africa?

FRY: Oh yes, I had inquiries all the way from Australia and the United States.

PLOWBOY: How did people here find out about you?

FRY: My operation was written up in a local South African farmers' weekly and the *National Hog Farmer* reprinted the article here in the States. I didn't even know the U.S. publication had run the piece until I got a batch of mail about a foot thick—some of it with return postage—from all over this country . . . and that caused me to do a singularly inept and stupid thing.

PLOWBOY: What was that?

FRY: Instead of answering the letters, I grabbed money that I should have used for pig feed and I came to the United States and bought a ramshackle car for a hundred dollars and I got a large map and put pins in it to represent all the people who had written me and I went and visited them one after the other. This was, of course, very foolish because not one of those good people was in a position where he could use a methane plant, let alone get the whole idea moving over here. This was in 1961 and I spent five weeks running down one blind lead after another before I finally sold the car and went back home.

PLOWBOY: That must have been very frustrating.

FRY: Quite. But it was far from the last time my enthusiasm for methane plants has run away with me. On my way back to South Africa, for instance, I learned that a United Nations conference on new sources of energy would soon be held in Italy. So I marched straight into the U.N. headquarters in Rome and found the chairman of the affair and told him of my successful experiments and offered to deliver a free lecture to the assembled delegates.

PLOWBOY: And?

FRY: And he said, "Well, look, buddy . . . if you had submitted your ideas nine months ago, we might have considered them. But you have to have a written paper on the concept. You can't just walk in here and give a speech."

So I dashed back to South Africa and wrote up a terrific report and had 60 copies—beautifully typed—whipped out in twenty-four hours flat and handed the whole stack to a South African delegate who was going to the conference. When he returned, he told me that he had delivered the papers directly to the U.N. headquarters. So I wrote them three months later and they said, "Yes, we still have all 60 copies." They had pigeonholed them and never given them to anyone.

PLOWBOY: You must have felt like a prophet without honor in . . .

FRY: In my own home country, actually . . . because in 1963 I demonstrated a generator on behalf of a British company at the Royal Agricultural Show in England. I'm afraid it wasn't a very good demonstration, though. Despite the fact that I had written the corporation four or five letters stating it would take me at least two weeks to put the finished digester into operation after it was assembled, the people in charge took no notice. They just gave me a flat 12 days to both set up the digester and put it into production. To add insult to injury, the unit they handed me wasn't even of my own design.

PLOWBOY: What happened?

FRY: We did get the unit to go for the show but it only produced about one or two percent of the gas that it should have made . . . and a very poor gas at that. Still, the unit drew tremendous interest. I especially remember one oldish couple who drove 200 miles from Wales to see the digester. Interest was very sharp indeed. So much so that, once again, I felt sure the time had come to introduce methane production to the world. I thought that all I'd have to do would be to go back to South Africa, sell out, set up a digester manufacturing facility in England and I'd be on my way.

Well that didn't work so well either. We—a family of five— uprooted ourselves after 17 years on the farm and just about got our money back and that was all. I then spent five months building and operating a methane composter on a pig farm in England and it worked just as it was supposed to . . . but the review board of the corporation that owned the operation decided they didn't want to produce and use the gas after all. That left us sort of stranded, of course, so we moved to the United States in late 1964 and finally settled here in Santa Barbara during January of 1965.

PLOWBOY: I assume that you continued to experiment with digester design once you arrived in California?

FRY: Not nearly as much as I would have liked. I've been sort of dogged by heart trouble since we got here and that has slowed me down quite a bit. I did put out a rather crude circular about my work but I didn't really send it to the people I should have. It's only been since I've been discovered by some of the local environmental organizations that I've kind of gotten my hand back in in a meaningful way.

Richard Merrill and his wife have been especially helpful. Rich learned of my work when he was with the Santa Barbara Ecology Center about three years ago. Then he joined the New Alchemists and convinced them to finance some of my experiments. That support has now been withdrawn—the New Alchemists really don't have a lot of money to work with—but Rich has continued to help me design, set up and test methane composters of various sizes.

PLOWBOY: Can you tell me anything about this work?

FRY: Well there's the very small unit I designed for VITA, Volunteers for International Technical Assistance. The group came to me and said, "Your methane idea is fine . . . but couldn't you do something with materials that any Asiatic person can find in quantity?"

I thought of goatskins and various things and finally struck on the idea of making a small composting unit from a truck inner tube. I devised a plastic insert that is shaped in a certain fashion and which has an inlet tube and an outlet. If you cut one of the truck tubes and insert this modification, you can mix one shovel of manure—animal or human—with a bucket of water, gravity feed the slurry into the unit . . . and produce enough gas in a day's time to cook a meal.

Placing cylinder in inner tube.

Now if you think of that in terms of the vast areas of the world where people forage for little sticks and twigs and carry them for miles, just to cook a meal . . . you can see what a valuable bit of technology this might be. Apart from anything else, these people are so desperate for fuel that they denude the soil of the last fragments of vegetation that could rot down and rebuild their earth. In fact, manure itself is burnt . . . and one side effect of that is the smoke from the dung. This smoke is very harmful to the eyes and people often go blind because of these fires, in addition to losing the total value of the manure.

PLOWBOY: Composting the droppings into methane and then burning the gas, I assume, would help to solve these problems.

FRY: Most certainly. With a simple digester, the same individuals could produce and burn nothing but the methane. What would probably be far more significant to them in the long run, however, is the fact that they'd have to get rid of the composted effluent somehow—once all the gas had been extracted—and they'd probably just drop it on the ground. And anyplace they dropped it, of course, plants which had been struggling along in a miserable fashion should start growing magnificently. Inevitably, these people will get around to using the effluent on their vegetable patches and they'll get better and better crops.

PLOWBOY: Do you have other experiments underway at this time?

FRY: Yes, we've set up three separate sump digesters made from 55-gallon drums. We're trying chicken droppings in one, dried steer manure—the kind you buy in a paper sack from garden supply stores—in the second and pig manure in the third. They're working quite well and we're comparing the output of the three units.

We've tried loading a generator with cactus juice, too, with very good effect—it produces a lot of gas—and Rich wants to try kelp. Seaweed, you know, contains none of the lignin that land plants need to hold them up. It should break down very rapidly and—because of the trace elements and minerals it contains—should produce some pretty good sludge.

PLOWBOY: I can definitely see the value of this work . . . but I would think that after running diesel engines day and night for six years on the waste of 1,000 hogs . . . well, wouldn't you really prefer to be designing and building much larger digesters?

FRY: Oh that's the next step I should think . . . we've already been asked to consider the construction of 40-to-50,000-gallon composting units for installation on some livestock and poultry farms in this part of the country.

PLOWBOY: Let's assume that you build one of these big units. How long would you have to test it before you'd feel safe in advising others that the design was good enough to duplicate on a wide scale? How soon after a pilot plant is put into operation, in other words, can we begin installing tested and proven digesters of this size on other farms?

FRY: That . . . I hadn't thought of, really. I suppose we could get facts and figures as we went along, but it's . . . with a unit of that size—40-or-50,000 gallons—I shouldn't think we'd get any conclusive results within a year or so. It would take quite a time to evaluate the flow of waste through the digester and compile absolutely accurate measurements. There's no question that the composter would work, of course . . . but to write a definitive report on its operation, you'd have to sample and test and weigh and measure and analyze for a year or more.

PLOWBOY: Would it be more difficult to start up a 50,000-gallon unit than, say, your inner tube model or a digester made from 55-gallon drums?

Digester with storage tank in background.

FRY: No, but you must remember that it always seems to take a disappointingly long time for any unit—even a 55-gallon model—to begin producing gas. You mix your manure and water into a slurry and pour it into the tank and you wait and wait and you wonder if this whole thing isn't just a complete farce. Will it *ever* work? And then one fine day—usually within two or three weeks—you look at your collecting tank and you see that it's been pushed way up in the air by the gas inside! And you put a dowel rod or a stethoscope against the main chamber and you can hear the bubbling and gurgling going on inside and there's no question . . . you really know that something's taking place in there.

PLOWBOY: Thanks partly to you and partly to Ram Bux Singh in India, MOTHER's methane digester is now producing a heavy flow of gas. We've set up a burner and fried eggs on it, as a matter of fact, and we're getting ready to put the fuel to more practical use. The point is that we now know—firsthand —that this thing *really does* work. We also know—firsthand— just how lonesome you can feel when you set up that first tank of waste and you wait a week or more for the start of gas production. Do you have any other reassurances or helpful hints for individuals who are just getting into this form of recycling?

FRY: Well I have to say that—while I admire Ram Bux Singh's work greatly and I have only the highest respect for his experiments and results—I have seen a few beginners become somewhat confused by Singh's writings on the subject.

In particular, it seems that neophytes have some difficulty understanding the ratio of 30 parts carbon to one part nitrogen with which Singh recommends that a generator be loaded. I've found that the simplest and easiest way to charge a digestion tank—at least in the beginning—is to fill it with nothing but pure manure and water. Mix the two together until you've formed a slurry that has the consistency of cream and put the liquid in your plant. That's all there is to it. Within two—or at most, three—weeks you should have gas. Just dump off the first couple of tanks to get rid of the oxygen and carbon dioxide and you should then collect a good flow of usable methane . . . assuming, of course, you hold the temperature of the slurry above 80° F.

PLOWBOY: Yes, our experiments have shown temperature to be quite important.

FRY: The anaerobic bacteria that produce methane are happiest at about 95° F. Their activity decreases by only 10% if you drop their environment to 80° . . . but it falls off by 50% at 60°. Since our ambient temperatures range between 60 and 80° in most of the inhabited areas of this country, some sort of heating or slight warming should be applied to any digester designed for maximum production. We've found that a heat engine—gasoline, diesel, whatever—is about as efficient for this purpose as a water heater. If you plan to drive a stationary powerplant with the gas you're making, then, it makes very good sense to simply put the bio-gas into the engine (thereby eliminating the need for a compressor) and run the waste heat from the engine back into the digester.

PLOWBOY: That's a very neat arrangement for stationary applications, but what about using methane to power something like a car or truck?

FRY: Well of course, the vapor has been used that way—during World War II, for instance, and currently on at least a demonstration basis by Harold Bate in England—but this most certainly does not seem to be the most practical application of the fuel. Methane, you know, is the lightest of the organic gases and it takes a pressure of nearly 5,000 pounds per square inch to liquify it for compact storage. If we only compress the vapor to 1,000 psi, we find that it takes something like 1,320 British thermal units of energy to put 6,350 Btu of usable "work" into a storage bottle. It may well be a better idea to burn the methane in a diesel engine near the digester, use the powerplant to drive an electrical generator, charge batteries with the output and run cars, tractors and trucks off the batteries.

PLOWBOY: Most of the people in the U.S. who theorize about anaerobic digestion seem to concentrate almost entirely on the idea of methane gas production . . . possibly because of the current pinch in gasoline supplies and the shortage of heating oil forecast for the coming winter. Actually, however, methane is only one by-product of the process . . . and not the major one at that. Can you tell me more about the others?

FRY: Yes. In addition to the gas—which bubbles off the top of digesting waste—a certain amount of sand and inorganic material always seems to settle in the bottom of a digestion tank. If this matter is allowed to build up too thickly it can hamper the operation of the unit . . . so I like to filter it out of the raw sewage, if at all possible, before the waste is run into the digester.

Next up from the bottom is the sludge. This is the approximately 40% of the original solids left over after digestion and just above the sludge we find the spent liquid—supernatant—that remains from the original slurry. Both the digested solids and the supernatant make an excellent fertilizer for crops and pond cultures.

Floating on top of the supernatant is a built-up scummy mixture of all the coarse, fibrous material released from the raw manure. In moderate amounts this scum can act as an insulation but greater quantities of the matter will virtually shut down a digester. This is the main reason I advise beginners to fill their units—as nearly as possible—with a mixture of just pure manure and water. An unseen by-product of anaerobic digestion, of course—at least the way I set it up in South Africa—was the saving of time and labor I realized in the handling of the manure.

PLOWBOY: What does all this translate to in dollars and cents?

FRY: The installation of my South African displacement digester cost me about $10,000, and the unit produced an average of 8,000 cubic feet of gas a day. The heat value of that gas at the farm's altitude of 5,500 feet above sea level was 585 Btu per cubic foot. Translated into present Santa Barbara prices for natural gas, this amounts to $7.57 per day or $16,578 over the six years that I operated the unit. Not that I *used* all that methane . . . the tank was bubbling all the time and gas was going out into the atmosphere constantly. You could hear the action in the inner tank from a hundred yards away.

At any rate, the gas alone must have paid for my installation in three or four years. I would say the digester saved me far more than that in labor and that I realized an even greater return again in the fertilizing value of the effluent I returned to the soil.

PLOWBOY: Although the gas alone more than paid for the digester over a six-year period, you feel certain that the labor you saved and the sludge and supernatant which came from the unit were even more valuable.

FRY: Yes.

PLOWBOY: You just mentioned that your big South African digester was a "displacement" unit . . . and you've called other plants "sump" designs. What do these terms mean?

FRY: I refer to the vertical digester—the inverted gas-collector tank inside an upright tank commonly used as a bio-gas plant in India—as a sump digester. My first experiments were with such units and I've learned a lot from them. Unfortunately, such a design can suffer quite severely from buildups of sand and other inorganic matter in the bottom of the main tank and scum on top of the decomposing waste. Due to the nature of the anaerobic process—which will often vigorously shove digesting waste up and down inside the main chamber—it's very easy for unprocessed material to find its way into the outlet pipe of a continuous-feed sump digester long before it should. This is both wasteful and unsanitary.

Accordingly, I've developed—and this is probably my major contribution to the furtherance of the anaerobic process—a digestion unit of horizontal design. I call it the displacement digester because the decomposing waste inside such a long, flat tank can only be moved along toward the outlet as it is displaced by fresh sewage introduced through the filler pipe on one end. I find the design much more trouble-free than a vertical sump digester.

PLOWBOY: Mr. Fry, you've told the beginners in our audience the easiest way in which to start processing their first batch of waste through a digester. Do you have any comparable tips for the fellow who's been having great luck with an anaerobic plant for a year or two . . . and then suddenly finds that the process has quit working for some reason?

FRY: Yes. Well, first of all, bear in mind that _any_ container or tank or vat will work as a digester after a fashion. I mean, you can dig a hole in the ground and put a slab of concrete over it and it will work . . . at least in the beginning. But what we want is a unit that will go on working year after year with an absolute minimum of difficulty and maintenance.

I'd advise your readers, therefore, to explore the benefits of the displacement design before they construct a digester. That will head off many later problems right there. Then make sure that the least possible amount of inorganic matter and scummy material is introduced into the plant whenever it's loaded. You should also plan to empty the digestion tank, clean it and start over at any time sand starts to build up in its bottom or the scum on top becomes a foot thick.

Remember, too, at all times that the ordinary cycling time for most organic waste processed at 95° is 30—35 days.

You've got to leave it in the tank at least 30 days in order to get full maturity out of the decomposition. Remember also, though, that the material is actually only 70% digested at the end of this period. The other 30% of gas production, however, isn't worth keeping the waste in the plant.

In other words, don't try to push your material through the digester too fast nor allow it to stay there an indefinite amount of time. Think of the bacteria as a great, massive brew that must be enriched at regular intervals but not constantly battered with massive injections of fresh acid-laden manure. Fit your schedule to the preferred schedule of the anaerobic bacteria and they'll reward you quite properly. If you become lax in feeding the little creatures, on the other hand, their production will fall off . . . and if you try to rush them too much you'll run the risk of upsetting the pH balance in the whole tank.

I had this happen once, by the way, and I couldn't do anything but sit and wait for three months until the condition righted itself. Luckily, someone quite recently discovered that a little ammonia can raise the pH value of a tankful of manure very fast. Just pour a little into your digester's inlet pipe and everything should be back to normal within hours.

PLOWBOY: I think it's only fair to tell our readers that there are many more tips of this nature, plus a very understandable explanation of the anaerobic process, plus a more detailed account of your South African and other experiments in a 48-page booklet that you and Richard Merrill have written.

FRY: Yes, the booklet—we call it a newsletter—was issued by the New Alchemists in the spring of this year and it contains a great deal of information about anaerobic digestion. Rich and I are currently expanding the publication into a full-fledged book which will be available a little later . . . but, for now at least, many people tell us they feel that the newsletter is the most concise and valuable piece of literature in the field.

PLOWBOY: There's no question that you're one of the most knowledgeable individuals in the world on the subject of small-scale anaerobic waste recycling . . . and I'd like to ask you what future you see for the process.

FRY: Well Rich and I feel that anaerobic digestion is, quite possibly, the only natural process that hasn't been really exploited . . . really integrated into the synergy of our society. Instead of admitting that the cycle of life *is* a cycle, you know, and that the decomposition of old life is a prerequisite for the building of new . . . we've traditionally pretended that the whole bottom half of the circle just somehow doesn't exist.

But it *does* exist and I find it tremendously exciting to reach halfway around the cycle of life to bottom dead center, so to speak, and use what I find there to literally construct new life and energy.

As others learn that this is possible, I think we'll all have our eyes opened to still unseen possibilities. We'll learn to value this natural and largely untapped resource enough to go far beyond just putting raw sewage into a tank and taking out fertilizer and fuel. We'll think about designing a homestead so that its livestock can run free . . . yet the animals' manure will be easily collectable for composting. Maybe we'll incorporate a pond into every small farm, dump sludge from the digested waste into the water, grow algae and grass on that and feed the resulting lush growth to chickens or pigs or other animals. Or maybe we'll let the algae support this little creature which will feed that one and so on right up through the chain of life to fish that we ourselves can eat . . . change waste very efficiently into protein, in other words.

If this were done on a large scale and we wanted to scrub all the methane our digesters produced and free the gas of CO_2 . . . we could do it by bubbling the bio-gas through water. Just bubble the methane through water and the carbon dioxide will go into solution. Great. We've done what we wanted to do. Interestingly enough, however, we've done something else. Plants, you know, thrive on CO_2, and the algae growing in that water should be even more productive than ordinary. The cycle, you see, is again complete.

The possibilities are endless and, at least to me, endlessly fascinating. I haven't been able to drop the subject of anaerobic digestion for 15 years now, despite heart attacks and various other setbacks that have nearly brought me to my knees. I'm convinced the process holds a very important key to our future. ●

If you'd like to purchase a copy of L. John Fry's 48-page book on methane production, you'll find sources of supply listed in the bibliography at the back of this book (look under Methane, Publications).

SCIENCE TEACHER ROBERT C. McMAHON TELLS...
HOW TO SET UP
A MODEST EXPERIMENT IN METHANE PRODUCTION

While you're waiting to build a digester large enough to process your farmstead waste into enough methane to heat the house . . . you may wish to try a simple, low (or zero) cost experiment that will familiarize you with the fuel's production and some of its characteristics.

Well, wish no more. Here's how to put together one of the simplest and least expensive methane production experiments of all. You'll need only a gallon cider jug, some sort of gas holder (I use a recycled, heavy-duty plastic bag) and—from the chemistry lab—some rubber tubing, a couple of tubing clamps, a two-hole rubber stopper, glass tubing and a glass "Y".

Your first step in constructing a mini-methane-generator will be to make a *manometer*. This is a U-shaped tube, partly filled with water, that will let you know when your little digester is producing gas, indicate the pressure of that gas and act as a safety valve (since excess pressure will blow the water out of the manometer). Any chemistry student should be able to show you the proper way to heat and form your glass tubing.

The four-inch manometer dimension shown in the drawing should be considered a maximum for both practical and safety reasons. Filling the tube with water to such a depth will give you eight inches of pressure . . . which is more than sufficient. Gas appliances usually operate on pressures of less than eight inches and there's no reason for you to risk blowing your jug apart with gas compressed beyond this amount.

Once your manometer is completed, you should make a "burner tip" by drawing out a piece of glass tubing in the approved manner (again, any chemistry student should be able to help you if you've never formed glass tubing before). I made my tip quite long as a precaution against the possibility of a backflash and advise you to do the same. Then attach the stretched-out burner to one arm of your glass "Y" with a short piece of rubber tubing on which a clamp is placed to act as a valve.

The other branch of the "Y" feeds directly to your gas collector through a longer section of rubber tubing (also fitted with a clamp). My collector is a polyethylene milk bag taken from a cafeteria-type dispenser. The cardboard cartons that fit inside such dispensers are thrown out after one use and you'll find that each box contains a bag-liner. Fully inflated, the bags are somewhat larger than a king-sized pillow. I washed one out, rolled it up to expel the air inside and hooked it to my "Y".

Now you're ready to place some manure in the jug. The best type appears to be a mixture of droppings and litter from a chicken barn but, if you can't get that, try something else. I used straight horse manure on my first run and it produced gas. The most efficient formula, of course, is 30 parts of carbon to one part nitrogen . . . but you can think about that later. Our objective right now is to get your methane experiment moving.

Mix the manure with water to form a slurry and pour it into the jug. (The narrower the container's opening, the more humbling the experience!) Fill the jug to about four inches below the stopper (there'll be some initial foaming and you want to keep it out of the tubing).

The most efficient generation of methane takes place at 90 to 100° F and, if your slurry's temperature drops much below

80°, the gas production will be slow or non-existent. You'll have to provide a sufficiently warm environment for your jug, then, if you want it to make gas. Bear in mind, though, that methane—carelessly handled—can explode ... and take suitable precautions in setting up your apparatus. I placed my mini-digester near the furnace and its gas-collector bag about five feet away. Enough said.

Start your generator working with all its valves (clamps) closed and, after a couple of days, the water being "pushed" up the long arm of the manometer will indicate that some pressure is beginning to build in the jug. This first production is mostly carbon dioxide, which will not burn. (Test the gas by holding an ignited match at the tip of the burner and opening its clamp. The amount of gas in the manometer is sufficient for such a trial, although—as stated—the carbon dioxide will not burn.)

Continue the tests until a match held at the burner tip does ignite the escaping gas. This may take a couple of weeks or more depending upon the acid conditions of the slurry in your jug. *(EDITOR'S NOTE: See the Gobar Gas article on pages 280–289 of this book for further discussions of acid balance, carbon to nitrogen ratio and other technical aspects of methane production.)*

Eventually, incorrect acidity levels will correct themselves and your model generator will begin to produce methane. When you're satisfied that such production is underway, open the clamp to the gas collector and you're in business. Methane production—depending on temperature—should last for from one to three months.

And what can you do with the gas? You can burn it off through the burner tip as a graphic demonstration that—by golly!—decomposed organic matter really does produce usable fuel. The quantity is too small for much else. To increase the pressure of the escaping gas (and, thereby, the spectacular nature of the resulting flame), place one or more bricks on the collector bag when you try this stunt. The manometer, of course, will faithfully indicate the pressure your gas reaches during such a demonstration.

Once the thrill of watching the flame passes, disconnect the collector bag, take it outside and expel the remaining methane. The residue left in the jug is an excellent fertilizer and you can use the liquid and some of the solids to seed your next batch

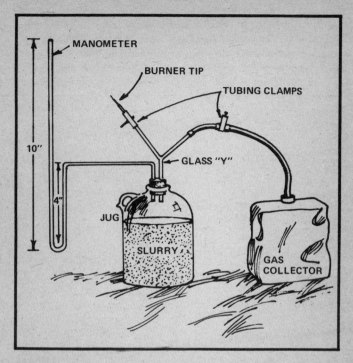

of waste (and thereby hasten its production of gas).

Even though I haven't personally tried them yet, I can suggest a couple of refinements on the above experiment. If you have a fish aquarium heater available, you might try putting your jug in a bucket of water warmed by the element. This would be a significant improvement in maintaining the digesting slurry at optimum working temperature. You can also improve the burning qualities of the resulting methane by bubbling it through a limewater solution to remove carbon dioxide and passing it over ferric oxide (rust) to remove hydrogen sulfide.

Although the above experiment is imprecise and yields only a small quantity of methane, it will familiarize you with the digestion process and, possibly, encourage you to investigate (if you haven't already) the construction of larger-scale generators that *will* produce usable quantities of gas. The independent production of energy is a worthwhile goal. ●

TO STOVE

It all began when Roy Dycus rescued a black steel barrel from the waters of Georgia's Lake Blue Ridge. Well now, a fellow can't have a painted drum sittin' around the homestead doin' nothing ... so Roy got to thinking and figuring and gathering up things like an old tractor tire. inner tube and plumbing tees and such as that. Pretty soon he had himself enough hardware to fabricate his very own mini-methane generator.

What he did was he put one gallon of liquefied chicken droppings, one gallon of liquefied cow manure, one gallon of "methane seeding material", ten gallons of water and enough shredded dry leaves and grass clippings (half and half) into the drum to fill the container slightly more than two-thirds full.

SMALL ENOUGH TO CONSTRUCT QUICKLY... AND LARGE ENOUGH TO BE PRACTICAL. THAT'S ROY DYCUS' DRUM METHANE GENERATOR

Dycus then sealed the large hole in the barrel's head with a steel screw-in plug and gasket ... and he fitted the small threaded hole with a 3/4-inch pipe nipple, a tee (which feeds off to an inner tube storage chamber) and a valve and length of copper tubing leading to an old propane stove (see the illustration with this article).

As you've probably figured out by now, when Roy shuts the valve leading from his rig's digester tank to the propane burner, the methane produced in the barrel will flow into the tractor tube collector. As the Georgia experimenter says, "A used tractor tube makes a good storage tank because, as it's inflated, it automatically provides the pressure you want to push the gas to the appliance when you open the valve. A water bed would also work."

Now it's easy to see that the operation of Roy Dycus' methane generator is simplicity itself: Close the tap leading to the stove and let the bubbling brew in the barrel work 24 hours a day blowing up the inner tube with methane. Then, once a day, when you're ready to use the gas . . . just open the valve and watch the fuel flow to the burners.

CAUTIONS AND FURTHER EXPLANATIONS

"When you run the filler hose from the tee on top of the barrel to the inner tube," Roy advises, "you'll probably have to install a reducer on the fitting to accept the tubing. And remember that methane is a 120-octane fuel. Be careful. Treat it as carefully as you'd handle propane or any other exotic propellant."

Dycus is nothing if not safety conscious: "Methane is especially explosive when one part of the vapor is mixed with 12 to 14 parts air . . . so be sure to purge your rubber storage tank as completely as possible before you even connect it to the generator. Remove the tube's valve core, roll the collapsible container as tightly as you can, cap the valve stem (so that air cannot re-enter the flattened doughnut) and set the inner tube aside until the barrel starts to produce gas. At that point, purge the filler hose (by letting vapor from the drum freely exhaust through the flexible line for a few minutes) before you again remove the valve cap and connect the hose to the stem of the inner tube. It's also a good idea to completely purge the digester, your storage tank and all connecting lines by opening the burners on the stove and releasing every bit of gas that's generated for the first two or three days."

If you decide to duplicate Dycus' installation, don't waste a lot of time fiddling around with half- or quarter-inch feeder lines to the gas burners. Roy says, "I quickly learned that it's best to run 3/4-inch tubing from the generator to the stove. We're dealing with low pressure, low Btu gas here and we need a good flow of it. A smaller pipe will work—you'll get a flame —but you'll find it takes more back pressure to push the methane through such a line. Increased back pressure means a greater volume of fuel left in storage where you can't use it . . . and that cuts the efficiency of your setup."

Dycus at first tried to burn his homemade natural gas

through the propane orifices that came with his stove. It was no go. Propane is a much "hotter" fuel and the tiny holes (which are entirely sufficient for that gas) were much too small to allow the passage of enough methane to sustain a flame. "I solved this hang-up," says Roy, "by getting some very large orifices from the ovens of natural gas stoves. When these were installed—and once I had turned down the air intakes on my burners—I obtained a beautiful blaze which I could fully control from low to high."

That sounds great . . . but does this barrel-inner-tube rig _really_ work? Yep. It really does. Our Georgia experimenter states that his tank (remember, now, he _did_ seed it with some bacteria-rich slurry) started producing gas within 48 hours of its initial loading. This was last summer, when temperatures in Dycus' area ranged from 60° F at night to 90° F during the day (a generator creates the optimum flow of methane when the slurry it contains is maintained at a constant temperature of approximately 95°).

Once he had his stove adjusted for maximum flame and lowest gas flow, Roy clocked the length of time one burner would stay lit on the methane his bio-gas plant made in one day. It was 30 minutes, sometimes more. He says: "A drum digester does not produce gas fast, but it does do it constantly . . . with no agitation, no stirring, no artificially introduced heat. This seems, to me, ideal for remote cabins or for people who want to make methane without getting into a major construction project. Three steel drums connected in series with three tractor tubes, or similar storage tanks, could provide a family with enough gas to cook three meals a day at practically no cost."

And when the drums have bubbled out all the methane they're going to make from their first filling? "I remove the piping and plug from the two holes in the end of my barrel and roll the container across the garden, letting 13 or 14 gallons of the rich effluent spread across the vegetable patch. What's left in the drum is used to seed the next batch."

One final tip: Roy Dycus says you can brew up a slug of starter for your tank's first loading by filling any airtight container with a slurry of manure, plant matter and water. Keep the bucket, jug or whatever sealed, hold it at a temperature of 70 to 90 degrees for six to eight weeks . . . and it should be absolutely teeming with anaerobic bacteria. ◖

ALTON ELIASON AND JOE PELLICCIO: THE
PARSONAGE HILL METHANE PLANT

*Here's yet another approach to methane production . . .
that uses readily available 275-gallon fuel oil tanks for both
digestion of waste and storage of the gas that results. Two
points: [1] we seriously doubt that Al's and Joe's composter
will produce enough methane to heat Al's greenhouse (that
particular job takes a lot of British thermal units), but [2] the
Eliason and Pelliccio unit is absolutely the finest looking
medium-sized digester we've heard about yet.*

It all started in March when Al and I met at an organic
gardening club gathering—held to discuss the principles of
methane production—in Madison, Connecticut.

Now I had the materials and the welding skill to construct a
digester but no place to put it . . . and Al (a gardening buff
who wanted to use methane to heat a greenhouse through the
winter) had the place but no materials. The two of us just
naturally got together.

We built our plant from an ordinary 275-gallon fuel oil tank

and, since we were undecided as to whether we wanted a batch- or continuous-feed digestion system, we planned a unit that could be loaded either way.

One major factor we kept in mind while designing the composting tank was our location. We figured that our low winter temperatures up here in the Northeast might really retard the digestion process (the anaerobic bacteria which produce methane work best when maintained at a constant temperature of 95° F). We didn't want to try to hold this level of warmth with a heated water jacket, however, because that approach seemed like a lot of extra work and added expense to us. Al and I finally decided that, since the greenhouse would be warmed to a steady temperature by burning the methane anyway, we'd just set the bio-gas plant right inside the building.

We began filling the tank during the second week in July and it started producing gas the first week of August. We had run a line from the digester into a bucket of water, figuring that bubbles would form in the liquid when the composter

commenced making methane.

As soon as the expected bubbles appeared, we called a chemist friend to evaluate the vapor we were producing (we wanted to make sure it was really methane). Our expert's scientific test, as it turned out, was conducted pretty much the way any backyard technician would approach the assignment: He lit the escaping gas with a match and determined that, yep, we were generating an ignitable fuel. And of good quality. Success at last.

We're now storing our "homemade natural gas" in a second 275-gallon tank while we finish Al's greenhouse and look for a space heater in which to burn the fuel. We'd surely like to hear from other MOTHER readers interested in methane and/or additional alternative energy sources. We'll be pleased to exchange information and compare notes. Write to either Joe Pelliccio, 34 Sheldon Terrace, New Haven, Connecticut 06511 or Alton Eliason, Parsonage Hill, Northford, Connecticut 06472. ●

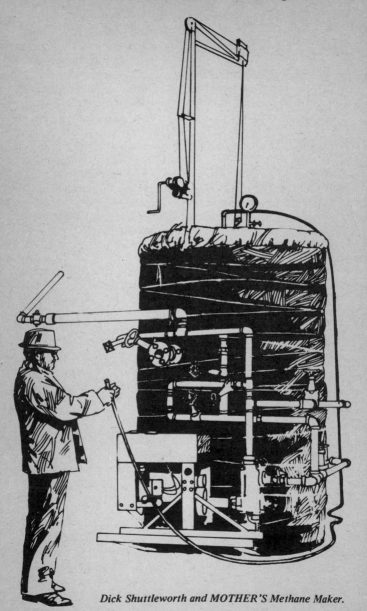

Dick Shuttleworth and MOTHER'S Methane Maker.

JOHN SHUTTLEWORTH: MOTHER'S METHANE MAKER

Thanks to a brief paragraph which appeared in *Mechanix Illustrated*, I first became aware that a burnable fuel could be produced from organic waste in the mid-1950's. The mini-article lightly mentioned that a few British sanitation engineers were powering their cars with some of the sewage gas generated by the garbage disposal plant at which they worked.

That skimpy but tantalizing report intrigued me and I squirreled it away in the files I've maintained since I was eight or ten years old. A few years later, I added a one-page article clipped from the May 1963 *Farm Journal.*

The second piece described a methane generator built by Dr. George W. Groth, Jr., on his 1,000-head pig ranch in San Diego County, California. According to the *Farm Journal* article, Groth used a 6,000-gallon composting unit to produce gas with which he fueled a war-surplus electrical generator. The generator, in turn, furnished electricity for the farm . . . but just how much, the report didn't say.

Over the years that followed, I collected other scraps of information about methane production. Stewart Brand's *Whole Earth Catalog* and *WEC Supplement* furnished some exceptionally valuable leads during 1969 . . . and a big packet of material from Clarence E. (Fireball) Burr in early 1970 really convinced me—once and for all—of the practicality of anaerobic bacteria and their useful by-products.

Burr, who served for years as Chairman of Health in the People's Lobby of Los Angeles, teamed up in the early 1930's with consulting engineer Russell P. Howard. The two men then

An air compressor is used to pump methane into storage tank.

spent the next 37 years fighting—together and singly—to introduce the merits of anaerobic waste digestion to municipal officials. It was a long, discouraging battle. So long and so discouraging that, when Clarence happened to see a copy of THE MOTHER EARTH NEWS in 1970, he more or less turned to the publication as a last resort.

Our fledgling magazine (we'd only published two issues when we received Burr's material) immediately printed Clarence's article . . . accompanied by a reprint of the 1963 *Farm Journal* piece and instructions for fabricating anaerobic latrines and digesters that another contributor seems to have "lifted" from the World Health Organization's book, *Composting.*

That opened the floodgate. MOTHER readers in the United States and Canada began digging up stray facts about methane production in fuel-poor sections of the planet and we started prodding our steadily expanding network of correspondents for still more information. Eventually, Ram Bux Singh (one of the world's foremost authorities on the subject) heard of this activity and—while visiting the U.S. during the summer of 1972—offered to oversee the fabrication of a "bio-gas plant" for the periodical.

Naturally, we were delighted to have the Director of India's famous Gobar Gas Research Station direct the construction of our experimental composting unit. We were somewhat less than delighted, however, when we later learned that a welder —imported from another state especially to help Singh put our demonstration bio-gas plant together—wasn't nearly as good a welder as he thought.

THE MOTHER EARTH NEWS' original digester, in short, leaked from every seam of its main tank and water jacket . . . and was absolutely worthless. We had hoped to have our waste disposal plant in operation a week after Singh returned to India so, of course, this was a major disappointment.

Disappointment soon turned to determination, however, and—in the spring of 1973—the maimed methane maker was transported to the Indiana farm owned by my parents, Richard and Esther Shuttleworth.

Now Dick Shuttleworth is one of those talented men who can make anything—mechanical, electrical, organic, whatever —perform as expected. Within weeks (and working only in his spare time), he had completely redesigned and rebuilt the digester. By mid-July, we were ready to load the composting unit with manure from the cattle on my parents' farm.

At that point, L. John Fry was brought into the act. I had first learned of his work (during the summer of 1972) when I had read a two-part article about Fry in *Survival Times,* an environmental monthly published in Santa Barbara, California. The piece was the inspiration for the L. John Fry interview in MOTHER NO. 23 (in which he outlined his digestion experiments during the past 20 years) . . . and our coverage of his methane experiments, in turn, had given me a great deal of respect for Fry's knowledge of the subject at hand.

Accordingly, I telephoned Mr. Fry, explained what we were doing and asked for any help he might extend. He was quite cordial, took a keen interest in our digester and gave me many valuable pointers . . . most of which boiled down to "mix your cow manure with enough water to form a slurry with the consistency of cream, put it into your airtight tank and be patient until gas production begins". That may not sound like a lot of help, but it was just the words we needed to hear . . . and we forged ahead.

I should pause here to admit that—even though I had known about anaerobic production of methane for approximately 17 years at that point and even though we had been

Frying eggs with methane produced by MOTHER'S digester.

advised by both Ram Bux Singh and L. John Fry and even though we had invested a great deal (for us) of time and money in our digester—none of us at MOTHER, in mid-July of 1973, were at all sure the danged idea would really, *really* work.

But what the heck. We had spent the money and time to put our composting unit together, and it certainly wasn't going to do anything if we left it empty . . . so what did we have to lose by filling it with cow manure and water?

The heart of our digester is a steel tank (bought at scrap price from a junkyard) approximately 48 inches in diameter and nine feet tall. It's surrounded by a larger water jacket, and a third tank (with a diameter halfway between the first two) is turned upside down over the digestion container to act as a gas collecting "bonnet".

Attached to the outside of the water jacket on one side (usually referred to as the "back") is a used 275-gallon fuel oil tank. This container has its top cut out and is used as a holding and mixing tank for the slurry that is pumped into the methane generator's main chamber. On the other side of the water jacket (the "front") is a Gorman-Rupp manure and trash

Dick Shuttleworth holds propane lamp as it burns on methane.

pump driven by a 12-hp engine taken off an old John Deere combine.

A maze of two-inch pipes and valves interconnects all these components so that we can force slurry into or out of the holding tank . . . into or out of the top, bottom or middle of the main digestion chamber . . . or completely out of the composter.

Our cow-manure-and-water slurry began producing gas a week after we half-filled THE MOTHER EARTH NEWS' digester with waste. This was unusually fast action (we had added no special cultures of bacteria or other starters to the slurry) and, as might be expected, we were quite excited by the activity. In the best "safety first" tradition, we bled off the first two bonnetfuls of gas (since the initial flow of methane could mix with air already inside the digestion chamber to form a potentially explosive combination). Dad then ran an ordinary garden hose from a petcock on the bonnet to an old two-burner gas stove, opened the valves, struck a match . . . and began frying eggs over a *very* hot flame.

From then until mid-October, the folks fried a lot of hen fruit for the dozens of visitors who trooped out to view the

The '48 Chevrolet engine on this welder has been run on methane.

wonders of "homemade natural gas". Somebody loaned dad a propane lamp and, after drilling out its orifice (methane is not as "hot" a fuel as propane, and more of it is required to do any given job), he began running the light on "cow power" that he had pumped into a pressure tank with the farm's air compressor.

As a matter of fact, my father spent most of the fall scrounging up all the old propane, bottled gas and other pressure tanks he could find. On its initial loading, you see, our generator produced a steady 41 cubic feet of high-quality methane a day for almost three months. Since he didn't really have any use for the fuel (other than demonstrating to the curious that it *would* burn) and since he was loath to let it go to waste, dad figured he ought to store the gas in some way.

So he did . . . by pumping the methane into pressure tanks with his air compressor. A standard (approximately four feet long) propane bottle would hold four days' production of gas when the methane was compressed to about 200 pounds per square inch. Which meant, of course, that dad needed another tank every four days. Pretty soon, it seemed, he had the containers sitting all over the farm.

Which makes this as good a place as any, I suppose, to clarify my above statement about "a steady 41 cubic feet of high-quality methane a day".

Actually, our generator produced more (sometimes *much* more) gas than that on a really warm day. When its collection bonnet had been pushed up 41 cubic feet worth, however, the collector either had to be emptied . . . or all the additional methane that was created merely bubbled out under the upside-down drum's lower edge. Since dad usually emptied the bonnet just once a day, it's obvious that we lost a lot of fuel we could have saved.

On the other hand, it's only fair to admit that gas production from THE MOTHER EARTH NEWS' digester ground to a complete halt one fine morning in late October. "What happened?" we wondered. "Has all the manure been digested? Is it getting too cold for the anaerobic bacteria? Did enough scum form on top of the slurry to shut down the bacterial action?"

It didn't take long to figure out the answer. Dad had mounted a small hand-cranked winch on top of the bio-gas plant and we used it to raise the bonnet so we could look down inside the main digestion tank. Sure enough, a tight cap of undigested material (mostly straw that had been mixed in with our slurry's manure) covered the top of the waste inside the composter. The cap was about 16 inches thick and dense enough (apparently) to shut down the digester.

So we removed it. Just stood up on top of the rig and reached down inside with a rake and a hoe, dug up the gummy scum, dumped it into the manure scoop mounted on the front of a tractor and hauled it away. Two days later, the generator was back in full production.

One further qualification about the "initial loading" of our digester and its "steady" production of methane: Singh and Fry had told us that we'd probably get a superior flow and quality of the gas by composting pure manure (no straw or other bedding) collected from the concrete floor of our barn (where we'd be sure to get every bit of urine along with the solids).

OK. The only trouble with that idea was the fact that the folks' cattle could freely ramble from the barn to the pasture and back . . . and they didn't stay inside much during the summer. There wasn't a whole lot of manure to collect off that concrete floor, in other words . . . just enough to fill our digester's main tank about half full.

That half charge was all we had with which to start our composter. I don't think anyone can say we were cheating, then, when dad added a scoop (tractor scoop) or two of manure to the slurry once or twice during the late summer . . . for the TV cameramen and newspaper photographers who came by and asked for some "action". At the time (late October) when we cleaned the scum from the digester, we also drained a couple of barrels of slurry from the plant and replaced it with fresh manure.

That was an interesting experiment, by the way, and you should know about it: We had heard that the spent slurry taken from a digester would be rich in nitrogen . . . but we weren't prepared for what happened when we dumped the composted waste on a bare patch of ground. The digested slurry actually soaked into the soil faster than plain water! The earth was that "hungry" for it. Furthermore, the particular spot of land in question was bare because dad had scraped off all its topsoil approximately 18 or 20 years before. Nothing had grown there since. But—now get this!—grass *did* start to grow on that same barren area two weeks after we doused it with the composted manure. A miraculous cure indeed . . . and it impressed the heck out of us.

Some MOTHER people who had been laboring in Ohio and our new headquarters in the mountains of North Carolina were also impressed—during our late October visit to Indiana—by another little demonstration staged by my father. Dad has a homemade portable welder which is powered by a 1948, 6-cylinder Chevrolet automobile engine. Not only did he run the Chevy powerplant on methane for us . . . but he did it by simply sticking his trusty garden hose (still fastened to the petcock on our generator's gas collector) directly into the air intake on the engine's carburetor. He had to regulate the mix of methane-to-air with his hand when he did this . . . but, dang it anyhow, there was absolutely no question that the gasoline engine would operate on methane with no real modifications whatsoever. We were excited!

On November 2, 1973, THE MOTHER EARTH NEWS held a press conference at the Richard Shuttleworth farm in Indiana. Many uses of methane were demonstrated . . . including the operation of a completely unmodified 1948 Chevrolet automobile engine on the fuel.

That excitement next turned to utter ecstasy when dad removed a small plug on the side of the Chevy's carburetor, just below the butterfly valve. By holding the end of the garden hose over this hole so that it fed methane to the engine downstream of the butterfly, the powerplant both ran on the "homemade gasoline" *and* was throttleable.

This left just one small bug in the ointment: Although the engine would run—and run well—when "hand fed" methane through a garden hose (at a pressure of 1-3/4 inches on a water gauge) . . . it wouldn't start on the vapor. Rather, we had to fire the powerplant up on gasoline, turn the regular fuel line off . . . and then "catch" the engine on methane as it starved out.

Was this because the methane, in some way, wasn't as "good" as the gasoline? Not at all. It was just because we were trying to meter one fuel through equipment designed to handle another. We now have a natural gas carburetor (it was

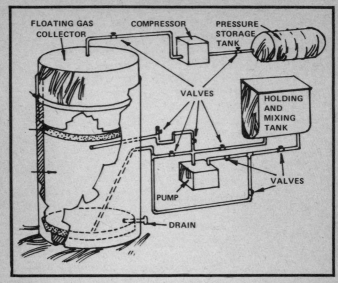

Relatively complicated vertical digester built by MOTHER.

considered "surplus" by an overstocked LP dealer and cost us only $12.00) on the engine and the powerplant currently both starts and runs quite well on nothing but "cow power".

We've put our homemade natural gas to other uses too. Besides regularly fueling a gas stove, propane lamp and automobile engine with the vapor, we've run a gas refrigerator, natural gas light, space heater and water heater on the methane. You don't have to take our word for it either: we held a news conference on Friday, November 2, 1973 and did all these things at random and upon request for a crowd of over 250 TV reporters, magazine editors, wire service stringers, United Auto Workers representatives, businessmen, government officials and interested farmers. Every demonstration worked exactly as we stated it would . . . and they've kept right on working for the steady stream of photographers, writers and other interested individuals who've visited our Indiana farm since the press conference.

As a matter of fact (and we're not really complaining, mind you!) our methane generator and the equipment it fuels have operated so well that they've become *too* popular. We have a gas chromatograph and some other test apparatus down here in North Carolina, you see, and we expected to move all our methane experiments south in mid-November so we could analyze the vapor we produce, test its Btu value, etc.

But first an independent TV news service, and then CBS wanted to film the composter while it was still on the farm in Indiana. Next, some manufacturers asked if they could see the unit operate up north. Somewhere along the line *Parade* and *National Geographic* and *Money* put in similar requests. As did several other publications and writers and photographers and commercial interests.

So at this writing (January 1974), our experimental methane maker is still parked in Hoosierland. This has, admittedly, slowed our research work somewhat . . . but not a lot. Our original generator was mainly put into operation just to prove once and for all (to ourselves, if to no one else) that a homestead-size methane production unit will really, really work. We now know that it will. We know some other things too:

[1] Our first methane maker has shown us that we don't much care for a digester of vertical design. Such bio-gas plants (as they're called in India) "want" to become plugged with scum and otherwise cause themselves trouble.

[2] It's ridiculous to spend a couple of thousand dollars for pipe, valves, a pump and engine when all you want to do is allow waste to flow through an airtight tank. We now believe that gravity can handle that job for us.

[3] It's almost equally as foolish to use electricity or another "outside" fuel (or even methane itself) to heat a digester to its optimum operating temperature of 95° F. The sun, we feel, should be allowed to maintain that temperature . . . virtually for free.

[4] No one design is going to be "best" for every size digester that everyone is going to want to build and every combination of material that everyone is going to want to process.

[5] The nitrogen-rich fertilizer produced by a composter is just as valuable as the methane it makes . . . and not everyone is going to get exactly the proportion of these

two end products that he wants from the waste he has to dispose of.

[6] Methane is a great fuel . . . for stationary applications such as heating a house, drying grain, cooking, running a gas refrigerator, electrical generator, etc. It's a very light gas, though, and not nearly as attractive as some people think for over-the-road use in internal-combustion-engine-powered vehicles.

[7] Perhaps most important of all, people who are accustomed only to the "free ride" we've all been getting from abundant and inexpensive fossil fuels are going to have to scale down their expectations when they begin (as we all will have to, sooner or later) plugging into anaerobic digestion and other renewable energy sources.

So where does that leave MOTHER and her methane experiments at this time?

Well, we're forging ahead with several designs for horizontal composting units that have absolutely no pipes, valves, pumps or engines. We'll just (in theory, at least) pour the slop in one end of these digesters and gravity will do the rest.

These waste disposal tanks will be housed in inexpensive solar energy collectors or buried underground (and warmed indirectly by the sun). If we find that gravity doesn't quite keep them operating the way we think they should, we'll add a simple little windmill—geared down 10,000-to-1 if necessary—to stir the slurry whenever there's enough breeze to turn the fan.

We're building models (55-gallon drums welded end to end make ideal experimental units with which to test our horizontal digester ideas) of these composters now and think we're onto something. We hate to get anyone else excited about the project, however, until we at least start producing methane and processed fertilizer with one of the new bio-gas plants.

Remember, it's not enough just to put together a digester that works: To be really practical, our new designs have to dispose of waste and produce methane and plant food at a price that is competitive with currently available effluent-treatment facilities and fuel and fertilizer sold on the open market.

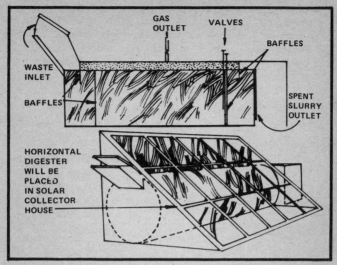

Simplified horizontal digester now being built by MOTHER.

Once again, then—as so often happens in our society—dollars and cents may well make the final decision on whether or not our "improved" methane generators are considered by the general populace to be an improvement after all. As recently as the summer of 1973 (before the so-called "energy crisis" fell out of the sky and dumbfounded most of them), few ordinary citizens of the United States and Canada paid much attention to our experiments. Now, however, every rise in gasoline prices, every hike in the cost of propane and fuel oil, every new government regulation and plea for voluntarily reduced fossil fuel consumption and every fresh statement about even tighter future energy supplies seems to tip the scales a little further in our direction.

Time and the tide, we'd say, are now most certainly running in favor of renewable energy sources of all kinds . . . including the lowly anaerobic bacteria and the methane they produce. MOTHER's new generation of digesters may well be riding the wave of the future. ☻

THE MOTHER EARTH NEWS regularly carries reports of alternative energy experiments of all kinds. To subscribe to the magazine, see bibliography in this book (look under Methane, Publications).

MOTHER'S ANAEROBIC-POWERED AUTOMOBILES

Our experiments with methane, here at THE MOTHER EARTH NEWS, have convinced us that over-the-road use of bio-gas is just about the poorest possible way to burn this fuel. Yet we're currently constructing several prototype "methane bugs" . . . ultra-small and ultra-light vehicles designed expressly for operation on our own homemade natural gas.

Why this apparent contradiction? Because we figure we'll be able to lick any methane problem we're likely to encounter if we can find a practical method of powering an automobile with the fuel.

Now there's no question in our minds about the actual operation of an internal combustion engine on "swamp gas". Dad's work with our trusty '48 Chevy powerplant and a few other research projects have proven—to our satisfaction—that homemade methane is a nearly ideal fuel for such beasties: it's easy enough to plumb up, it deposits far less crud in an engine than gasoline and it spews a relatively low amount of pollutants into the air as it burns.

This wonder fuel does have one slight drawback, however: methane is the lightest of the gaseous hydrocarbons and—at atmospheric pressure—it takes approximately 135–160 cubic feet of pure methane (or 180–250 cubic feet of bio-gas) to equal one gallon of gasoline. This presents a problem of sheer bulk: unless you want to tow a dirigible around behind you, you're going to find your range severely limited if you try to operate the typical Detroit Juggernaut on homemade natural gas.

There are at least six or seven possible ways around this situation, however, and we're going to try them all:

[1] Homemade methane can be "refined" so that each cubic foot of the gas has the maximum possible Btu value.

[2] A special lightweight (it takes less fuel to push around less pounds) mini-vehicle can be designed just for operation on bio-gas.

[3] That super-compact automobile can be fitted with as large a fuel tank as possible.

[4] The ultra-light car's methane tank should be a pressure bottle able to withstand from 400 to 3,000 psi so that relatively large quantities of bio-gas can be compressed into the container.

[5] The vehicle's engine/transmission/drive-train assembly should be the smallest, most efficient combination possible. "Most efficient"—in this case—probably meaning a four-cycle, high-compression, air-cooled powerplant coupled to a stick shift.

[6] The mini-car should be carefully conceived to deliver maximum utility when operated within a particular—and somewhat limited (by 1972, but certainly not 1980 standards)—performance envelope: two place, minimum luggage, rather leisurely acceleration, 55 mph top speed, 200-mile range.

[7] The operator of the vehicle should be trained to drive the car for maximum fuel economy: easy starts, constant cruising speeds, etc.

If this all sounds like something of a drag . . . well, we're sorry about that. The alternative may well be no driving at all (or motoring down the highway on gasoline that costs better than $1.00 a gallon). ●

BIBLIOGRAPHY

STANDARD REFERENCE SOURCES

SPECIAL NOTE: THE FOLLOWING NINE REFERENCES ARE LISTED SO MANY TIMES IN THIS BIBLIOGRAPHY THAT THEY'RE CONSIDERED TO BE STANDARD REFERENCES. TO SAVE SPACE, THEIR FULL ADDRESSES ARE GIVEN JUST THIS ONE TIME.

Alternative Sources of Energy, Rt. 1, Box 36-B, Minong, Wis. 54859
Brace Research Institute, Macdonald Campus of McGill University, Ste. Anne de Bellevue 800, Quebec, Canada
Electrical Research Association, Cleeve Road, Leatherhead Surrey, England
Low Impact Technology Ltd., 73 Molesworth St., Wadebridge, Cornwall, England PL27 7DS
The Mother Earth News, P.O. Box 70, Hendersonville, N.C. 28739
Mother's General Store, P.O. Box 506, Flat Rock, N.C. 28731
National Research Council of Canada, Building M-2, Montreal Road, Ottawa K1A OR6, Ontario, Canada
Solar Energy Digest, P.O. Box 17776, San Diego, Calif. 92117
VITA (Volunteers for International Technical Assistance), College Campus, Schenectady, N.Y. 12308

WOOD, PUBLICATIONS

The Coming Age of Wood, Egon Glesinger, Simon & Shuster, 1949
Forest Farming and Rural Employment, Stoddard and Lathrop, Pack Forestry Foundation, Washington, D.C., 1949
Fuel Values of Wood, Sandy Eccli, Alternative Sources of Energy, No. 11, pp. 46—47 (Taken from Technical Note No. 98, U.S. Dept. of Agriculture, Forest Service, Forest Products Lab, Madison, Wis.)
The Gas-Burning, Wood-Burning Stove, Stuart Silverstein, The Mother Earth News®, No. 10, pg. 54
Gengas (Wood Gas): Swedish experiences with wood gas from 1935—1945, collected and published by the Academy of Sciences of Swedish Engineering, Stockholm, 1950, Reviewed in Alternative Sources of Energy, No. 11, pg. 23
Heating Your Home Without Harming Nature, Jeff Cox, Organic Gardening and Farming, March 1973, pp. 90—93
Letters on Alcohol and Wood Gas, Phil Carabateas, Ted Ledger, John Cuddy and Robert M. Monsen, Alternative Sources of Energy, No. 10, pp. 21—23
Waste to Wood, George R. Stephens and David E. Hill, Canada Poultryman, Feb. 1972
You Can Make a Barrel Stove By:, The Mother Earth News®, No. 8, pg. 73

WOOD, HARDWARE

Ashley Automatic Heater Co., 1604 17th Ave. S.W., P.O. Box 730 Sheffield, Ala. 35660 (Thermostatically Controlled Wood-Burning Heaters)
Avondale Stove & Foundry Co., Inc., 2500 27th Ave. North, Birmingham, Ala. 35207 (Heating Stoves)
Birmingham Stove & Range Co., Box 2647, Birmingham, Ala. (Coal-

and Wood-Burning Cookstoves, Heaters and Ranges)

Comstock-Castle Stove Co., Quincy, Ill. 62301 (Commercial Ranges: Coal, Gas, Oil, Wood)

Gold Coin Furnace & Machine Co., Inc., 795 Broadway, Albany, N.Y. 12207 (Coal and Wood)

Jackes-Evans Manufacturing Co., 11737 Administration Drive, St. Louis, Mo. 63141 (Wood-Burning Stoves)

Jacobs Manufacturing Co., Bridgeport, Ala. 35740 (Cookstoves)

King Stove & Range Co., Sheffield, Ala. 35660 (Cast Iron for Coal and Wood)

Louisville Tin & Stove Co., 737 S. 13th St., Louisville, Ky. 40210 (Stovepipe Ovens)

Marco Industries, Inc., P.O. Box 6, Harrisonburg, Va. 22801 (Furnaces: Wood, Coal, Oil or Gas, Residential, Commercial and Industrial)

Marine Works, Inc., 237 Water, New York, N.Y. 10038 (Hotel, Steamship and Institution, Wood, Coal and Oil)

Mission Foundry & Stove Works, 554 Treat Ave., San Francisco, Calif. 94110 (Coal and Gas Stoves)

Montag Furnace Co., 3432 S.E. Belmont, Portland, Ore. 97214 (Domestic, Wood, Coal, Oil and Electric Stoves and Furnaces)

Mother's General Store, (Wood-Burning Stoves, Fireplace Equipment) Axes, Hatchets, Crosscut Saws, etc.)

Orbon Stove Co., Belleville, Ill. 62221 (Coal, Gas, Oil, Wood and Heating)

Pittsburgh Stove & Range Co., Preble Ave. at Superior Bridge, Pittsburgh, Pa. 15233 (Coal, Gas and Wood, House and School Heating Stoves and Domestic Ranges)

Portland Stove Foundry Co., 57 Kennebec, Portland, Maine 04101 (Coal, Wood, Oil and Gas and Electric Combination Ranges and Coal, Wood and Oil Furnaces)

Riteway Manufacturing Co., Inc., P.O. Box 6, Harrisonburg, Va. 22801 (Furnaces: Wood, Coal and Oil, Automatic)

Sam Daniels Manufacturing Co., Inc., Hardwick, Vt. 05843 (Furnaces: Wood and Coal)

Skaggs Manufacturing & Foundry Co., Crocker, Mo. 65452 (Furnaces: Wood and Coal)

Union Stove Works, Inc., 12 Columbia Ave., Paterson, N.J. 07503 (Wood and Coal, Railroad Caboose Heating Stoves)

Washington Stove Works, 3402 Smith Ave., Everett, Wash. 98201 (Camp Ranges: Wood, Coal and Oil)

WATER, PUBLICATIONS

Apparatus for Providing AC Electrical Energy at a Preselected Frequency, U.S. Patent No. 2,663,945, May 16, 1972, with W.L. Hughes and R.G. Ramakumar, Oklahoma State University, Stillwater, Okla.

Design of Small Dams, U.S. Dept. of the Interior, Bureau of Reclamation, U.S. Government Printing Office, Washington, D.C.

Domestic Water Supply and Sewage Disposal Guide, A.P. Anderson, Theo. Audel Co., New York, 1967

Farm Water Power, George Warren, U.S. Dept. of Agriculture, Feb. 1931, Washington, D.C.

Hydraulic Ram Forces Water to Pump Itself, A.W. Kaufman, Popular Science, Oct. 1948, pp. 231—233

A Hydraulic Ram for Village Use, Ersal W. Kindel, VITA

Letter Concerning Hydraulic Rams, Edward Barberie, The Mother Earth News® Issue No. 21, pg. 3

Low Cost Development of Small Water-Power Sites, Hans W. Hamm, VITA, 1967

Measuring Water Flow, Don Marier, Alternative Sources of Energy, No. 1 (July 1971), pp. 8—10

The Owner-Built Hydroelectric Plant, Access Catalog, Vol. 1, No. 7, pp. 12—15

Power Development of Small Streams, Harris and Rice, Rodney Hunt Machine Co., Orange, Mass., 1920

Power for the Farm from Small Streams, A.M. Daniels, U.S. Dept. of

Agriculture, Washington, D.C., 1925
Power From Small Streams, C.A. Crowley, Popular Mechanics, Sept. 1940 (Part 1), pp. 466—473 and Oct. 1940 (Part 2), pp. 626—630
Power, Water and Food for Desert Coasts: An Integrated System for Providing Them, Carl N. Hodges and Carle O. Hodge, Environmental Research Laboratory, University of Arizona, 1969
Savonius Rotor for Water Pumping, VITA, Pub. No. 11132.1 ($ .75)
Some Practical Advice, Don Marier, Alternative Sources of Energy, No. 5 (April 1972), pp. 7—9
Village Technology Handbook, VITA
Water Lifting Devices for Irrigation, Daniel Johnson, VITA, Report No. 4
Water Power Development, Emil Mosonyi, Vol. 1, Low-Head Power Plants, Akademiai Kiado, Budapest, 1967
Water in the Service of Man, H.R. Vallentine, Baltimore: Penguin Books, 1967
Windmills and Watermills, John Reynolds, Praeger Publishers, New York, 1970 (available from The Mother Earth News® for $13.95)

WATER, HARDWARE

Allis-Chalmers, P.O. Box 512, Milwaukee, Wis. (Water Wheels and Turbines)
Asea Electric, Inc., 2 Kaysal Court, Armonk, N.Y. 10504 (Hydraulic Turbines and Water Wheels)
Baldwin-Lima-Hamilton, 111 E. Wacker Drive, Chicago, Ill. 60601 (Turbines, Governors and Wheels)
Edward Barberie, Box 104, Green Spring, W. Va. 26722 (Hydraulic Rams, Designs and Material Lists)
Ce Co Co Chuo Boeki Goshi Kaisha, P.O. Box 8, Ibaraki City, Osaka, Japan (Hydraulic Rams)
Davis Foundry & Machine Works, Rome, Ga. 30161 (Water Wheels and Hydraulic Turbines)
Dresser Industries, Inc., Machinery Group, 3201 Wolf Rd., Franklin Park, Ill. (Water Wheels and Hydraulic Turbines)
The James Leffel & Co., Springfield, Ohio 45501 (Manufacturer of Water Power Stations. Request Pamphlet A and the Hoppes Bulletin H-49 for instructions for measuring the potential of your water source. Upon receipt of this information, Leffel will give quotation on the best design for your application.)
J.W. Jolly, Inc., Holyoke, Mass. 01040 (Water Wheels and Hydraulic Turbines)
Low Impact Technology Ltd., (Hydraulic Rams, Water Wheels and Purifiers)
Mother's General Store, (Hand Pumps, Books and Manuals)
Newport News Shipbuilding & Dry Dock Co., Newport News, Va. (Hydraulic Turbines and Water Wheels)
Ossberger-Turbinfabrik, 8832 Weissenberg, Bavaria, Germany (Small-Sized Water Power Stations)
Rife Hydraulic Engine Mfg. Co., Box 367, Millburn, N.J. 07041 (Hydraulic Ram Manufacturers)
Sulzer Bros., Inc., 19 Rector, New York, N.Y. 10006 (Water Wheels and Turbines)

WIND, PUBLICATIONS

Achievements of Soviet Wind Power Engineering, E.M. Fateev and I.V. Rozhdestvenskii, "Vestnik Machinostroeniya", No. 9, 1952, pp. 24—27, Electrical Research Association, Trans. No. IB 1334
Advanced Study Institute for Solar and Aeolian Energy/Proceedings of the Greek Atomic Energy Commission and the Hellenic Scientific Society of Solar and Aeolian Energy, Sounion, Greece, 1961
The Aerodynamic Layout of Wind Blades of Wind Turbines with High Tip Speed Ratios, Ulrich Hütter, U.N. Conference on New Sources of

Energy, Rome, 1961

The Aerodynamics of Windmills Used for the Generation of Electricity, L.H.G. Sterne and G.C. Rose, Electrical Research Association, Pub. No. IB/T 4, 1951, 12 pp.

Airscrew Blade Vibration, B.C. Carter, 619th Lecture of the Royal Aeronautical Society, Mar. 11, 1937

Airscrew Blade Vibration, J. Morris, Aeronautical Research Committee, Reports and Memoranda No. 1835, June 9, 1937

Apparatus for Providing AC Electrical Energy at a Preselected Frequency, U.S. Patent No. 2,663,945, May 16, 1972, with W.L. Hughes and R.G. Ramakumar, Oklahoma State University, Stillwater, Okla.

Burgess Engineering Manual, Gould Burgess Battery Division, Freeport, Ill. 61032, 1970

Climatic Atlas of the U.S., S.S. Visher, Harvard University Press, 1954

Construction and Performance of an Experimental Rechargeable Fuel Cell Battery, R.G. Ramakumar, Paper presented at Frontiers of Power Technology Conference, Oklahoma State University, Oct. 1970

Current State of Wind Power Research in the Soviet Union, N. Levy, Brace Research Institute, Pub. No. T. 56, Sept. 1968

The Design, Development and Testing of a Low-Cost 10 hp Windmill Prime Mover, R.E. Chilcott, Brace Research Institute, Pub. No. MT. 7, 1970, 113 pp.

The Design of High Speed Windmills Suitable for Driving Electrical Generators, National Research Laboratories, Ottawa, Report No. PAA-32

Design Study of Hydrogen Production by Electrolysis, Allis-Chalmers Mfg. Co., Milwaukee, Wis., Pub. No. ACSDS 0106643, Oct. 1966

The Development of a Method for Measurement of Strains in the Blades of a Windmill Rotor, J.G. Morrison, British Electrical and Allied Industries Research Association, Technical Report C/T 117, 1957, 28 pp.

Dynamic Analysis of High Speed Wind Turbine Systems, J.S. Duggal, Brace Research Institute, Pub. No. MT. 9, 1971, 92 pp.

An Economical Energy Storage System Utilizing Hydrogen-Oxygen Regenerative Fuel Cells, W.L. Hughes, R.G. Ramakumar and H.J. Allison, Presented at I.E.E.E. Summer Power Meeting, New York City, Paper No. 70 CP 212 PWR, Jan. 1970

Economic High-Pressure Hydrogen-Oxygen Fuel Cell, R.G. Ramakumar, W.L. Hughes and H.J. Allison, Presented at 5th Intersociety Energy Conversion Engineering Conference, Washington, D.C., Sept. 1969

The Economics of Generating Electricity from the Wind Power in India, R. Ramatathan, Indian Quarterly Journal of Economics, Jan. 1970, pp. 245—255

The Economic Utilization of Wind Energy in Arid Areas, E.W. Golding, Wind and Solar Energy, UNESCO, 1956

The Economic Value of Hydrogen Produced by Wind Power, A.H. Stodhart, Electrical Research Association, Pub. No. C/T 111, 1954, 8 pp.

Electric Battery Directory, Starting, Lighting, Ignition, and Generating Systems Buyers Guide, Independence Battery Manufacturers Association, Inc., Largo, Florida (annual)

Electric Energy from the Wind, R.G. Kloeffler and E.L. Stiz, Kansas State College Bulletin, Vol. XXX, No. 9, Sept. 1946

Electric Power from the Wind, Henry Clews, Solar Wind Publication, 1973, 29 pp.

Estimation of the Maximum Drag and Root Bending Moment on a Stationary Brace Airscrew Windmill Blade and Variation of Airscrew Starting Torque with Blade Angle, P.K. Ghosh, Brace Research Institute, Pub. No. CP. 19, May 1969, 13 pp

Ever-ready Battery Applications—Engineering Data, Union Carbide Corporation, Consumer Products Division, 270 Park Avenue, New York, N.Y. 10017, 1971

The Experimental and Theoretical Investigation of Windmills, Matsunosuke Iwasaki, Reports of Research Institute for Applied Mechanics, No. 8, Japan, 1953, pp. 181—229

Experimental Data on Models of Devices for Accumulating Wind Energy in Space, R. Vezzani, "Elettrotecnica" Vol. 35, Dec. 1948, pp. 488—493, Electrical Research Association, Trans. No. IB 1046

Feasibility of Energy Storage by Water Electrolysis and High Pressure Hydrogen Storage, W.L. Hughes, C.M. Summers and H.J. Allison, Engineering Research Report, Oklahoma State University, 1962

Final Report on the Wind Turbine, Research Report PB 25370, New York University, for Office of Production, Research and Development, War Production Board, Washington, D.C., 1946

First Progress Report on Research on Wind Power Potential in Selected Areas in Oregon, E. Wendell Hewson, Oregon State University, Report No. PUD73-1, Mar. 1973

Fix Your Own Alternator, M. Schultz, Popular Mechanics, Aug. 1972

Foundation for the Generation of Electricity by Windmills, B.W. Colenbrander, Secretary, Jan Steenlaan 12, Heemstede, Netherlands

The Generation of Electricity by Wind Power, E.W. Golding, E. & F.N. Spon Ltd., 22 Henrietta St., London, 1955

A Graphic Method of Calculating the Performance of an Airscrew, C.N.H. Lock, Aeronautical Research Committee, Reports and Memoranda No. 1849, 1938

Helical Sail Windmill, VITA, Pub. No. 11131.1 ($ .75)

A High Power Output DC-AC Inverter with Sinusoidal Output, G. Salters, Electronic Engineering, Sept. 1961, pp. 586—591

Homemade Six-Volt Wind-Electric Plants, H.F. McColly and Foster Buck, North Dakota State University, Revised 1936 (available from The Mother Earth News ® for $1.00)

How to Construct a Cheap Wind Machine for Pumping Water (instructions for building a Savonius Rotor for water pumping), A. Bodek, Brace Reserach Institute, Do-It-Yourself Leaflet No. L.5, 1965

Investigation Concerning Savonius Rotors and Related Turbomachines, G. Bach, Forschung auf dem Gebiete des Ingenieurwesens, Vol. 6, June 1931, pp. 218—231, German to English translation by G.T. Ward, Brace Research Institute, Pub. No. T. 41

Is There a Place for the Windmill in the Less Developed Countries?, The East-West Center, Technology and Development Institute, Honolulu, Hawaii 96822

LeJay Manual, LeJay Manufacturing Co., Inc., Belle Plains, Minn. 56011, 1945, 48 pp.

List of Past and Present Windmill Manufacturers, Gerry Smith, editor, University of Cambridge, 1 Scroope Terrace, Cambridge CB2 1 PX (GB)

Low Cost Windmill for Developing Nations, Hartmut Bossel, VITA, Oct. 1970

Low Drag, Laminar Flow Aerofoil Section of Windmill Blades, P.K. Ghosh, Brace Research Institute, Pub. No. CP. 20, May 1969, 8 pp.

Modern Electrolyser Technology, A.K. Stuart, Paper presented at the American Chemical Society Symposium on Non-Fossil Fuels, Boston, April 13, 1972

A New Propeller Type High Speed Windmill for Electric Generation, E.N. Fales, ASME Transactions, Vol. 19, Paper AER-50-6, 1928

New Sources of Energy, Proceedings of Conference, Rome, August 21—31, 1961, Vol. 7, Wind Power, United Nations Publication (out of print), 1964, 409 pp.

Notes on the Development of the Brace Airscrew Windmill as a Prime Mover, R.E. Chilcott, The Aeronautical Journal of the Royal Aeronautical Society, Vol. 73, No. 700, Apr. 1969, pp. 333—334, or Brace Research Institute, Pub. No. R. 38

Notes on Jopp and Jacobs, Alternative Sources of Energy, No. 12

Novel Aerodynamic Wind-Power Pumps, Lubing Maschinenfabrik, 2847 Barnstorf, Postfach 110, West Germany, 1970

A 1-kw Wind Driven Domestic Lighting Plant at Spring Head, St. James, Barbados, M. Simonds, Brace Research Institute, Pub. No. T. 7, 1964, 11 pp.

Optimization and Development of the Savonius Wing Rotor for Power Generation, R.B. MacPherson, University of Massachusetts, Department of Civil Engineering

Parallel Operation of a Wind Power Station with a Powerful Grid, V.M. Andiranov and D.N. Bystritskii, "Elektrichestvo", No. 5, 1951, pp. 8—12, Electrical Research Association, Trans. No. IB 1161

Performance Characteristics of the Macdonald College Fanmill, D. Croney and G. Thierstein, Brace Research Institute, Pub. No. CP. 18, May 1969, 6 pp.

Performance Test of an 8-Meter-Diameter Andreau Windmill, A. Bodek, Brace Research Institute, Pub. No. T. 12, 1964, 24 pp.

Performance Test of a Savonius Rotor, M.H. Simonds and A. Bodek, Brace Research Institute, Pub. No. T. 10, Jan. 1964, 20 pp.

The Physics of Airfoils, from Physics by H.E. White, Lifestyle! No. 3, pg. 49

Planning and Balancing of Energy of Small Output Wind Power Plant, Ulrich Hütter, Wind and Solar Energy, UNESCO, 1956

Plans for the Construction of a Small Wind Electric Plant, Arnold Benson, Pub. No. 33, Oklahoma State University, Stillwater, Okla. 74079

Potential for Medium-Power, Fixed-Pitch, Variable-Speed Airscrew Wind Machines in Canadian Agriculture, R.E. Chilcott and G.T. Ward, Brace Research Institute, Pub. No. T. 47, 1968

Potential for Wind Power Development, M.S. Kadivar, Brace Research Institute, Pub. No. MT. 10, July 1970, 171 pp.

The Potentialities of Wind Power for Electricity Generation (with reference to small-scale operation), E.W. Golding and A.H. Stodhart, British Electrical and Allied Industries Research Association, Technical Report W/T 16, 1949

Practical Experience Gained from the Development of a 100-kw Wind Power Installation, Ulrich Hütter, Brennstoff-Waermekraft, Vol. 16, No. 7, July 1964, pp. 333—341, German to English translation by G.T. Ward, Brace Research Institute, Pub. No. T. 42

A Preliminary Report on the Design and Performance of Ducted Windmills, G.M. Lilley and W.J. Rainbird, British Electrical and Allied Industries Research Association, Technical Report C/T 119, 1957, 65 pp.

Preliminary Tests of a High Speed Vertical Axis Windmill Model, P. South and R.S. Rangi, National Research Council of Canada, Laboratory Technical Report LTR-LA-74, Mar. 1971

The Present State of Planning and Erection of Large Experimental Wind Power Stations, V.R. Sektorov, "Elektrichestvo", No. 2, 1933, pp. 9—13, Electrical Research Association, Trans. No. IB 1052

Principles of Inverter Circuits, Bedford and Hoft, John Wiley and Sons, New York, 1964

Proceedings of NASA's Wind Energy Porgram, NASA, Lewis Research Center, Mail Stop 500-201, Cleveland, Ohio 44135

Proceedings of the U.N. Conference on New Sources of Energy, Vol. 7, Wind Power, U.N. Sales No. 63.I.41, 1964 ($3.50)

Production and Distribution of Hydrogen as a Universal Fuel, D.P. Gregory and J. Wurm, Proceedings of 1972 Intersociety Energy Conversion Engineering Conference, American Chemical Society Paper No. 729208, 1972

Rebuilt Wind Chargers, Bill Gibbons, Lifestyle! No. 3, pg. 51

Regulation of the Output of a Wind Power Station, V.M. Andrianov and A.I. Polataev, "Elektrichestvo", No. 6, 1952, pp. 19—24, Electrical Research Association, Trans. No. IB 1249

A Report on Preliminary Testing of a Lubing Windmill Generator (M022-3G024-400) of the Brace Research Institute, H.L. Nakra, Brace Research Institute, Pub. No. T. 75, 5 pp.

Rotor High Speed Performance, Theory vs. Test, F.D. Harris, F.J. Tarzanin and R.K. Fisher, JAHS, Vol. 15, No. 3, July 1970

Sail Windmills in India, Alternative Sources of Energy, No. 12

Savonius Rotor Windmill, VITA, Pub. No. 11132.1

Shrouded Aerogenerator Design Study 1, A. Kogan and E. Nissim, Haifa Institute of Technology, Dept. of Aeronautical Engineering, Report 17, Jan.-June 1961

Shrouded Aerogenerator Design Study 2, Israel Society of Aeronautical Sciences, 5th Conference on Aviation and Astronautics, 1963, pp. 49—56

A Simple Electric Transmission System for a Free Running Windmill, T.H. Burton, Brace Research Institute

60-Cycle Inverter, Electronic Circuit Design Handbook, TAB Books, Blue Ridge, Summit, Pa. 17214, 1968

Solar and Aeolian Energy, A.G. Spanides and A.D. Hatzikakidis, Proceedings of International Seminar on Solar and Aeolian Energy, Sept. 1961, Plenum Press, 1964, 423 pp.

Solar Windmill, Henry Clews, Alternative Sources of Energy, No. 8, pg. 14, Jan. 1973

Specifications of the Brace 10-hp Airscrew Windmill (15 Assembly and 70 Detail Drawings), Chilcott, Budgen, Goldstein and Weyts, Brace Research Institute, Pub. No. T. 43, Feb. 1971

The S-Rotor and Its Applications, S.J. Savonius, Mechanical Engineering, Vol. 53, No. 5, May 1931, pp. 333—338

Standard Handbook for Mechanical Engineers, Marks, Theodore Baumeister, editor (six-page section by E.N. Fales on wind power)

The Testing of Wind Driven Generators Operating in Parallel with a Network, D.E. Villers, Electrical Research Association, Pub. No. C/T 116, 1957, 22 pp.

Theory and Calculation of a Wind Turbine, G.D. Mattioli, Padua, Oct. 1944, Electrical Research Association, Trans. No. IB 1381

Theory of Propellers, T. Theodorsen, McGraw-Hill, 1948

Two Plans for a Fan-Bladed Turbine Type Windmill with Applications ($1.00), VITA

US/AID Fan Blade Windmill, Pub. No. 11133.3, VITA

The Use of Wind Power in Denmark, E.W. Golding and A.H. Stodhart, Electrical Research Association, Pub. No. C/T 112, 1954, 16 pp.

VITA-ESSEX Windmill, Pub. No. 11133.1 ($1.00), VITA Handbook

Wind Bibliography, Alternative Sources of Energy, No. 9

Wind Blown Generator, Aerowatt S.A., 37 Rue Chanzy—75—Paris 11[e] (company report)

Wind Driven Generator, Kendall Ford, Popular Science, Aug. 1938

Wind-Driven Generators: The Difference Between the Estimated Output and Actual Energy Obtained, J.R. Tagg, Electrical Research Association, Pub. No. C/T 123, 1960

Wind Electric Research Report (Evaluation of the Performance of a Commercial Aerogenerator), C. Sanchez-Vilar, Brace Research Institute, Pub. No. DT. 4

Wind Energy, Hans Meyer, Domebook 2, Pacific Domes, Box 279, Bolinas, Calif. 94924

Wind Energy Bibliography, Windworks, Rt. 3, Box 329, Mukwonago, Wis. 53149

A Wind Energy Storage Technique Utilizing a Hydrogen Oxygen Electrolysis Cell System, H.J. Allison, Presented at Frontiers of Power Technology Conference, Oklahoma State University, Oct. 29, 1968

Wind-Generated Electricity—Prototype 100-kw Plant, Engineering, Vol. 179, No. 4652, Mar. 1955, pg. 371

Wind Machines, J. Juul, Wind and Solar Energy, UNESCO, 1956

Windmill Cut-Out Works on Back Pressure, R.G. Wilson, Queensland Agriculture Journal, Vol. 87, 1961, pp. 621—622

Windmill Electric Lighting and Power, W. Manikowske, North Dakota Agricultural Experiment Station, Bulletin No. 105, Aug. 1913

Windmills, E.N. Fales, Standard Handbook for Mechanical Engineers, McGraw-Hill

Windmills for Electricity Supply in Remote Areas, G. Gimpel and A.H. Stodhart, Electrical Research Association, Pub. No. C/T 120, 1958, 24 pp.

Windmills and Fans, H. Glauert, Aerodynamic Theory, Vol. IV, W.F.

Durand, editor, Dover Publications, 1963, pp. 324—332

Windmills for the Generation of Electricity, Cameron Brown, National Institute of Agricultural Engineering Library, 1933

Wind Power Glossary (translated title), Ulrich Hütter, In Beitrag zum Lueger Lexikon der Technik, BD 6/7 Stuttgart, Deutsche Verlagsanstalt, 1965

Wind Power and Solar Energy, Proceedings of the New Delhi Symposium, UNESCO, 19 Avenue Kloher, Paris—16, France, 1956, 235 pp.

Wind Power Stations Working in Connection with Existing Power Systems, A. Kroms, Alternative Sources of Energy Bulletin, Vol. 45, No. 5, Mar. 1954, pp. 135—144, Electrical Research Association, Trans. No. IB 1371

A Wind Tunnel Investigation of a 14-ft.-Diameter Vertical Axis Windmill, P. South and R.S. Rangi, National Research Council of Canada, Laboratory Technical Report LTR-LA-105, Sept. 1972

WIND, HARDWARE

Aerowatt S.A., Distributed in the U.S. by: Automatic Power Division, P.O. Box 18738, Houston, Tex. 77023 (Builds expensive but reliable wind generators . . . five models, the largest rated at 4.1 kw in a 16-mph wind)

Boston Gear Division, North American Rockwell, 14 Hayward St., Quincy, Mass. 02171 (Gears for Windplants)

Bucknell Engineering Co., 10717 E. Rush St., South El Monte, Calif. 91733 ($3.00 for company literature. Plans for sale for 250-watt wind generator. Completed unit also for sale)

Cullman Wheel Co., 205 Huehl Rd., Northbrook, Ill. 60062 (Catalogue 67, Sprockets and Chains)

Domenico Sperandio, Via Cimarosa 13-21, 58022 Follonica (GR), Italy (Windmills . . . seven models, from 100 to 1,000 watts)

Dunlite Electrical Co. Pty. Ltd., 21-27 Frome St., Adelaine, South Australia (Windplants)

Dyna Technology, Inc., P.O. Box 3263, Sioux City, Iowa 51102 (Windplants)

Elektro gmbH, Winterthur, Switzerland (Windplants)

The Heller-Aller Co., Napoleon, Ohio 43545 (Manufacturer of Baker Run-In-Oil Water-Pumping Windplants)

Low Impact Technology Ltd., (Windplants and Dempster Water-Pumping Windmills)

Lubing Maschinenfabrik, 2847 Barnstorf, Postfach 110, West Germany (Manufacturer of Electric-Generating Windmills [400-watt, 24-volt DC System] and Water-Pumping Windmills)

Mother's General Store, (Baker Run-In-Oil Water-Pumping Windmill, Windplants, Air Speed Indicators, Books and Manuals)

Nova Manufacturing Co., 263 Hillside Ave., Nutley, N.J. 07110 (Inverters)

Jim Sencenbaugh, 678 Chimalus Drive, Palo Alto, Calif. 94306 (Distributor of Dunlite windplant. Also has wind charger plans)

Windworks, Rt. 3, Box 329, Mukwanago, Wis. 53149 (Windplant Plans)

SOLAR, PUBLICATIONS

An Analysis of Solar Energy Utilization, J.H. Fisher, WADC Technical Report 59-17, Vols. 1 & 2, Wright Air Development Center, ASTIA Document No. AD 2146111, 1959

Are Solar Power Systems Really Pollution Free?, Richard Cellarius, Alternative Sources of Energy, No. 11, pp. 8—10

Climatic Atlas of the United States, S.S. Visher, Harvard University Press, 1954

The Coming Age of Solar Energy, D.S. Halacy, Jr., Harper & Row, New York, Evanston and London, 1964 (available from The Mother Earth News® for $7.95)

Design Approach for Application of a Solar Energy System to Geodesic Structure, Dept. of Design, Southern Illinois University, 1971

Design and Initial Test of a Stirling Engine for Solar Energy Applications, J.A. Utz and R.A. Braun, M.S. Thesis, Mechanical Engineering Department, University of Wisconsin, 1960

A Directory of World Activities and Bibliography of Significant Literature, Association for Applied Solar Energy, Phoenix, Ariz., 1959

Direct Use of the Sun's Energy, Farrington Daniels, Yale University Press, New Haven and London, 1963 (available from The Mother Earth News ® for $12.50)

Dome Home: Heat From Sun, Electricity From Wind, St. Paul Pioneer Press, Jan. 21, 1973

Domestic Solar Water Heater, Khanna Mathur et al., Journal of Scientific Industrial Research, No. 18A, pp. 15—58, Feb. 1959

Drying Lumber by Solar Energy, E.C. Peck, Sun at Work, 3rd quarter, pp. 4—6, 1962

Energy Balances on a Parabolic Cylindrical Solar Collector, Transactions of the Society of Mechanical Engineers, pp. 24—32, G.O.G. Löf, D.A. Fester and J.A. Duffie, 1962

Energy For Man, Hans Thirring, Harper Torchbook 556, Harper & Row, New York, 1958

Energy in the Future, P.C. Putnam, Princeton, N.J.: Van Nostrand, 1956

Engineering of Thermoelectricity, Interscience, New York, 1961

Everything You've Always Wanted to Know About Solar Energy, but Were Never Charged Up Enough to Ask, Jerome Weingart, Environmental Quality Magazine, Dec. 1972

Experiments with Solar Energy, D.S. Halacy, Jr., W.W. Norton & Co., New York, 1969

Floating Station Collects Sunlight, Industrial Research, June 1972 (Escher's Helios-Poseidon Project)

Heliotechnology (Geliotekhnika), Faraday Press, New York

A High-Speed Cylindrical Solar Water Heater, Stephen A. Vincze, Solar Energy, Nov. 1971, Vol. 13, No, 3, pp. 339—344

Home Storage of Vegetables and Fruits, Evelyn Loveday, Garden Way Publishing, Charlotte, Vt., 1972

How to Make a Solar Steam Cooker, Brace Research Institute, Jan. 1965 ($ .75)

Image Furnace Techniques, T.S. Laszlo, Interscience, New York, 1965

Intermittent Absorption Cooling Systems with Solar Regeneration, D.A. Williams et al., Refrigeration Engineering, Nov. 1958, No. 66, pg. 33

Introduction to the Utilization of Solar Energy, A.M. Zarem and D.D. Enway, McGraw-Hill, New York, 1963

ISES Newsletter, International Solar Energy Society, c/o National Science Center, P.O. Box 52, Parkville, Victoria, Australia 3052, U.S. Section: c/o Smithsonian Radiation Biology Laboratory, 12441 Parklawn Dr., Rockville, Md. 20852

Large Enclosures and Solar Energy, Dietz, Architectural Design, April 1971

Living Off the Sun, Andrew MacKillop, Ecologist, 73 Molesworth St., Wadebridge, Cornwall-PL27 7DS, England, Vol. 3, No. 7 (July 1973), pp. 260—265

Low Temperature Engineering Application of Solar Energy, Ashrae Technical Committee on Solar Energy Utilization, American Society of Heating, Refrigeration and Air Conditioning Engineers, 345 E. 47th St., New York, N.Y. 10017, 1967

MIT Builds Solar Heated House, Architectural Engineering, Apr. 1949, Vol. 105

More Comfort at Less Cost, C.A. Mills, Refrigerating Engineering, Jan. 1955

New Sources of Energy and Energy Development, U.N. Conference on New Sources of Energy, Rome, 1961, U.N. Dept. of Economic and Social Affairs, New York, 1964, E/3577/Rev. 1 Doc. ST/ECA/72

Optics in Solar Processes, V.B. Veynberg, State Publishing Office for the Defense Industry, Moscow (1959), English translation from: U.S.

Dept. of Commerce, Pub. No. 255-609

Optimization of Focusing Solar-Collector Design, G.O.G. Löf and J.A. Duffie, Journal of Engineering for Power, July 1963, pp. 221—228

The Owner-Built Home, Ken Kern, Sierra Route, Oakhurst, Calif. 93644 (book and preliminary house design available from author® for $10.00; book alone available from The Mother Earth News® for $5.00)

The Performance of Flat-Plate Solar Heat Collectors, H.C. Hottel and B.B. Woertz, Transactions of the American Society of Mechanical Engineers, No. 64, pp. 91—104, 1942

Physics Looks at Solar Energy, Meinel and Meinel, Physics Today, Feb. 1972

Proceedings of the Advanced Study Institute for Solar and Aeolian Energy, A.G. Spanides, editor, Greek Atomic Energy Commission and the Hellenic Scientific Society of Solar and Aeolian Energy, Sounion, Greece, 1961

Proceedings of the Space Heating Symposium, Massachusetts Institute of Technology, Cambridge, Mass., 1950

Proceedings of the World Symposium on Applied Solar Energy, Phoenix, Arizona, 1955 (1965 reprint available from: Johnson Reprint Corporation, 111 5th Ave., New York, N.Y. 10003, Cloth: $15.00)

A Proposal for a Joint Industry-University-Utility Task Group on Thermal Conversion of Solar Energy for Electrical Power Production, Aden B. Meinel, Optical Sciences Center, University of Arizona

Radiant Conditioning in Use at "Reflection Point", C.A. Mills, Heating, Piping and Air Conditioning, Dec. 1950, pg. 88

Report No. 27 (list of reports available), Brace Research Institute, June 1973

Report, Solar Energy Laboratory, R. Seyboldt, University of Wisconsin, 1957

Research Frontiers in the Utilization of Solar Energy, Proceedings of the National Academy of Science, No. 47 (1961), pp. 1245—1306

A Slit and Expanded Aluminum Foil Solar Collector, J.J. Chiou, M.M. El-Wakil and J.A. Duffie, Solar Energy Symposium, University of Florida, April 1964

Solar and Aeolian Energy, A.G. Spanides and A. Hatzikakidis, editors, Plenum Press, New York, 1964

Solar Cooker Construction Manual, VITA, June 1967

Solar Cooking Ovens, Dr. Maria Telkes, Solar Energy, Jan. 1959

Solar Distillation, U.N. Dept. of Economic & Social Affairs, New York, U.N. Publications Sales, No. E. 70. II. B. 1. (1970)

Solar Electricity From the High Places, Paul Sturges, Alternative Sources of Energy, No. 10, pp. 3—5

Solar Energy, Richard Blazej, New England Coalition on Nuclear Pollution, P.O. Box 637, Brattleboro, Vt. 05301

Solar Energy, Day Chahroudi, Domebook 2, pg. 120, Pacific Domes, Box 279, Bolinas, Calif. 94924

Solar Energy, Hans Rau, Macmillan Co., New York, 1964

Solar Energy Conversion, John A. Strother, I.E.E.E. Spectrum, April 1971, pp. 11—12

Solar Energy: A Feasible Source of Power, Allen L. Hammond, Science, May 14, 1971, Vol. 172(3984), pg. 660

Solar Energy for Heating, Hoyt Hottel, Mechanical Engineers' Handbook (5th edition), pp. 1636—1638, L.S. Marks, editor, McGraw-Hill

Solar Energy for House Heating, Irving Hand, Heating and Ventilating, Dec. 1947, pp. 80—94

Solar Energy as a National Energy Resource, NSF/NASA Solar Energy Panel Report, Dec. 1972, Solar Energy Panel, Dept. of Mechanical Engineering, University of Maryland, College Park, Md. 20742

Solar Energy Technology: New Seriousness, Science News, Vol. 101, No. 15, pp. 225—240, Apr. 8, 1972

Solar Energy and its Use for Heating Water in California, F.A. Brooks, U.C. Agricultural Experiment Station, Bulletin 602, Nov. 1936, University of California at Berkeley

The Solar Era: Part 2 (Power Production with Small Solar Engines), Farrington Daniels, Mechanical Engineering, Sept. 1972

Solar Greenhouse, James Bowden, Alternative Sources of Energy, No. 10, pg. 7

The Solar Heater, A.W. Farrall, University of California at Berkeley, Bulletin 469, June 1929

Solar Homes, Sen. Mike Gravel, Congressional Record, Vol. 117, No. 194, Washington, D.C., Dec. 11, 1971

Solar House, Lifestyle! No. 5, pg. 58

Solar House, Steve Baer, Alternative Sources of Energy, No. 10, pg. 8

Solar House Models, Dr. Harry E. Thomason (available from: Edmund Scientific Co., 300 Edscorp Building, Barrington, N.J. 08007)

Solar House Plans, Dr. Harry E. Thomason (available from: Edmund Scientific Co., 300 Edscorp Building, Barrington, N.J. 08007, and: The Mother Earth News® for $10.00)

Solar Power, Ford and Kane, Bulletin of the Atomic Scientists, Oct. 1971

Solar Power—Reality or Vision?, P.E. Glaser, A.S.M.E.-I.E.E.E. National Power Conference, Albany, N.Y., Sept. 19—22, 1965

Solar Radiation, N. Robinson, Elsevier Publishing Co., New York, 1965, 347 pp.

Solar Shingles and Crops of Clean Energy, Sen. Mike Gravel, Congressional Record, Vol. 118, No. 106, Washington, D.C., June 28, 1972

Some Thoughts on an Experimental Solar Laboratory, Eugene Eccli, Alternative Sources of Energy, No. 10, pp. 6—7

Specifications of a 12-hp Solar Steam Turbine, J.C. Georgian, Brace Research Institute, Pub. No. T. 44, July 1968

Sun-Heated Ski Lodge Slit into Mountain Slope, Paul Jacques Grillo, Interiors, Jan. 1951

Sun Machine Previews Shadows, Paul Wohl, Popular Science, Aug. 1971, pg. 121

Surface Treatment and Finishing of Aluminum and its Alloys, S. Wernick and R. Pinner, Robert Draper, publisher, Teddington, England, 1959

Thermal Conversion of Solar Energy into Power, Aden B. Meinel and Marjorie P. Meinel, Citizen's Organization for the Study of Solar Energy, Rt. 8, Box 550-B, Tucson, Ariz. 85710

Thermal Heliotrope: A Passive Sun-Tracker, NASA Technical Brief, July 1971, Technology Utilization Officer, Goddard Space Flight Center, Greenbelt, Md. 20771, Reference: B71-10260

Thermoelectric Materials and Devices, B.C. Irving and E. Miller, Reinhold, New York, 1960

Thermoelements and Thermoelectric Cooling, D.K.C. MacDonald, Infosearch, London, 1957 (Trans. from Russian)

Thin Films and Solar Energy, Optical Coating Laboratory, Inc., P.O. Box 1599, Santa Rosa, Calif. 95403

Transactions of the Conference on the Use of Solar Energy: The Scientific Basis, University of Arizona Press, Tucson, 1958

The Trapping of Solar Energy, W.C. MacNevin, Ohio Journal of Science, 1953, Vol. 53(5), pp. 257—319

Use of Solar Energy for Heating Water, F.A. Brooks, Pub. 3557, Smithsonian Institution, Washington, D.C., 1939

Village Technology Handbook, VITA, 1970

Wind Power and Solar Energy: Proceedings of the New Delhi Symposium, UNESCO, 19 Avenue Kloher, Paris-16, France, 1956

Year-Round Residential Conditioning by Reflective Radiation, C.A. Mills, Refrigerating Engineering, 1953

Your Engineered House, Rex Roberts, J.P. Lippincott, 1964 (available from The Mother Earth News® for $8.95)

SOLAR, HARDWARE

Beasley Solar Hot Water Systems Co., Holton Ave., Devon Park, Adelaide, South Australia (Solar Water Heaters)

Davis Instruments, 857 Thornton, San Leandro, Calif. 94577 (Solar Cooker)

Edmund Scientific Co., 300 Edscorp Building, Barrington, N.J. 08007,

(Solar Furnaces, Lenses, Photocells, Mirrors and Space Heating Plans)

Fafco, Inc., 2860 Spring St., Redwood City, Calif. 94063 (Solar Heat Exchangers)

Fred Rice Productions, Inc., 6313 Peach Ave., Van Nuys, Calif. 91401 (Solar Water Heaters)

Gaydardt Industries, RD 1, Box 319-A, Brandywine, Md. 20613 (Flat-Plate Solar Collectors)

Intercontinental Enterprises Co., 69 Stewart Ave., Eastchester, N.Y. 10707 (Solar Cooker)

Don Johnson, 3013 Hennepin Ave., Minneapolis, Minn. 55408 (Solar Cooker)

Ken Fischer Sun Systems, 716 Main St., Berlin, Pa. 15530 (Parabolic Reflectors)

George O.F. Löf, Cherry Hills Village, Denver, Colo. (Solar Space Heating)

Low Impact Technology Ltd., (Solar Heat Collectors)

Mother's General Store, (Solar-Powered Collectors, Water Heaters, Ovens, Stoves, etc., and Books and Manuals)

National Products, Inc., 900 Baxter Ave., Louisville, Ky. 40204 ("Flex-Sheet" Mirrors)

Platecoil, 735 E. Hazel St., Lansing, Mich. 48909 (Manufacturer of Solar Collectors)

The Rayosol Co., Carretera de Cadiz, 32, Torremolinos (Málaga), Spain (Manufacturer of Solar Hot Water Heaters)

Sky-Therm Processes and Engineering, Harold Hay, 945 Wilshire Blvd., Los Angeles, Calif. 92017 (Solar Space Heating)

Solar Energy Digest, (Solar Collectors [Solapak])

Solar Energy Systems, 669 Boston Post Rd., Guilford, Conn. 06437 (Flat-Plate Solar Collectors)

Solar Power Corporation, 186 Forbes Rd., Braintree, Mass. 02184 (Solar Cells)

Solar Systems, 323 Country Club Drive, Rehoboth Beach, Del. 19971 (Commercial Solar Heating Systems)

Sunwater Co., 10404 San Diego Mission Rd., San Diego, Calif. 92108 (Solar Stills)

Transparent Products Co., 1727 W. Pico Blvd., Los Angeles, Calif. 90015 (Aluminized Mylar for Solar Reflectors)

Zomeworks Corporation, Steve Baer, P.O. Box 712, Albuquerque, N.M. 87103 (Solar Water Heaters and Solar Space Heating Systems)

METHANE, PUBLICATIONS

Agricultural Utilization of Sewage Effluent and Sludge, James P. Law, Federal Water Pollution Control Administration, U.S. Dept. of the Interior, Superintendent of Documents, U.S. Government Printing Office, Washington, D.C. ($ .45)

Anaerobic Composting for the Farm, The Complete Book of Composting, Rodale Press, 1971, Emmaus, Pa., pp. 412—418

Anaerobic Digesters, The Complete Book of Composting, Rodale Press, 1971, Emmaus, Pa., pp. 258—259

Anaerobic Digestion of Hog Wastes, E.P. Taiganides, E. Baumann, H. Johnson and T. Hazen, Journal of Agricultural Engineering, Research, Vol. 8(4)

Anaerobic Digestion of Poultry Manure, Eliseos P. Taiganides, World's Poultry Science Journal, Vol. 19(4), 1963

Anaerobic Digestion of Solid Wastes, S. Klein, Compost Science Journal, Feb. 1972

The Biochemistry of Methane Fermentation Using C^{14} Tracers, John S. Jeris and Perry L. McCarty, Journal of the Water Pollution Federation 3900 Wisconsin Ave. N.W., Washington, D.C. 20016, Vol. 37, No. 2, pp. 178-192.

Bio-Gas Plant, Ram Bux Singh, Gobar Gas Research Station, Ajitmal, Etawah (U.P.), India (available from The Mother Earth News® for $5.00)

Biological Conversion of Light Energy to the Chemical Energy of Methane, C.G. Golueke and W.J. Oswald, Applied Microbiology, No. 7, pp. 219—227, 1959

Biological Transformation of Solar Energy, W.J. Oswald and C. Golueke, Advances in Applied Microbiology, No. 2, pp. 223—262, 1960

Carbon-Nitrogen Ratios in Organic Fertilizer Materials in Relation to the Availability of their Nitrogen, E. Rubins and F. Bear, Soil Science, No. 54, pp. 411—423, 1942

Characteristics and Treatment of Wastes from a Confinement Hog Production Unit, Eliseos P. Taiganides, Ph.D. Dissertation, Iowa State University, Science and Technology, Agricultural Engineering, 1963 (available from University Microfilm, Inc., Ann Arbor, Mich., No. 63-5200, 177 pp.)

Chicken Power, Maine Times, Vol. 4, No. 33, pp. 2—3

A Clean New Gas, Hinrich L. Bohn, Environment, Dec. 1971, Vol. 13(10), pp. 4—9

Composting: Sanitary Disposal and Reclamation of Organic Wastes, H. Gotaas, World Health Organization, Geneva, 1956

Comprehensive Studies of Solid Waste Management, C.G. Golueke and P.N. McGauhey, U.S. Dept. of Health, Education and Welfare, Public Health Service Pub. No. 2039, 1970 (for sale by Superintendent of Documents, U.S. Government Printing Office, Washington, D.C. 20402, $4.25)

Convert Your Car to Propane, Jerry Friedberg, The Mother Earth News®, No. 15, pp. 78—82

Cow Dung Gas and Manure Plant for Village, Indian Agriculture Research Institute, VITA, 5 pp.

Digestion of Human Fecal Matter, S. Mishihara, Sewage Works Journal, Vol. 7(5), pp. 798—809, 1935

Disposal of Sewage and Other Water-Borne Wastes, K. Imhoff, W. Müller and D. Thistlethwayle, Ann Arbor Science Publishers, Ann Arbor, Mich., 1971

The Effect of Nitrogen to Carbon Ratio on Anaerobic Decomposition, F.A. Sanders and D. Bloodgood, Journal Water Pollution Control Federation, No. 37, pg. 1741, 1965

Evaluating Adaptability of Pasture Grasses to Hydroponic Culture and Their Ability to Act as Chemical Filters, H. Iby, Symposium on Farm Animal Wastes, May 5—7, 1966, Beltsville, Md.

Farm Animal Waste Management, J.R. Miner, Iowa State University Dept. of Science and Technology, Agricultural and Home Economics Experimental Station, Ames, Iowa, Special Report 67, May 1971

Free Clean Fuel: Methane Power, Jim Stumm, The Green Revolution, Jan. 1972, Vol. 10(1), pp. 9—12

Fuel Gas from Cow Dung, B.R. Saubolle, VITA

Harvesting and Processing Sewage-Grown Planktonic Algae, C.G. Golueke and W.J. Oswald, Journal Water Pollution Control Federation, 1965

A Homesite Power Unit: Methane Generator, Les Auerbach, 242 Copse Road, Madison, Conn. 06443 ($5.40)

How to Build a 100 Cubic Foot/Day Methane Gas Plant, from Bio-Gas Plant by Ram Bux Singh, The Mother Earth News®, No. 12, pg. 31

How to Generate Power From Garbage, Kieth D. Gilbert, The Mother Earth News®, No. 3, pp. 45—53

Important Considerations in Sludge Digestion—A Discussion, M.W. Tatlock, Sewage Works Journal, Jan. 1947, pp. 36-38

Important Considerations in Sludge Digestion, Part II—Microbiology and Theory of Anaerobic Digestion, Dr. A.M. Buswell, Sewage Works Journal, Vol. 19, No. 1, pp. 28—36

Increased Production of Bio-Gas from Cow Dung by Adding Other Agricultural Waste Materials, R. Laura and M. Idnai, Journal of the Science of Food and Agriculture, No. 22, pp. 164—167, 1971

Jerry Friedberg on Harold Bates, Jerry Friedberg, The Mother Earth News®, No. 15, pg. 78

Letter on Gas Refrigerators, Dan Detwiler, The Mother Earth News®, No. 14, pg. 118

Making Gas and Oil—Part I, Sen. Mike Gravel, Congressional Record,

Dec. 11, 1971, Vol. 117, No. 194, Washington, D.C.

Making Oil and Gas—Part II, Sen. Mike Gravel, Congressional Record, June 28, 1972, Vol. 118, No. 106, Washington, D.C.

Management of Farm Animal Wastes, Proceedings of the National Symposium on Animal Waste Management, May 5—7, 1966, East Lansing, Mich. (available from American Society of Agricultural Engineers, St. Joseph, Mich. 49085 for $5.00)

Manure Gas Plants, E. Paul Taiganides, National Hog Farmer, Swine Information Service, Bulletin No. F 13

Manure Smell Furnishes Farmstead's Power Needs, L. John Fry, National Hog Farmer, March 1961, pg. 35

Methane Digesters, L. John Fry and Richard Merrill, New Alchemy Institute Newsletter No. 3, Spring 1973 (available from The Mother Earth News® for $3.00)

Methane Gas—An Overlooked Energy Source, Organic Gardening and Farming, June 1972, pp. 98—101

Methane Production from Farm Wastes as a Source of Tractor Fuel, G. Rosenberg, Journal of Mining and Agriculture (England), No. 58, pp. 487—494, 1952

Methane Systems, Earthmind, 26510 Josel Drive, Saugus, Calif. 91350 ($1.25)

Mother's Methane Maker, The Mother Earth News®, No. 18, pp. 12—13

Mother's Methane Maker Meets Mass Media, The Mother Earth News®, No. 24, pp. 78—81

New Alchemy Methane, Earl Barnhardt, Alternative Sources of Energy, No. 11, pp. 12—17

Now . . . Electricity from Manure Gases, Farm Journal, May 1963

Nutrient Removal from Enriched Waste Effluent by the Hydroponic Culture of Cool Season Grasses, James P. Law, Federal Water Quality Administration, Dept. of the Interior, 1969 (available from Superintendent of Documents, U.S. Government Printing Office, Washington, D.C. for $ .50)

Operation of Sludge Gas Engines, S. Greeley and C.R. Velzy, Sewage Works Journal, Vol. 8(1), pp. 57—62, 1936

Photosynthetic Reclamation of Agricultural Solid and Liquid Wastes, Gordon L. Dugan et al., Sanitary Engineering Research Laboratory, University of California at Berkeley SERL Report No. 70—1, 1970

Power From Solar Energy Via Algae-Produced Methane, C. Golueke and W. Oswald, Solar Energy, Vol. 7(3), pp. 86—92, 1963

Properties of Farm Animal Excretia, E. Taiganides and T. Hazen, Transactions of American Society of Agricultural Engineering, Vol. 9(3), pp. 374—376, 1966

Reclamation of Energy from Organic Refuse, John T. Pfeffer, Dept. of Civil Engineering, University of Illinois, Urbana, Ill. 61801, April 1973

Sewage Sludge for Soil Improvement, M.S. Anderson, U.S. Dept. of Agriculture Circular No. 972, 1955, Superintendent of Documents, U.S. Government Printing Office, Washington, D.C. ($ .25)

Sewage Treatment (2nd edition), K. Imhoff and G. Fair, John Wiley & Sons, New York, 1956

Sludge Digestion Tests of Livestock Manures, Samuel Hart, Dept. of Agricultural Engineering, University of California at Davis, 1960

Solar Power Via a Botanical Process, W.J. Oswald and C.G. Golueke, Mechanical Engineers, Feb. 1964, pp. 40—43

Solution to Pollution, Clarence E. Burr, 1361 Gravenstein Highway North, Sebastopol, Calif. 95472, The Mother Earth News®, No. 3, pp. 41—43

Special Review: Methane Digesters for Fuel Gas and Fertilizer, Barbara and Chris Logan, Alternative Sources of Energy, No. 11, pp. 18—19

METHANE, HARDWARE

Low Impact Technology Ltd., (Generators)
Mother's General Store, (Books, Manuals and Do-It-Yourself Plans)

INDEX